WILD FLOWERS

THE MACMILLAN COMPANY
NEW YORK · CHICAGO
DALLAS · ATLANTA · SAN FRANCISCO
LONDON · MANILA

IN CANADA
BRETT-MACMILLAN LTD.
GALT, ONTARIO

HOMER D. HOUSE

WILD FLOWERS

THREE HUNDRED AND SIXTY-FOUR FULL-COLOR
ILLUSTRATIONS WITH COMPLETE DESCRIPTIVE TEXT

THE MACMILLAN COMPANY   NEW YORK

Popular Edition in one volume published October, 1934
Reissued from new plates, 1961

WILD FLOWERS is based on a work of similar title originally issued
by the State of New York. The illustrations, the originals of which
are in the State Museum in Albany, are reproduced by permission of
the Board of Regents of the State of New York.

The Macmillan Company, New York
Brett-Macmillan Ltd., Galt, Ontario

Color plates printed in Holland by Smeets Lithographers
Text printed in the United States of America

DEDICATED TO MY WIFE

ERMA N. H. HOUSE

IN GRATEFUL TRIBUTE TO HER ASSISTANCE IN

THE PREPARATION OF THE TEXT AND PLATES

ACKNOWLEDGMENTS

I am indebted to Mr. Edward A. Eames of Buffalo for photographs and autochromes of certain orchids, to Mr. G. A. Bailey of Geneseo, Mr. O. O. Nylander of Caribou, Maine, and Mr. Edward Hale Lincoln of Pittsfield, Mass., for additional photographs used in the text. The autochromes used as guides in making the colored illustrations were made under the author's supervision by Mr. Harold Snyder and Mr. Walter Starr.

INTRODUCTION

SCARCELY a reminder is left of the unbroken forested area which once stretched from the Atlantic seaboard westward toward the Mississippi valley. It is only within the memory of those now living that any serious effort has been made to preserve certain areas for the safe abode of what wild life may have survived the lumbering age. By the establishment of State Parks, wild life sanctuaries, and State, municipal and private forests and large private estates, there is abundant hope that there will be preserved for future generations some measure of the woodland beauty that has all but vanished from our horizon.

In this course of destruction made necessary in large part by the economic development of a new country, it is not only gratifying but to a large measure marvelous, that so many of the native wild flowers have persisted and often against great odds have held their own in the restricted habitats left to them. These woodlands of ours are not merely growths of trees. They are the protection, the home, and the sustenance of a wonderful variety of wild life. In their shade is the source of waters, the home of wild flowers, countless birds and other forms of wild life.

In addition our native flora has been enriched by a multitude of immigrants, many of them with attractive flowers; but unfortunately most of them are to be classed as undesirable weeds from the agriculturist's point of view. On the other hand a few of these immigrants have established themselves in woodlands, along streams and in other places where they are not thus objectionable, and have added much to the beauty of our plant life.

Anyone who has observed the natural vegetation in such unlike parts of the country as the salt marshes and sandy coastal areas along the Atlantic, the higher mountains of New Hampshire, New York and the southern

7

Appalachians, must have been impressed by the obvious difference in the wild flowers of those several sections, and especially by the fact that very few of the wild flowers which bloom between early spring and late autumn in the uplands and mountainous regions are to be found on Cape Cod, Long Island or the pine barrens of New Jersey.

Such differences in the character of the vegetation of widely separated areas are explained partly by soil conditions and geological origin and partly by differences in climate, especially the length of growing season and relative humidity. Climatically the eastern United States is a forest region, and hence favorable for a luxuriant variety of herbaceous and shrubby plants; a region in which forests would naturally dominate all other vegetation if not cut down.

In the changes which have taken place in our forested areas since the settlement of the eastern United States, corresponding changes have occurred in the relative abundance and distribution of the smaller elements of the flora, including the wild flowers. Plants which require the undisturbed, cool recesses of the semi-primeval forest have in most instances become greatly restricted in range and abundance. On the other hand many plants which prefer open woodlands, thickets, and open fields have prospered amazingly, and hence we find a greater abundance and increased range of many wild flowers of this sort which were comparatively scarce in the primeval forest.

To know and appreciate the native wild flowers as well as other forms of wild life is the stimulus back of all efforts to conserve these elements of nature, and this appreciation of their beauty and place in nature is more effective in their preservation than any man-made laws devised for their protection.

Many of our wild flowers are very attractive and possess a high decorative value. Care should be exercised, however, not to injure the roots or leaves in gathering those which are scarce or easily destroyed. The only satisfaction to be gained by their destruction is a few brief hours of doubtful pleasure which the flowers may yield from bowls and vases. Where they formerly grew in the woods, their beauty may never again delight the passer-by. Thus have many of our byways and woodlands, formerly so attractive with native wild flowers, become the abiding place of weeds. Even more regrettable is the fact that the disturbance does not end with the mere change of plant life. The insects, animals and bird life also suffer a marked change, adding nothing to the attractiveness of such byways and woodlands. Such roadside and meadow flowers as the goldenrods, asters, buttercups and violets can be gathered without fear of extermination. Many woodland wild flowers like the Trailing Arbutus, Trilliums, Windflower, Moccasin Flower (and other Lady's Slippers) and Gentians are easily destroyed by picking. Care should be taken to pick as few of such flowers as possible. The Flowering Dogwood, Azalea and Mountain Laurel suffer greatly from their overenthusiastic admirers and need every possible protection from vandalism and fire. The sale of such flowers at wayside stands should be discouraged whenever possible. To those who would attempt to bring wild flowers into their gardens a word of caution is offered. Many of them are very exacting in their requirements for soil, moisture and protection. A knowledge of these factors is essential for their successful cultivation.

Several states have enacted laws designed to prevent vandalism and destruction of wild flowers, but the real preservation of our wild flowers and all other forms of wild life depends ultimately upon the coöperation of all those who traverse our fields and forests.

The present volume is offered, with its wealth of color and form, scarcely approaching the beauty of the growing and living plants depicted, with the hope that the interest which it may stimulate in our native and naturalized wild flowers will become a potent force for their preservation and protection.

PLANT STRUCTURE[1]

No one who loves plants, either cultivated or wild, has failed to note how they differ from one another in shape, size, color and arrangement of the flowers, the leaves and other parts. These features are essentially the same in all individuals of a given species, but differ greatly in individual plants not belonging to the same species or variety.

To express these differences requires a terminology that is familiar largely only to those who have studied botany. The fact that it is practically impossible to describe a plant accurately without the use of a certain number of these special terms is a great impediment to a broad familiarity with our wild flowers on the part of all those who would like to study them with the aid of botanical guides. Because of the great variety of flowering plants and the minuteness of the flowers on many of them, the difficulty of identification is even greater than that connected with the study of bird and animal life.

The following brief summary of the terms necessary to an accurate description of a flowering plant, taken alone, means little to the average reader. Taken in connection with the plants as they are found growing and carefully studied, these terms, as soon as understood, place one on a footing of easy familiarity with the wild flowers, so that an accurate description as given in books means something definite and enables one to decide if the given description applies to the plant under consideration. Supplemented by illustrations, a study of the terminology used enables the student to acquire a much wider knowledge of our wild flowers.

Leaves

The leaf is an essential organ of all plants which live independently, that is, are not parasitic upon other plants (like the Dodder) or saprophytic upon dead plant remains (like the Indian Pipe). The leaf manufactures

---

[1] The cuts in this section are adapted from Gray's Lessons in Botany. Copyright by Asa Gray. Reproduced by permission of the American Book Company, publishers.

food for the plant, gives off excess water (transpiration) and is the breathing
organ of the plant.   To accomplish these functions the leaf is built up by
a complex arrangement of cells and is variously modified in different groups
of plants to meet the external conditions of environment and competition
by other plants.

The parts of a leaf are designated as
blade, petiole and **stipules.**   The **leaf blade**
(figure 1A) is the broadly expanded portion,
although in some species the leaf blade is
very narrow or even threadlike.   The **petiole**
(figure 1B) is the stalk which supports the
blade, and may be lacking in some cases, when

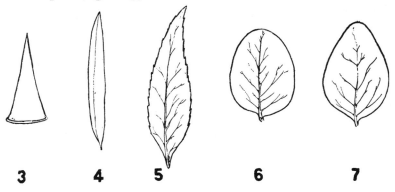

the leaf is said to be **sessile.**   The **stipules** (figure 1C) are small, leaflike
organs at the base of the petiole, and are best typified by the rose leaf.
Frequently the stipules encircle the stem at the base of the petiole and often
they are entirely lacking or fall away so soon after the leaves expand that
they are not found when the plant is in bloom.

Terms of leaf outline: The various shapes of leaf blades may be
expressed by the following terms:

Subulate; awl-shaped, without visible expansion of blade, and usually
tapering to the apex (figure 3).

3   4   5   6   7

Linear, or ribbon-shaped; elongated and several times longer than
wide (figure 4).

Lanceolate; in which the leaf blade is three times as long as wide, or longer, and broadest at or below the middle (figure 5).

Oblong; in which the blade is somewhat longer than wide, broadest in the middle or with sides almost parallel (figure 6).

Ovate; shaped like an egg; that is, broadest below the middle or near the base (figure 7).

Elliptical; rounded at both ends, somewhat longer than wide (figure 8).

Orbicular or **rotund;** in which the blade is nearly or quite circular in outline (figure 9).

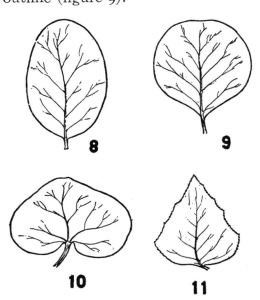

Reniform; in which the blade is broader than long, with a heart-shaped base (figure 10).

Deltoid; triangle-shaped, similar to **ovate** but conspicuously broadened at the base and pointed at the apex (figure 11).

Consideration of a few leaf blades shows immediately that these terms are not always sufficient to express accurately the shape and we may have recourse to combinations of terms, such as **oblong-lanceolate, ovate-lanceolate** (figure 13), etc.

The shape of leaf blades which are broadest above the middle may be expressed by the following terms:

Obovate; ovate in shape, but broadest near the apex or above the middle (figure 14).

Oblanceolate; lanceolate in shape but broadest above the middle or near the apex (figure 15).

Spatulate; in which the blade is oblanceolate or obovate in shape with the base conspicuously elongated (figure 12).

Terms applied to the apex of the leaf:

Obcordate; broad and heart-shaped at the apex (figure 16).

Emarginate; with a slight depression at the somewhat narrowed apex (figure 17).

Retuse; terminating in a semicircular end, the center of which is somewhat indented (figure 18).

Truncate; with a flat or abrupt apex (figure 19).

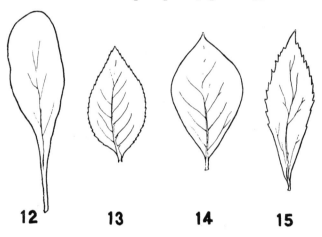

Acuminate; when the apex of the blade is longer than broad (figure 20).

Acute; when the apex of the blade is about as broad as long (figure 21).

Obtuse or **blunt;** when the apex is much broader than long (figure 22).

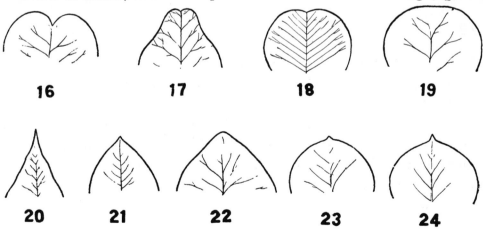

Mucronate; when the apex is terminated by a short blunt tip (figure 23).

Cuspidate; when the tip of the blade is hard and stiff (figure 24).

Terms applied to the base of the leaf:

The terms **truncate, acuminate, acute, obtuse** (defined above) may also be applied to the shape of the base of the leaf blade, in addition to the following:

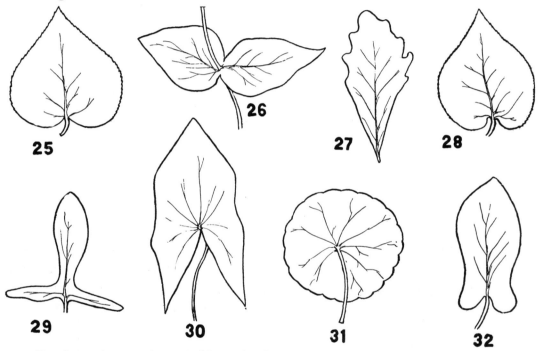

Cordate; heart-shaped (figure 25).

Cuneate, or wedge-shaped; when the sides of the leaf blade taper to an acute angle at the base (figure 27).

Auriculate, when the depression at the base of the blade is deep and produces on either side conspicuous basal lobes (figures 28 and 32).

Sagittate; when the basal lobes point downward like the head of an arrow (figure 30).

Hastate; when the basal lobes are turned outward (figure 29).

Peltate; a rounded leaf blade with the petiole attached at or near the middle of the lower surface (figure 31).

Perfoliate; when the bases of leaf blades meet and join around the stem of the plant (figure 26).

Terms applied to the marginal segmentation of leaf blades:

Sinuate; when the marginal lobes of the leaf blade present a wavy outline (figure 33).

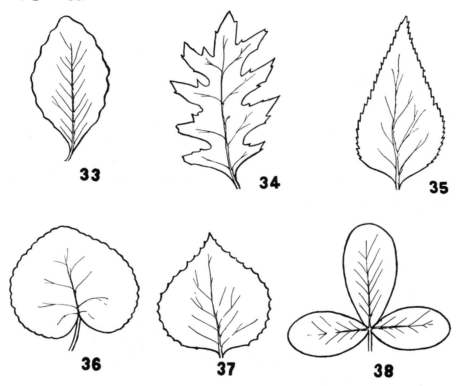

Pinnately lobed; when the tissue between the veinlets is cut out nearly to the midrib of the leaf and the divisions are arranged like the pinnae of a feather (figure 34).

Palmate; when the blade is deeply divided nearly or quite to a common base (figure 38).

Serrate (figure 35); when the margin is sharply toothed with coarse teeth, like a saw. When the teeth are rounded inward or are concave, the margin is said to be **dentate** (figure 37). When the margin is formed of rounded teeth it is said to be **crenate** (figure 36). If the teeth are very small, the diminutives of the above terms are used, namely, **serrulate** (figure 39), **denticulate** (figure 40) and **crenulate** (figure 41).

39 40 41

Compound leaves:

When a leaf possesses several divisions or segments upon a common petiole or rachis, it is said to be compound. The distinction between a simple leaf, which is deeply divided, and a compound leaf, rests upon the presence of distinct articulation between the leaf segment of the compound leaf and the petiole. Compound leaves may be **pinnate** (figure 42), when the leaflets are arranged on either side of a common petiole (Ash, Rose, Walnut etc.) or **palmately compound** (figure 43), when the leaflets all join the petiole at its summit (Horse-chestnut).

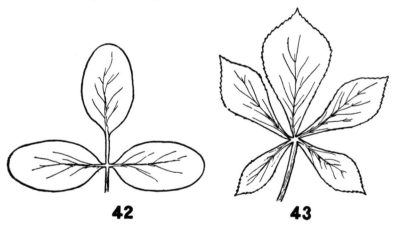

42   **43**

Leaf arrangement:

Alternate, when the leaves are arranged one at a node and each leaf is opposite and above the preceding leaf; **spirally arranged,** when the nodes are not opposite; and **opposite** when the leaves are in pairs opposite each other on the same node. When several leaves are inserted on the same node they are said to be **whorled** or **verticillate**.

Flowers

The flower of a plant is a group of organs (figure 44) which exist for the purpose of producing seed. The parts of a flower fall into two general groups: those which actually function as seed producers (essential organs), and those which act as protective organs or organs for the attraction of insects (floral envelops or perianth). These might also be designated as non-essential organs, since they are lacking in certain flowers.

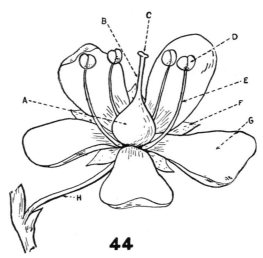

44

The essential organs consist of two parts, the **pistils** (figure 44A) and the **stamens** (figure 44D, E), often designated as the pistillate and staminate parts of a flower; and when a flower contains only pistils it is called a **pistillate flower,** and when it contains only stamens it is called a **staminate flower.**

When both stamens and pistils are present in the same flower, it is said to be **perfect.** If, in addition, the flower possesses the floral envelops, calyx and corolla, it is called a **complete flower.** Hence a flower which lacks any of these sets of organs is **incomplete** (that is, if it lacks either calyx or corolla); if it lacks either stamens or pistils it is **imperfect.**

The perianth or floral envelopes:

The ideal flower contains two sets of floral envelops, the **calyx** (figure 44F) and the **corolla.** In some flowers the corolla is entirely or partly divided into a certain number of divisions, each of which is called a **petal** (figure 44G). They are usually but not always brightly colored. Subtending or beneath the corolla is the calyx, which is usually, but not always, green, and is likewise in many plants divided into a number of distinct parts or **sepals.** When an incomplete flower has but one set of floral envelopes, it is usually the petals (or corolla) which are lacking, and in such cases the calyx may be brightly colored and function as a corolla (a petaliferous calyx).

The essential organs:

The number and arrangement of stamens varies in different kinds of plants, but nearly always a stamen consists of a **filament** or **stalk** (figure 44E), which bears at its apex the **anther** (figure 44D), or pollen-bearing sac. The shape of the anther, and the manner by which it dehisces, or opens to emit the pollen, likewise varies in different groups of plants.

The **pistil** (figure 44A–C), or seed-bearing organ, consists of an **ovary** (figure 44A), **stigma** (figure 44C) and **style** (figure 44B). The **ovary** is at the base of the pistil and contains the **ovules** or **eggs,** which after fertilization ripen into **seeds.** The **ovary** usually contains several or many ovules, but may contain as few as a single ovule. The **stigma** is that part of the pistil which acts as a receptive organ for pollen in the process of pollination. Its surface is usually moist and minutely granular and its position and shape are dependent upon the mode of pollination (insects or wind)

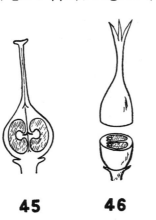

45   46   47

made use of by the particular plant. The **style** connects the stigma and ovary. It may be long or short, slender or stout, or sometimes entirely lacking when the stigma is situated directly upon the ovary.

The ovary itself may contain one or several chambers or cells (figures 45–47), and very frequently the number of chambers in the ovary and the lobes or divisions of the stigma bear a direct relationship to the number of petals, sepals and stamens. The term **carpel** (or **carpophyllum**) is used to designate the seed-bearing leaf. A **carpel** may be a pistil of itself, or it may be a constituent of a more complex pistil. In either case, a carpel is the homologue of a leaf. The surface within the ovary to which the ovules are attached is called the **placenta.**

Simple pistils may be solitary, or several together on a common receptacle within the flower, as in the Buttercup. A **compound pistil** consists of two, three or more carpels united into one body.

The apex of the flowering stem, which supports the flower, is designated as the **receptacle.**

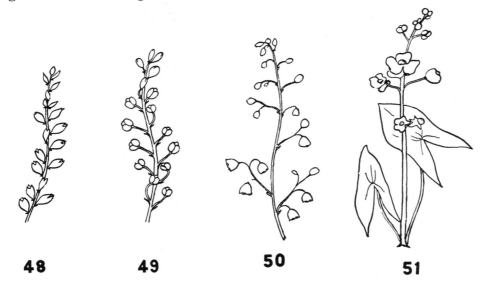

48 **49** **50** **51**

Arrangement of flowers:

Flowers are either solitary or clustered, but their arrangement varies in different kinds of plants, and may even vary to some extent in the same species. The arrangement or disposition of the flowers may be designated as the **inflorescence.** The following are the most frequent arrangements of flowers:

Spike (figure 48), in which the flowers are arranged along the flowering stem, and sessile (that is, without stalks) or with very short stalks (**pedicels**). When the flowering stem is naked (devoid of leaves) and rises directly from the root or crown of the plant, it is called a **scape** (figure 51).

Raceme (figure 49), in which the flowers are arranged along a flowering stem and each flower possesses a distinct stalk or pedicel. The lower pedicels may be somewhat longer than the upper ones.

Umbel (figure 52), when the flowers arise from the same point, which is usually the apex of the flowering stem or of a lateral flowering stalk, and

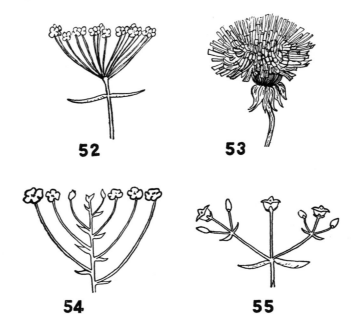

52   **53**

54   **55**

radiate like the rays of an umbrella. If the radiating stalks of such an inflorescence bear smaller umbels at their tips, it is called a **compound umbel.**

Corymb [**corymbose**] (figure 54), when the branches of an inflorescence are of unequal length, but the lower or outer ones are longest so that they all form a flat-topped, or nearly flat-topped, cluster.

Cyme (figure 55), when the flowers each terminate an axis or stem arising successively from a new axis or stem.

A **spadix** is a spikelike inflorescence with a fleshy stalk and with sessile flowers; the floral leaf or bract which subtends it or surrounds it partially is called the **spathe** (Skunk Cabbage, Wild Calla).

A **panicle,** or **compound raceme** (figure 50), is formed by the arrangement of flowers along the plant stem, similar to a raceme, but each flower stem has two or more branches.

Head (figure 53), an arrangement of flowers compactly on a common receptacle and surrounded by bracts (**involucral bracts**).

Modification and arrangement of the perianth:

Among the simpler groups of flowering plants the perianth is wanting, as in the Cat-tail and Willow. In the Sweet Flag, Oak and others, the perianth consists of a few scales, but in the higher plants, the perianth appears as a conspicuous portion of the flower, as in the Lily. Finally, as in the Rose family, there appears a clearly differentiated calyx and corolla.

In the simpler types of flowers, the sepals, petals and the stamens arise at the top of the receptacle. Such flowers are called **hypogynous,** meaning the insertion of these parts below the ovary (figure 56).

When the basal portion of the receptacle is continued upward, forms a cup-shaped growth around the ovary and bears the sepals, petals and stamens upon its margin, the flower is called **perigynous** (figures 57 and 59), meaning the insertion of the parts of the flower around the ovary.

Frequently the growth of the receptacle adheres to the ovary, and the sepals, petals and stamens appear to arise from above the position of the ovary, in which case the flower is called **epigynous** (figure 58), meaning above the ovary.

There may be varying degrees of cohesion or union of the parts of one or both of the floral envelops (perianth). When the sepals are united with each other the calyx is said to be **gamosepalous,** while a **gamopetalous** corolla (figures 62, 63, 64 and 65) refers to a union of the petals, as in the flower of the Morning-glory.

The degree of coalescence or union of parts of a gamopetalous corolla

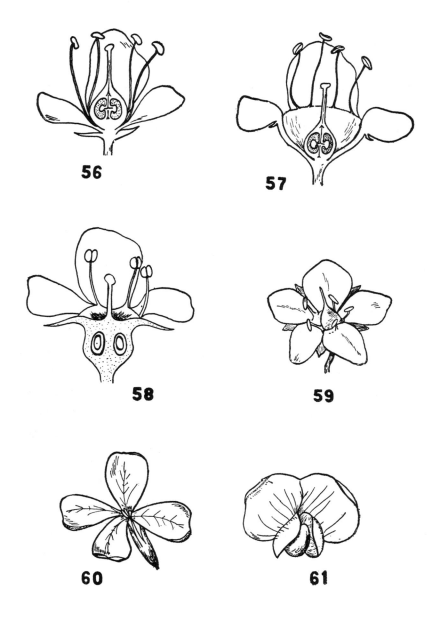

56

57

58

59

60

61

varies in different flowers.   When the calyx or corolla is divided almost to the base it is said to be **parted** (figure 63); when divided to about the middle it is said to be **cleft** (figure 64); when still less separated it may be said to be **lobed** or **toothed** (figure 65); or if entire on the margin it is said to be **entire** (figure 62).

When the parts of each set of organs of a flower are alike or equal in size, the flower is said to be **regular,** which means that the petals are alike, the sepals are alike and the stamens are alike.   A **symmetrical** flower is one in which the sepals, petals and stamens are of the same number; **unsymmetrical** when there are unequal numbers in each **cycle,** that is, an unequal number of sepals, petals or stamens.

Certain groups of plants may often be recognized by the form of the corolla of some of its members.   This character seems to be quite constant and the names of several large or important families of flowering plants are derived from this source.   Of these groups we may mention the **cruciferous** (figure 60) type of flower of the Mustard family (Cruciferae), in which there are four spreading petals forming a cross, as in the flower of the Spring Cress (C a r d a m i n e   b u l b o s a); the **labiate** corolla (figure 66) of the Mint family (Labiatae) in which the corolla is more or less two-lipped; the **papilionaceous** type of flower (figure 61) of the Pea family (Leguminosae), in which the petals are characteristically grouped into two lateral (wing) petals, a single upper (banner) petal and a pair of lower petals, often more or less united to form the **keel.**

Stamens:

The general characteristics of the stamens have already been described. In the stamens, as in the case of the petals and sepals, the number and arrangement are subject to great variation in different kinds of plants. **Monandrous** refers to a flower with a single or solitary stamen; **polyandrous** to a flower containing several stamens.   The stamens may be **monodelphous,** in which the filaments are united into a tube, as in the Wild Lupine (figure 67), or the stamens may be **diadelphous** (figure 68), which means two sets

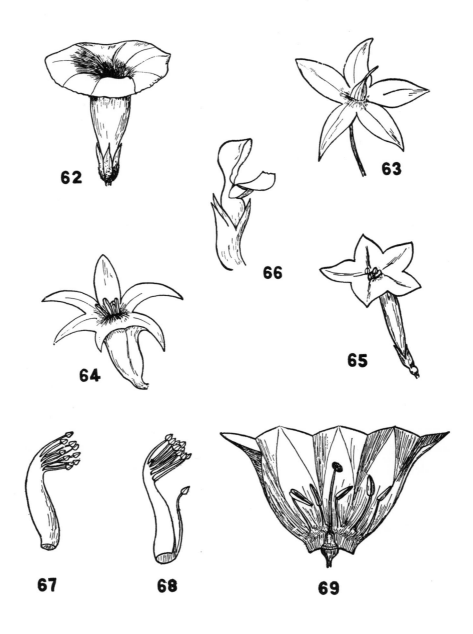

of united stamens. In this form of arrangement there may be a union of the filaments of all the stamens except one, which is a common diadelphous arrangement of stamens in many of the species of the Bean family. When there are several sets of united stamens, the arrangement is said to be **polydelphous.**

Adnation or union of the stamens with other parts of the flower is of frequent occurrence, and the terms employed depend upon the degree of adnation, or the absence of it, namely, **hypogynous** (meaning beneath the pistil), applied to parts, including stamens, which are inserted or borne on the receptacle of the flower (figure 56). This is the absence of adnation and indicates an unmodified type. **Perigynous** (around the pistil) implies an adnation which carries up the apparent origin or place of insertion of the parts of the flower to some distance above or away from the receptacle and thus placing the insertion around instead of beneath the pistil (figure 57). **Epigynous** (on the pistil), where the adnation is complete to the very top of the ovary (figure 58).

When the stamens are borne upon the corolla, or upon the tube of the corolla, they are said to be **epipetalous** (figure 69), and when they are borne upon the pistil, as in the Orchid family, they are said to be **gynandrous.**

The most important part of a stamen is the **anther** (figure 44D), which contains the pollen. It normally consists of two lobes or sacs; but as each sac is often, and in most of our common flowers, divided into two cavities, it appears to possess in such instances four pollen sacs. For the discharge of the pollen, the cells of a normal anther open along a definite line, usually extending from top to bottom. This suture or line of dehiscence may be lateral or marginal, or centrally located.

In the genus Solanum, to which the Potato belongs, in most members of the Heath family (Ericaceae), in Polygala, and certain other species, the anther cells open only by a hole or pore (figure 71). In the Blueberry, Cranberry etc. the pore-bearing tip of the anther cell is prolonged considerably, often into a slender tube. In the Barberry, and in most other members of that family, and in the Lauraceae, the whole face of each anther cell separates by a continuous line, forming a kind of door, which is attached at the top, and turns back, as if on a hinge; and the anther is said to open by uplifted valves (figure 72).   In the Sassafras and certain other members of the Lauraceae, each lobe of the anther opens by two smaller valves, like trapdoors.

The attachment of the anther to the filament (or stalk) presents three

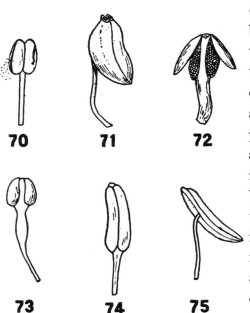

70   71   72

73   74   75

different modes, frequently connected by gradation: **Innate** (figure 70), in which the anther is a direct continuation of the axis of the filament, the cells usually opening by marginal slits, and the lobes or cells of the anther project neither inward nor outward; **adnate** (figure 73), in which the anther is a direct continuation of the filament but having the anther cells adherent to the anterior or posterior face of the filament; the Wild Ginger (Asarum) furnishes a good example of this, on account of a prominent prolongation of the connective or tip of the filament (figure 74); **versatile** (figure 75), when the anther is attached at some part only of its back or front to the tip of the filament, on which it lightly swings when the pollen is discharged; examples of this are seen in members of the Lily family, the grasses, Evening Primrose (O e n o t h e r a   b i e n n i s) and others.

Pollination

The structure of most flowers affords an excellent indication of the device used for the transference of pollen from one flower to another (pollination).   Long ago it was assumed that Nature wished no flower to be fertilized by its own pollen, but in the light of present knowledge we know this is not wholly true. The subject of pollination of flowers by insects received a great light through the investigations of Charles Darwin and the publication in 1862 of his well-known book on the fertilization of orchids by the aid of insects.

As we understand the matter today, it appears that flowers are habitually intercrossed (flowers of the same species), and that there are manifold structural adaptations which secure or favor this interchange of pollen. Separation of sexes (stamens and pistils) is a direct adaptation to cross-pollination, rendering it necessary between individuals with dioecious flowers, and favoring it in most plants with monoecious and polygamous flowers. Strictly, close fertilization can take place in hermaphroditic flowers only.

Flowers depend upon certain external agencies for the transference of pollen from one flower to the flower on another plant. These agencies are wind (anemophilous flowers) and insects (entomophilous flowers). Other agencies are of minor importance, although water must be considered in connection with some aquatic plants.

Wind-pollinated flowers are mostly dull in color, destitute of odor and nectar, since these qualities attract insects. Wind-pollinated flowers usually have the sexes separated, the flowers borne in great abundance and have very light pollen. Most of our common trees (the Pines, Oaks, Hickories etc.) depend upon wind for the transference of pollen, as do also the grasses, sedges, Plantain and others.

Insect-pollinated flowers are correlated with showy coloration (including white, which is most showy at dusk), odor or secretion of nectar. Structural adaptations of the flower in reference to insect visitation are wonderfully various, and most of these are found upon investigation to favor, or often to necessitate, cross-pollination. The range of these variations is too extensive to be treated here. Literature upon this subject is easily available and most textbooks of botany contain chapters upon the subject.

After pollination the pollen grain germinates upon the surface of the stigma, sends a tube down through the tissue of the stigma and style and discharges into the ovule a male nucleus which unites with a nucleus in the embryo sac of the ovule, fertilizing the ovule, and stimulating its development into an embryonic plant.   By a process of hardening of the coats of the ovule its development is arrested and the seed is produced.

The Fruit

The fruit of a plant (in the case of our flowering plants) consists of the matured pistil (or gynoecium), including also whatever parts of the perianth or other floral organs may be joined to it.   Fruits are of various degrees of simplicity or complexity, and may consist of a matured simple ovary, a cluster of such ovaries, at least when they are somewhat coherent, or a ripened ovary with calyx and other floral parts consolidated with it.

The **pericarp,** or seed vessel, is the ripened ovary and should therefore accord in structure with the ovary from which it is derived.   In the development of a simple ovary into a simple fruit certain alterations sometimes take place, either by the abortion or obliteration of certain parts, or by accessory growth.   The **dehiscence** is the method by which a pericarp opens to discharge its seeds and may be regular (normal) or irregular (abnormal).   The word " pod " is frequently applied to dehiscent pericarps.

A **capsule** is a dehiscent pericarp formed of two or more carpels.   Such carpels are **septicidal** (figure 80) when the dehiscence is such that the carpel is divided into its constituent carpels.   Members of the St John's-wort family afford a good example of this method as do also Rhododendron and Kalmia.   Carpels are called **loculicidal** (figure 79) when each of the component carpels splits down its dorsal suture, as in Iris, Hibiscus, Oenothera etc.

Kinds of fruits.   For ordinary purposes it is sufficient to classify fruits into four classes:

1   Simple fruits, those which result from the ripening of a single pistil.

2   Aggregate, those of a cluster of carpels of one flower crowded into a mass.

3 Accessory fruits, where the principal mass consists of the surroundings or support of either a simple or an aggregate fruit.

4 Multiple or collective fruits, formed by the union or compact aggregation of the pistils of several flowers.

1 *Simple Fruits*

Upon the basis of texture, simple fruits may be designated as dry fruits, stone fruits and baccate fruits.

Dry fruits which are dehiscent:

Follicle (figure 78), a pod formed by a simple pistil, and dehiscent along one line (suture, and almost always the inner or ventral suture), as in the Columbine, Marsh Marigold, Milkweed and Dogbane.

Legume (figure 77), a pod formed of a simple pistil which is dehiscent by both sutures, so dividing it into two pieces or valves. The fruits of the Bean or Pea family are of this sort. Some members of this family (Meibomia), however, have legumes reduced to indehiscent achenes, joined together end to end, and to which a special term **"loment"** (figure 76) is applied.

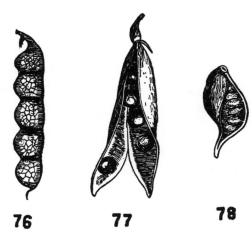

76   **77**   **78**

Capsule (figures 79 and 80), a pod or dehiscent fruit, of any compound pistil. The modes of regular dehiscence are mentioned above in the paragraph on dehiscence, and it remains here to describe two modifications of the capsule, namely, the **pyxis,** in which the dehiscence is along a circular line, cutting off the upper part as a lid, examples of which are seen in the common Plantain, Purslane and Henbane, small plants or weeds not illustrated in this work; and the **silique,** a narrow, two-valved capsule, with two parietal placentae, from which the valves separate in dehiscence, as in the Mustard family, where there is usually a false partition stretched across between the two placentae.

Dry fruits which are indehiscent:

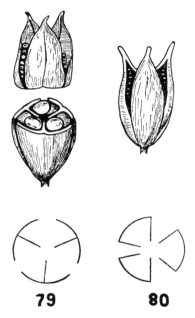

79   **80**

Samara, an indehiscent, one-seeded fruit provided with a wing. In the Ash, the wing is terminal; in the Elm, the wing surrounds the body of the pericarp; and the Maple fruit is a double samara or pair of such fruits.

Achene (figures 81–88), a general term for all one-seeded, dry and hard, seedlike fruits. The best examples are the fruits of the Buttercup, Anemone, Clematis and Avens. The style sometimes remains on the fruit as a long and feathery tail (Dandelion, figure 85), and in others merely as a short hook (Buttercup, figures 86 and 87). In the Compositae (Sunflower family) the tube of the calyx is joined with the surface of the ovary, and its border or upper edge appears as a crown or cup, or a set of teeth or of scales, or very often as a tuft of bristles or hairs, called the **pappus** (figures 82–84, 88).

Utricle, a dry achenelike fruit with a thin and bladdery loose pericarp, like that of the Goosefoot (Chenopodium).

Caryopsis or **grain,** differs from the achene in having the seed completely filling the cell and its thin coats firmly consolidated throughout with the very thin pericarp. This term is applied to the fruits of the grass family, including Indian corn and all other cereals.

Nut, a hard one-celled and one-seeded, indehiscent fruit which finds its best examples in the fruit of the Hazel, Beech, Oak, Chestnut etc. The smaller nutlike fruits of the Borage family and of the Mint family are usually called **nutlets.**

Stone fruits:

Drupe (figures 90 and 92), of which the best examples are the fruit of
the Cherry, Plum, Peach etc., are one-seeded or rarely two-seeded, in the
ripening of which the outer portion of the pericarp becomes fleshy or pulpy
and the inner portion becomes much hardened. The term is also commonly
applied to similar fruits of the Hackberry, Cornus, Rhamnus etc. In the
case of the Blackberry (figure 89) and Raspberry, the several pericarps of
the aggregate fruit are called **drupelets.**

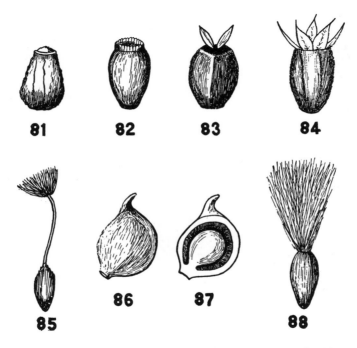

Pome (figure 91), the name of the fruit of the Apple, Pear, Quince etc.,
which are fleshy fruits, composed of two to several carpels, of parchment-
like texture (or hard in the Thorn Apples), inclosed in flesh which has
developed from the inclosing calyx and receptacle. Indeed, the fruit of
the Thorn Apple might well be called a " several-seeded drupe."

Pepo, or Gourd-fruit, a type of fruit typified by the Melon, Squash,
Cucumber, Gourd and other members of that family.

Berry [baccate] (figure 93), a simple fruit in which the pericarp is fleshy throughout and without a hardened inner coat. The fruit of the Grape, Currant, Gooseberry, Cranberry, Banana and Tomato furnish good examples.

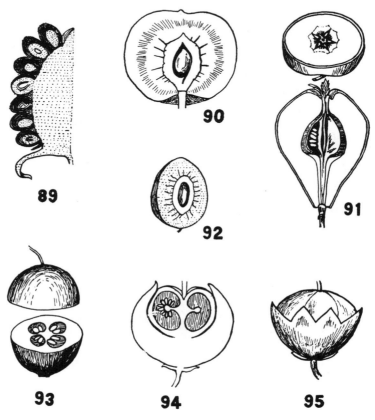

2 Aggregate Fruits

Aggregate fruits are those in which a cluster of carpels, all belonging to one flower, are crowded on the receptacle into one mass, as in the Blackberry (figure 89) taken as a whole. They may be aggregates of any kind of simple fruits. But when dry and not coherent, the mass would simply be described as a head or spike of carpels (or achenes, as in Buttercup and Anemone).

3 *Accessory Fruits*

Accessory fruits are those in which some conspicuous part of the fruit is derived from some portion not organically connected with the ovary or pistil. This part might be called a pseudocarp, and this condition may occur either in simple, in aggregate, or in multiple fruits. The Wintergreen (G a u l t h e r i a p r o c u m b e n s) affords a good example (figures 94 and 95), the fleshy part of the fruit being the enlarged calyx. Likewise the torus, although not conspicuous, may be said to be an accessory part of the fruit of the Blackberry, being the fleshy or pulpy center of the fruit. In the Strawberry it is very conspicuous and comprises the sole edible part of the fruit, the achenes or true fruits being dispersed over the surface and comparatively insignificant.

4 *Multiple or Collective Fruits*

Multiple or collective fruits are those which result from the aggregation of several flowers into one mass. The simplest of these is the fruit of the Partridge Berry (M i t c h e l l a r e p e n s) and certain Honeysuckles (Lonicera) formed of the ovaries of two blossoms united into one fleshy fruit. More typical examples of this are seen in the Pineapple fruit, the Mulberry and others.

WILD FLOWERS

DESCRIPTIONS OF SPECIES

Cat-tail Family

Typhaceae

Broad-leaved Cat-tail

Typha latifolia Linnaeus

Figure I

A marsh or aquatic plant, usually growing in thick colonies from creeping perennial rootstocks provided with fibrous roots. Stems stout, round in cross-section, glabrous, 4 to 8 feet high. Leaves numerous, linear, flat, swordlike, sheathing the stem at the base and rather stiffly ascending. Flowers monoecious, that is, staminate and pistillate flowers separate but on the same plant; densely crowded into terminal spikes; the staminate spikes uppermost and scarcely or but slightly separated from the dark brown or nearly black pistillate spike, each 3 to 12 inches long and often an inch or more thick. Perianth of the individual flowers composed merely of bristles which subtend two to seven stamens (in the staminate spike), or a small, short-stalked ovary (in the pistillate spikes). Mingled among the stamens and pistils are bristly hairs, and among the pistillate flowers many sterile flowers with clavate tips. The fruit consists of many small nutlets, surmounted by the persistent bristles which aid in wind dissemination of the seeds when the head of fruit breaks up.

Common everywhere in marshes and swamps, and also in Europe and Asia. Flowering in June and July; fruit ripe in August and September, frequently persistent until the following spring.

The Narrow-leaved Cat-tail (Typha angustifolia Linnaeus), is more abundant in marshes along the coast, but is sometimes found inland. The leaves are narrower than those of the preceding species, being one-sixth to one-half of an inch wide; spikes lighter brown in color, not so thick, and the staminate and pistillate spikes separated from one another.

WILD FLOWERS

Figure I
Broad-leaved Cat-tail
(T y p h a l a t i f o l i a Linnaeus)

Water Plantain Family

Alismaceae

Broad-leaved Arrowhead

Sagittaria latifolia Willdenow

Plate 1

A perennial aquatic herb with thickened base and numerous long, fibrous roots. Leaves long petioled and extremely variable in form and size, sometimes wider than long and obtuse, sometimes linear-lanceolate and acuminate at the apex; the basal lobes of the leaf blades one-quarter to one-half as long as the blade. Flowers monoecious or sometimes dioecious, pediceled and borne near the summits of the scapes in verticels of three, the staminate usually uppermost, each verticel subtended by three bracts. Calyx of three persistent sepals. Stamens numerous; anthers two-celled, dehiscent by lateral slits. Pistillate flowers with numerous distinct ovaries and sometimes with imperfect stamens. The ovaries ripen into a globose or compact head of achenes, each achene broadly winged on both margins, with a beak about one-third its length and horizontal or nearly so.

Common in shallow water almost everywhere and offered by dealers in native plants for colonizing lily ponds and shallow waters. Such situations are scarcely complete without its presence. Flowering from July to September.

There are several closely related species such as Sagittaria cuneata Sheldon, with a minute beak to the achene, which is erect over the ventral wing; Sagittaria pubescens Muhlenberg, which is strongly pubescent; Sagittaria graminea Michaux, which has long-petioled, linear, lanceolate or elliptical leaf blades, acute at both ends, and much smaller flowers than S. latifolia, and other less abundant species. A nearly related genus is Alisma, represented in our range by the very common Alisma subcordatum Rafinesque (American Water Plantain), with oblong, elliptic, oval or ovate leaf blades which are cuneate, truncate or cordate at the base, the flowering scapes rather tall, bearing numerous branches and pedicels in whorls of three to ten, with very small, white flowers. Like most other members of the Alismaceae, it inhabits shallow water or muddy places.

Sedge Family

Cyperaceae

Sheathed Cotton Grass or Hare's Tail Rush

Eriophorum callithrix Chamisso

Plate 2a

The Cotton Grass may be regarded not so much as a wild flower as one of the most ornamental of the sedges, since it is not a true grass. It is an inhabitant of cold, mossy bogs. The stiff culms, forming tussocks, rise eight to twenty inches above the surface of the bog and each culm bears at the summit a solitary spikelet of small, perfect flowers; each flower with six scalelike divisions, three stamens and a three-cleft style. Within the scalelike perianth are numerous soft, white bristles, which become greatly elongated in fruit, at which time the bog where the plant is growing becomes beautiful with hundreds or thousands of these waving white plumes.

Common in sphagnum bogs from Newfoundland to Alaska, south to Massachusetts, Pennsylvania and Wisconsin. Flowering in early spring, the white plumes being at their best in June or, in the far north, in July.

The Sheathed Cotton Grass is but one of a number of related species which add much to the beauty of our wet meadows, swamps and bogs in summer. Perhaps even more abundant in the north is the Thin-leaved Cotton Grass (E r i o p h o r u m   v i r i d i c a r i n a t u m   (Engelmann) Fernald) with five to thirty nodding white plumes, and the Virginia Cotton Grass (E r i o p h o r u m   v i r g i n i c u m   Linnaeus), in which the soft bristles of the mature plume are of a dingy brown color.

Arum Family

Araceae

Jack-in-the-pulpit; Indian Turnip

Arisaema triphyllum (Linnaeus) Torrey

Plate 3

A perennial herb, 1 to 3 feet tall, from a rounded, acrid corm. Leaves one or two, nearly erect, and exceeding the scape, three-foliate, the segments or leaflets pale green beneath, ovate, acute, rounded or pointed at the base, 3 to 8 inches long, 1 to 3 inches wide, unfolding with the flowers. Flowers dioecious, borne on the basal part of the club-shaped spadix, which is naked, blunt and green or purple above; spathe green and purple-striped, curving in a broad flap over the top of the spadix, long pointed, sometimes whitish with green stripes or almost uniformly greenish. The crowded ovaries of the pistillate flowers ripen into a cluster of bright-red, shining, globose berries.

A common plant of moist woods and thickets, flowering from early spring until June. The fruit ripens in July, and in late summer the leaves frequently wither and die, leaving the stalks of bright-red berries conspicuous objects in the woods.

Two closely related species are sometimes recognized, Arisaema pusillum (Peck) Nash, with leaves green beneath, a cylindrical spadix and spathe deep brown to almost black in color; Arisaema stewardsonii Britton, with a conspicuously fluted spathe which is whitish below and green or green-striped toward the tip, but otherwise resembling A. pusillum.

The Green Dragon or Dragon-root (Arisaema dracontium (Linnaeus) Schott) (figure II) has solitary leaves divided into five to seventeen segments, and a narrow greenish or whitish, long-pointed spathe enwrapping the spadix, the upper part of which tapers into a slender appendage exserted 1 to 7 inches beyond the spathe. The mature berries are reddish-orange in color. This plant is less abundant than the Jack-in-the-pulpit, and much less conspicuous.

Figure II
Green Dragon or Dragon-root
(A r i s a e m a   d r a c o n t i u m (Linnaeus) Schott)

Wild Calla; Water Arum

Calla palustris Linnaeus

Plate 4

A perennial herb of swamps and bogs with long, acrid rootstocks, covered with sheathing scales and with fibrous roots at the nodes, from which arise numerous petioled leaves with thick, entire, glossy green, broadly ovate or suborbicular leaf blades 2 to 5 inches wide, cuspidate or pointed at the apex and deeply cordate at the base. Flowering scapes about as long as the petioles, sheathed at the base, bearing at the summit an ovate-lanceolate or elliptic, acuminate, open spathe, white within and greenish without, sometimes with a second spathe nearly opposite the first and smaller in size, or rarely the two of equal size. Spadix cylindric, much shorter than the spathe, densely covered with perfect flowers, or the uppermost flowers staminate. The individual flowers on the spadix possess usually six stamens and no perianth. Ovaries ripening into a large head of red berries.

Frequent in swamps and bogs, especially northward. Rare in the southern part of its range. Flowering from late May to early July, the fruit ripening from June to August.

Skunk Cabbage

Spathyema foetida (Linnaeus) Rafinesque

Plate 5

A fetid herb, and the first plant to flower in the spring. The leaves are large, ovate, cordate, numerous in dense crowns, becoming in summer 1 to 3 feet long and 1 foot wide, but at flowering time scarcely beginning to unfold. Rootstock thick, descending, terminating in whorls of fleshy fibers. Spathe preceding the leaves, erect, 3 to 6 inches high, 1 to 3 inches in diameter, convolute, firm and fleshy, often one-fourth to one-half of an inch thick in the middle, pointed, completely inclosing the spadix, brown to greenish yellow, usually mottled, its short scape usually below the surface.

Spadix about 1 inch in diameter, entirely covered by the perfect flowers, greatly enlarged and sometimes 6 inches in diameter in fruit. The perianth of each flower consists of four hooded sepals.

A common plant of low, wet woods, meadows and swamps. When the spathes first appear, they possess little of the rank odor which characterizes them when older and which renders them objects of opprobrium. They appear almost before the last snowdrifts have disappeared and indicate the first awakening of plant life in spring.

The Arum family (Araceae), to which belong the Jack-in-the-pulpit, the Wild Calla, and the Skunk Cabbage, also contains several other native plants usually found in wet or damp places. The Green Water Arum (Peltandra virginica (Linnaeus) Kunth) with bright-green, hastate-sagittate leaves, often 1 to 2 feet long and 3 to 8 inches wide, possesses an inconspicuous green spathe, 4 to 8 inches long, with a strongly involute undulate margin. The Golden Club (Orontium aquaticum Linnaeus), found from New England and southern New York, southward, possesses a cylindric, golden yellow spadix, from which the spathe falls at flowering time.

The Sweet Flag, Calamus or Flagroot (Acorus calamus Linnaeus) (figure III) belonging also to this family is a common plant of wet meadows, with long, linear, flaglike leaves and the spathe a leaflike extension of the scape, the spadix spikelike, 2 to 3 inches long and about one-half of an inch in diameter, compactly covered with minute greenish yellow flowers.

Yellow-eyed Grass Family
Xyridaceae
Carolina Yellow-eyed Grass
Xyris caroliniana Walter

Plate 2b

A small, tufted, grasslike plant of wet meadows and bogs, with numerous fibrous roots and flat, linear, grasslike leaves 4 to 15 inches long. Flowering scapes as long or usually much longer than the leaves. Sometimes over a foot tall, bearing at the summit a dense, ovoid, obtuse spike

Figure III
Sweet Flag, Calamus or Flagroot
(A c o r u s c a l a m u s Linnaeus)

of coriaceous, overlapping bracts or scales. Flowers bright yellow, about one-fourth of an inch broad, on short, slender peduncles; each flower consisting of three oblong divisions to the corolla, three stamens inserted on the corolla and a three-branched style. Flowers appearing from the axils of the bracts comprising the spike.

In swamps, bogs and borders of streams from Maine to Florida and Louisiana, mostly near the coast. Flowering from June to August; in New York usually flowering in July.

Several closely related species are recognized by botanists. X y r i s f l e x u o s a Muhlenberg, of about the same range, has the scapes bulbous-thickened at the base. X y r i s m o n t a n a H. Ries, in bogs from Nova Scotia to Michigan and Pennsylvania, is frequent in the mountainous parts of New York, and resembles very closely the Carolina Yellow-eyed Grass.

Pipewort Family

Eriocaulaceae

Seven-angled Pipewort

Eriocaulon septangulare Withering

Plate 6a

A small, tufted plant with pellucid, fenestrate-nerved leaves arising from the crown, 1 to 3 inches long. Flowering scapes weak, twisted, usually about seven-angled, 1 to 8 inches tall, or when submersed, both the leaves and the scapes considerably elongated, bearing at the summit a small subglobose head of woolly white flowers, interspersed with numerous bracts; most of the flowers staminate and about one-eighth of an inch long, the few pistillate flowers scarcely more than half as large.

In still water and on shores of ponds, lakes and streams, usually where it is sandy, from Newfoundland to Minnesota, Florida and Texas. Usually in flower in the north in July and August. In the south are numerous other species of this and related genera.

Spiderwort Family

Commelinaceae

Asiatic Dayflower

Commelina communis Linnaeus

Plate 6b

A glabrous plant with decumbent or ascending branching stems, often rooting at the nodes, 1 to 3 feet long with numerous oblong-lanceolate leaves 3 to 5 inches long and 1 to 1½ inches wide, acuminate at the tips and narrowed or rounded at the base, smooth and dark green, the stem with white-membranous, green-veined sheaths below each leaf. Flowers toward the ends of the branches or stems, each subtended by green leaflike spathes about 1 inch long, deep blue, one-half of an inch broad or broader, irregular, consisting of three sepals and three petals, two of them much larger than the third; three fertile stamens, one of them incurved and its anther larger than the others. In addition there are three sterile stamens. Fruit a small, two-celled capsule, each cell with two seeds; seeds compressed, dark brown and roughened.

A native of Asia, commonly naturalized or adventive in southern New York and southward, and occasionally appearing farther north. Sometimes called " Wandering Jew."

Spider Lily; Spiderwort

Tradescantia virginiana Linnaeus

Plate 7

A tall, smooth or slightly pubescent plant, belonging to the same family as the Dayflower, often 1 to 3 feet tall, with long, linear or linear-lanceolate, long-pointed leaves, often a foot long and one-half to 1 inch wide, usually more or less channeled along the middle. Flowers in terminal umbels or clusters on slender pedicels, one-half to 2 inches long; blue or purplish, rarely white, 1 to 2 inches broad with three small sepals, three large, obovate, similar petals, and six equal and fertile stamens.

In rich soil, mostly in woods and thickets, from southern New York, Ohio and South Dakota, south to Virginia and Arkansas. A common plant in cultivation farther north where it is a frequent escape to roadsides and fence rows. Although of great beauty, the flowers are of brief duration, and the delicate petals soon wither, the flowers being followed by others until all the numerous buds of each cluster have bloomed. Northward it usually flowers in June and July or sometimes as late as August, especially since not all the stems appear to reach maturity at the same time.

Pickerel Weed Family

P o n t e d e r i a c e a e

Pickerel Weed

Pontederia cordata Linnaeus

Plate 8

A perennial aquatic herb, rising from a thick, horizontal rootstock, with thick, glossy, dark-green, ovate to lanceolate leaves, cordate-sagittate, truncate or narrowed at the base, 2 to 10 inches long, 1 to 6 inches wide, the apex and basal lobes obtuse. Flowering stems erect, 1 to 4 feet tall, glandular-pubescent above, one-leaved, with several sheathing, bractlike leaves at the base. Flowers blue, ephemeral, numerous, in a dense head or spike (spadix) subtended by a thin bractlike spathe. Each flower is tubular, about one-fourth of an inch long, curved, two-lipped, the upper lip composed of three ovate lobes, of which the middle one is the longest, and with two yellow spots at the base within, the lower lip of three linear-oblong spreading lobes. Stamens six, the filaments, anthers and style bright blue. After flowering, the lobes and upper part of the perianth tube wither above, while the persistent base hardens around the fruit.

Frequent along the borders of ponds and streams and shallow margins of lakes, where it flowers from June to September, usually at its best in August. One of the most attractive of our native aquatic plants.

The Pickerel Weed belongs to the Pontederiaceae, represented in our flora by but one other genus, the Mud Plantains (Heteranthera), with two species of small, inconspicuous herbs of shallow water or wet muddy shores.

Bunchflower Family

Melanthaceae

Glutinous Triantha or False Asphodel

Triantha glutinosa (Michaux) Baker

Plate 9b

A perennial, herbaceous plant, somewhat bulbous at the base; stems 6 to 20 inches high, viscid pubescent with black glands, bearing a few leaves near the base; most of the leaves basal and tufted, linear and grasslike, 2 to 7 inches long. Flowers numerous in an oblong raceme at apex of the stem, subtended by minute involucral bracts, each flower about one-fourth of an inch broad, the perianth white, divided into six nearly equal oblong segments; stamens six, with pink or reddish anthers; fruit a small oblong capsule, the tiny seeds with a curved appendage at each end.

An inhabitant of sphagnum or marly bogs from Newfoundland to Minnesota, Michigan and the southern Alleghanies. By no means a common plant, and one which the wild flower connoisseur always likes to locate, and which repays by its rarity rather than its beauty the inevitable journey to the boggy place where it grows.

Glaucous Anticlea

Anticlea chlorantha (Richardson) Rydberg

Plate 9a

A slender, herbaceous, perennial plant from a membranous coated, ovoid bulb which is about an inch long. Stems slender, 6 inches to 3 feet tall; leaves linear, one-eighth to seven-eighths of an inch wide, keeled, the lower ones 4 to 12 inches long, the upper ones much shorter. Inflorescence a simple, open raceme or large, loose panicle, 4 to 12 inches long, with slender, ascending branches. Flowers perfect, greenish or yellowish, about three-fourths of an inch broad; perianth segments oval or obovate, obtuse, bearing a large obcordate gland just above the short claw, the perianth persistent and adnate to the lower part of the ovary after withering. Fruit an oblong, three-celled capsule, about 1 inch long.

An inhabitant of marshes, bogs and moist places, New Brunswick to Vermont, New York, Manitoba and Missouri. Flowering in August. Not so rare as the Glutinous Triantha, but usually growing in similar locations.

Bunchflower

Melanthium virginicum Linnaeus

Plate 10

A rather tall, leafy, herbaceous plant, perennial by a thick rootstock; stems slender to somewhat stout, 2 to 5 feet high. Leaves linear, acuminate, often a foot long, but only one-third to 1 inch wide, the lower ones sheathing the stem, the upper ones smaller and sessile. Inflorescence a many-flowered panicle, 6 to 18 inches long, pubescent; flowers about three-fourths of an inch broad, greenish yellow, turning brown with age; perianth of six spreading, separate, persistent segments, each segment consisting of an oblong, obtuse, flat blade, sometimes obcordate, about twice as long as the claw, and bearing two dark glands at its base; stamens shorter than the segments and adnate to them; fruit a three-lobed capsule, about two-thirds of an inch long.

In meadows, wet woods and marshes, Rhode Island to southern New York and Minnesota, south to Florida and Texas. Flowering in July and August.

The Bunchflower is not a common plant in New York, and is found only in a few localities in the southern part of the State. Two closely related species are equally uncommon and also restricted to the southern part of the State. These are: (1) the Crisped or Broad-leaved Bunch-flower (M e l a n t h i u m l a t i f o l i u m Desvaux), with broader leaves and the blade of the perianth segments undulate, crisped and scarcely longer than the claw; (2) the Pine-barren Oceanorus (O c e a n o r u s l e i m a n t h o i d e s (A. Gray) Small), with linear, blunt leaves, the outer ones becoming fibrous, and small whitish flowers with oblong perianth segments, which are sessile.

American White Hellebore; Indian Poke
Veratrum viride Linnaeus

Plate 11

A tall, leafy, perennial herb; stem simple and branched only in the inflorescence, stout, 2 to 8 feet tall, from a poisonous, perennial, erect rootstock 2 to 4 inches long and 1 to 2 inches thick with numerous fleshy-fibrous roots. Leaves alternate, clasping, strongly veined and plaited, all pointed at the apex; the lower leaves broadly oval or elliptic, 5 to 12 inches long, 3 to 6 inches wide; the upper ones successively narrower and shorter, those of the inflorescence very small; stem and inflorescence pubescent. Flowers greenish or greenish yellow, two-thirds to 1 inch broad arranged in a many-flowered panicle at the summit of the stem, the panicle often 8 to 20 inches long, its lower branches spreading or drooping. Segments of the perianth six, without glands or claws, oblong or oblanceolate, ciliate-serrulate, twice as long as the curved, yellow stamens which are six in number and opposite the perianth segments. Fruit a three-lobed, three-celled, many-seeded capsule, three-fourths to 1 inch long and one-third to one-half of an inch thick.

In swamps and wet woods, New Brunswick, Quebec and Ontario to Minnesota, south to Georgia and Tennessee. Flowering in May and June, or July in the far north.

Lily Family
Liliaceae
Day Lily
Hemerocallis fulva Linnaeus

Plate 12

A tall, glabrous herb with fibrous roots, usually growing in dense clusters. Leaves mostly basal, linear, erect or spreading, 1 to 2 feet long and one-half to two-thirds of an inch wide, channeled and tapering to an acute tip. Flowering scapes leafless, 2 to 5 feet tall, bearing a few short bracts above, and six to fifteen flowers on short pedicels. Perianth funnelform, tawny-orange, 4 to 5 inches long, opening for a day, its lobes oblong, somewhat spreading, netted-veined, the three outer nearly flat and more acute; the three inner ones undulate on their margins and blunt. Stamens six, inserted at the top of the perianth tube, shorter than the lobes of the perianth and declined. Fruit an oblong, thick-walled, three-angled, wrinkled capsule.

Native of Europe and Asia. Frequent in cultivation in this country and commonly escaped to meadows, along streams and roadsides or persistent in old yards and cemeteries. A flower of early introduction into the eastern states where it has made itself quite at home as an escape, and thrives and spreads with amazing rapidity under favorable conditions.

The Yellow Day Lily (Hemerocallis flava Linnaeus), with yellow flowers, their lobes parallel-veined, is occasionally found near old gardens and on roadsides, but not so frequently as the tawny-orange flowered Day Lily.

Red Lily; Wood Lily; Philadelphia Lily

Lilium philadelphicum Linnaeus

Plate 13

Stems 1 to 3 feet tall from a bulb about 1 inch in diameter and composed of numerous narrow, jointed, fleshy scales. Leaves lanceolate, acute at both ends, or the lower leaves sometimes obtuse, in whorls of three to eight on the stem, or a few of the upper leaves alternate, thin, with finely roughened margins. Flowers one to five at summit of stem, erect, 3 to 4 inches high; perianth reddish orange, its six equal segments spatulate, somewhat spreading, pointed or obtuse, one-half to 1 inch wide, gradually narrowed below, spotted with purple toward the base; stamens six, about as long as the club-shaped style. Capsule oblong-ovoid, 1 to 2 inches long.

In rather dry woods and thickets, more often in sandy regions than elsewhere, Maine and Ontario to North Carolina and West Virginia.

Wild Yellow Lily; Canada or Nodding Lily

Lilium canadense Linnaeus

Plate 14

Stems 2 to 5 feet tall, from a stout rootstock bearing several subglobose, scaly, white bulbs. Leaves in whorls of four to ten or some of them alternate, lanceolate or oblong-lanceolate, acuminate, 2 to 6 inches long, one-fourth to $1\frac{1}{4}$ inches wide, finely roughened on the margins and on the veins beneath. Flowers one to sixteen, nodding on long peduncles at the top of the stem; perianth segments 2 to 3 inches long, yellow or red, usually thickly spotted, recurved or spreading; fruit an oblong, erect capsule 1 to 2 inches long.

Common in swamps, moist meadows, and fields, Nova Scotia to Minnesota, Georgia, Alabama and Nebraska. Flowering in July and August. A common and most attractive wild flower of the east, more abundant than the Turk's-cap Lily (L i l i u m   s u p e r b u m Linnaeus), which has similar but usually larger flowers, usually orange-red and purple-spotted, more strongly recurved flower segments and leaves smooth and not roughened on the margins or veins as in L.   c a n a d e n s e.

Yellow Adder's-tongue; Dog's-tooth Violet

Erythronium americanum Ker

Plate 15a

A low, herbaceous plant arising from a deeply buried corm which propagates by offshoots; the simple stem 6 to 12 inches long, bearing a pair of equal or somewhat unequal, oblong or oblong-lanceolate, flat leaves, dark glossy green, usually mottled with brown, sometimes green all over, narrowed into clasping petioles; the flower stem arising from between the leaves, bearing a single nodding flower; perianth yellow or rarely purplish-tinged, the segments oblong, seven-eighths to 2 inches long, about one-fourth of an inch wide or less, recurved, dotted within, the three inner ones auricled at the base; style club-shaped; capsule obovoid.

In moist woods and thickets, Nova Scotia to Ontario and Minnesota south to Florida and Arkansas. Flowering in April and May.

One of the commonest and best known of our spring flowers, coming in company with the Hepatica, Spring Beauty, and Squirrel Corn, but usually in its prime a little later than these. The white Dog's-tooth Violet (E r y t h r o n i u m   a l b i d u m   Nuttall), with leaves less or not at all spotted and pinkish white flowers, is very rare.

Ague or Colicroot; Star Grass

Aletris farinosa Linnaeus

Plate 16

Leaves mostly basal, lanceolate and spreading, forming a dense cluster, lanceolate, long pointed, narrowed at the base, pale yellowish green, 2 to 7 inches long, one-fourth to 1 inch wide. Roots numerous, tough and very bitter. Stem or scape 1 to 3 feet tall, bearing a few distant bractlike leaves. The terminal raceme of flowers 4 to 12 inches long; flowers erect on short pedicels subtended by small bracts; perianth tubular-oblong, six-lobed, white or the short lobes yellowish, about one-fourth to one-third of an inch long and less than half as thick, mealy-roughened without; capsules ovoid, about one-sixth of an inch long, inclosed by the withering-persistent perianth.

In dry, mostly sandy soil, Maine to Ontario and Minnesota, south to Florida and Arkansas. Flowering in June and July. In New York rarely seen except in the sandy regions adjacent to the coast. Extremely abundant on sterile sandy fields like the Hempstead plains of Long Island, where it is very conspicuous in early summer. It possesses a number of vernacular names, such as Ague Grass, Blazing Star, Bitter Grass, Crow Corn, Mealy Starwort, Aloeroot, Starroot, Huskroot, and others.

Lily of the Valley Family
Convallariaceae
Yellow Clintonia; Dogberry
Clintonia borealis (Aiton) Rafinesque

Plate 17

Flowering scape or stem 6 to 15 inches high, with two to five (usually three), oval, oblong or obovate, thin, glossy green leaves at the base, their petioles sheathing the base of the stem which arises from a slender rootstock. Leaves ciliate, 5 to 8 inches long, and $1\frac{1}{2}$ to $3\frac{1}{2}$ inches wide. Flowers three to six, forming an umbel at the top of the stem, sometimes a secondary cluster of flowers below the top, drooping, greenish yellow, three-fourths to 1 inch long, on pedicels about as long as the flowers; perianth segments distinct, six in number, equal and somewhat spreading, the six stamens about as long as the perianth. Fruit an oval, dark blue, shining berry about one-fourth of an inch in diameter.

In moist woods and thickets, Newfoundland to Manitoba, south to North Carolina and Wisconsin. Very common in the rich, moist woodlands of northern New York, but rare or absent from the coastal region. Flowering from the latter part of May until the last of June. The fruit ripe in September.

The White Clintonia (Clintonia umbellulata (Michaux) Torrey), with smaller white flowers, not drooping, and black berries, leaves and scapes more pubescent but otherwise similar, which is common in the southern Appalachians, reaches New York in the southwestern counties of the State.

Wild or False Spikenard; False Solomon's-seal
Vagnera racemosa (Linnaeus) Morong

Plate 18

Stem slender or stout, erect or ascending, sometimes zigzag, 1 to 3 feet tall, simple, bearing numerous alternate, sessile or nearly sessile oblong-lanceolate or oval, acuminate leaves, 3 to 6 inches long, 1 to 3 inches wide, which are finely pubescent, especially beneath, and sometimes also above, their margins minutely ciliate. Rootstock rather thick and fleshy with numerous long, fibrous roots, the scars of former stems irregular and ring-like. Flowers white; many, forming a large terminal panicle, 1 to 4 inches long; each flower about 2 lines broad; perianth of six oblong, equal, separate, spreading segments. Fruit a red, aromatic berry about 3 lines in diameter and speckled with purple. In Bergen swamp, New York, occurs a variety with three to six purple stripes like the fruit of V. s t e l l a t a .

In moist woods and thickets, Nova Scotia to British Columbia, south to Georgia, Missouri and Arizona.

The Star-flowered Solomon's-seal (V a g n e r a s t e l l a t a (Linnaeus) Morong) is scarcely less abundant, but seems to prefer thickets and banks with more moisture. The leaves are smaller and narrower, the flowers fewer in number, larger, white, and racemed; the berries green with six black stripes, or entirely black.

Three-leaved Solomon's-seal

Vagnera trifolia (Linnaeus) Morong

Plate 32a

Stem and leaves glabrous from a slender, elongated rootstock, the erect stem 2 to 15 inches high with two to four (usually three) oval, oblong or oblong-lanceolate, sessile leaves 2 to 5 inches long, one-half to 2 inches wide with sheathing bases. Flowers white, few, racemed at the top of the stem; perianth segments oblong or oblong-lanceolate, obtuse, finally somewhat reflexed and longer than the stamens. Fruit a dark-red berry about one-fourth of an inch in diameter.

In bogs and wet woods, Newfoundland to British Columbia, south to Connecticut, New Jersey, Pennsylvania and Michigan. Usually abundant in sphagnum under or near spruces and tamaracks, and therefore rare outside of the mountainous and northern sections of its range. A boreal species, found also in Siberia, and associated in my mind with the Black poll and Myrtle warblers of similar habitat across the northern evergreen forest region.

False or Wild Lily of the Valley
Two-leaved Solomon's-seal

Unifolium canadense (Desfontaines) Greene

Plate 19

A low, herbaceous perennial with slender rootstock, and slender, erect and often zigzag stem, 2 to 7 inches high, bearing one to three (usually two) ovate or ovate-lanceolate, pointed leaves, cordate at the base and sessile or short-petioled; stemless plants frequent and consisting of a single leaf on a petiole 1 to 4 inches long arising from the rootstock. Flowers white, numerous, forming a rather dense terminal raceme, 1 to 2 inches long; perianth about one-fifth of an inch broad with four spreading, separate segments, which slightly exceed the four stamens in length; fruit a cluster of pale-red, speckled berries, each with one or two seeds.

In moist woods and thickets, Newfoundland to the Northwest Territory of Canada, south to the mountains of North Carolina, Tennessee, Iowa and South Dakota. Flowering in May and June.

A common wild flower of most parts of New York, especially in the moist cool forests of the northern and mountainous sections.

Sessile-leaved Bellwort

Uvularia sessilifolia Linnaeus

Plate 20a

Stems slender, glabrous, 4 to 12 inches high, naked or with one or two leaves below the fork. Leaves oblong or oblong-lanceolate, 1 to 3 inches long when they mature, thin, sessile, acute at each end, slightly rough-margined, pale or glaucous beneath; flowers greenish yellow, two-thirds to $1\frac{1}{4}$ inches long; the six perianth segments smooth, the stamens shorter than the styles; anthers blunt; fruit a sharply three-angled capsule, narrowed at both ends, about 1 inch long and two-thirds as thick.

In moist woods and thickets, usually most abundant where the soil is sandy, New Brunswick and Ontario to Minnesota, south to Georgia and Arkansas. Unlike the larger flowered bellworts (U . g r a n d i f l o r a and U . p e r f o l i a t a), this small-flowered bellwort is most abundant in sandy or acid soils.

Large-flowered Bellwort

Uvularia grandiflora J. E. Smith

Plate 20b

An erect herb with smooth, leafy, forked stem from a perennial root-stock; stem with one or two leaves below the fork, 6 to 20 inches high. Leaves perfoliate, oblong, oval or ovate, pubescent beneath, glabrous above, becoming 2 to 5 inches long, acute at the apex, rather smaller and often scarcely unfolded at flowering time; flowers solitary at the ends of the branches, peduncled, drooping, narrowly bell-shaped, lemon-yellow, 1 to 1½ inches long, perianth segments six, distinct, smooth on both sides or very slightly granular within; stamens six, longer than the styles which are united to about the middle; anthers linear, the connective blunt; fruit a three-angled, truncate capsule, about one-half of an inch long.

In rich upland woods, Quebec to Ontario, Minnesota, Georgia and Kansas. Flowering in April and May. A common flower of most sections, especially in rich woodlands. In the Ontario lowlands and Hudson valley it is largely replaced by the Perfoliate Bellwort (U v u l a r i a p e r-f o l i a t a Linnaeus), which differs chiefly in having smooth and glaucous foliage, and slightly smaller flowers with the perianth segments papillose within.

Sessile-leaved Twisted-stalk

Streptopus roseus Michaux

Figure IV

Stems 1 to 3 feet high from a short, stout rootstock covered with fibrous roots. Branches usually three or four in number and obliquely ascending, all leafy and sparingly pubescent. Leaves alternate, thin, many-nerved, ovate or ovate-lanceolate, 2 to 4½ inches long, long pointed at the apex, sessile, rounded or slightly clasping the stem at the base, green on both sides, but usually paler beneath, their margins finely ciliate. Flowers purple or rose colored, about one-third of an inch long, slender-peduncled, solitary or two together from the axil of each of the upper leaves on slender peduncles, one-half to 1 inch long, the peduncle bent or twisted at about the middle; perianth bell-shaped, its six segments lanceolate and pointed, their tips somewhat recurved or spreading. Stamens six, shorter than the perianth. Fruit a globose, red berry about one-third of an inch or less in diameter.

In moist woods, Newfoundland to Manitoba, Georgia and Michigan. Flowering in May and June.

The Clasping-leaved Twisted-stalk (S t r e p t o p u s a m p l e x i - f o l i u s (Linnaeus) De Candolle) is similar but the leaves are clasping around the stem at their bases, glaucous or whitish beneath and the flowers are greenish white in color.

The Hairy Disporum (D i s p o r u m l a n u g i n o s u m (Michaux) Nichols.) resembles the Twisted-stalks in manner of growth, but the leaves are somewhat narrower and not clasping and the flowers are solitary or few together at the ends of the branches, one-half to three-fourths of an inch long and greenish in color.

Hairy Solomon's-seal

Polygonatum biflorum (Walter) Elliott

Plate 21

Stems slender, smooth, arching, often zigzag above from a thick, horizontal, jointed rootstock, bearing the raised orbicular scars of the stems of former years; stem naked below, above bearing six to many opposite or nearly opposite, oval or ovate leaves, 2 to 4 inches long, one-half to 2 inches wide, acute or acuminate at the apex, narrowed or obtuse at the base, pale or pubescent beneath, glabrous above, the upper leaves commonly narrower than the lower; flowers in drooping, axillary clusters of one to four (often two), perianth greenish or greenish yellow, tubular, one-third to one-half of an inch long, with six short lobes; the six stamens shorter than the tube, their anthers sagittate and filaments minutely roughened. Fruit a dark blue, pulpy berry about one-fourth of an inch in diameter.

WILD FLOWERS

Figure IV
Sessile-leaved Twisted-stalk
(S t r e p t o p u s   r o s e u s Michaux)

A common but not showy plant of woods and thickets from New Brunswick to Ontario and Michigan, south to Florida and Tennessee.

Resembling this but usually larger in every way, with glabrous leaves and smooth filaments, is the Smooth or Giant Solomon's-seal (P o l y g o n a t u m   c o m m u t a t u m (Roemer & Schultes) Dietrich), which ranges northeastward only to Rhode Island, New Hampshire and Ontario. It seems to prefer moist thickets and woods along streams and on bottomlands, while the Hairy Solomon's-seal is more commonly met with in rich upland woods.

Wake-robin Family

T r i l l i a c e a e

Indian Cucumber Root

Medeola virginiana Linnaeus

Plate 22

A slender, erect, unbranched herb from a perennial rootstock 1 to 3 inches long; stem 1 to 2½ feet high, loosely covered with deciduous wool, bearing the lower whorl of leaves above the middle or, in flowerless plants, at the summit; leaves of the lower whorl sessile, 2 to 5 inches long, 1 to 2 inches wide; acuminate at the apex, narrowed at the base, three to five-nerved; leaves of the upper whorl 1 to 2 inches long, one-half to 1 inch wide, short petioled or sessile, often turning reddish at the base; umbel of two to nine flowers on filiform pedicels, 1 inch long or less, declined in flower, erect or ascending in fruit; perianth segments one-fourth to one-half of an inch long, obtuse, the six equal segments recurved, the three long styles recurved. Fruit a dark blue or purplish berry one-fourth to one-half of an inch in diameter.

In moist woods and thickets, Nova Scotia to Ontario, Minnesota, Florida and Tennessee. Flowering in May and June. Fruit ripe in September.

The thick, tuberlike, white rootstock is brittle with numerous slender fibrous roots and has the odor and taste of cucumbers.

Red Trillium; Wake-robin or Birthroot

Trillium erectum Linnaeus

Plate 23a

Stem rather stout, 8 to 16 inches high, from a thick, short rootstock. Leaves rather dark green, very broadly rhombic, 3 to 7 inches long, often as wide or wider, sessile or nearly so, acuminate at the apex, narrowed at the base, peduncle 1 to 4 inches long, erect or nearly so, bearing a single, unpleasantly scented, large flower; sepals lanceolate, acuminate, spreading, one-half to $1\frac{1}{2}$ inches long; petals lanceolate to ovate, acute, spreading, equalling the sepals or a little longer, dark purplish-red, varying to pink; greenish, white, or reddish yellow in certain aberrant forms; anthers longer than the filaments and exceeding the stigmas; ovary purple with short-spreading or recurved styles; fruit an ovoid, somewhat six-lobed, reddish berry, 1 inch thick or less.

In woods and thickets, Nova Scotia to Ontario, south to North Carolina and Tennessee.

White Trillium; Large-flowered Wake-robin

Trillium grandiflorum (Michaux) Salisbury

Plate 23b

A glabrous, erect, unbranched herb from a stout, perennial, short, scarred rootstock, 8 to 18 inches high; bearing at the top of the stem three light-green, broadly rhombic-ovate or rhombic-oval leaves, 2 to 6 inches long, acuminate at the apex, narrowed and sessile at the base, peduncle erect or nearly so, 1 to 3 inches long, bearing a single flower 2 to 3 inches broad. The three sepals lanceolate, pointed and spreading. Petals three, erect-spreading, oblanceolate, obovate, or rarely ovate-oblong, obtuse or cuspidate, thin, strongly veined, white, usually turning pink with age, much longer than the sepals. Stamens six, with yellow anthers which are about one-half of an inch long; the three styles slender and ascending. Fruit a globose, black, slightly six-lobed berry, three-fourths to 1 inch in diameter.

In rich woods, preferring ravines and wooded upland slopes, Quebec to Ontario and Minnesota, south to North Carolina and Missouri.

Various monstrous forms sometimes occur with two to several long-petioled leaves, double flowers, and even forms with green, variegated or leaflike petals.

Painted Wake-robin

Trillium undulatum Willdenow

Plate 24a

Stem slender, 8 to 20 inches high, bearing three ovate, petioled, bluish green, waxy leaves, 3 to 8 inches long, 2 to 5 inches wide, long-acuminate at the apex, obtuse or rounded at the base. Flowers on erect or somewhat inclined peduncles, 1 to $2\frac{1}{2}$ inches long; sepals lanceolate, acuminate, three-fourths to $1\frac{1}{4}$ inches long, spreading; petals ovate or ovate-lanceolate, acuminate or acute, white and marked with magenta veins at the base, thin, and longer than the sepals, widely spreading, wavy-margined; the ovoid ovary with three slender spreading styles, ripening into an ovoid, obtuse, bluntly three-angled bright red shining berry.

Common in woods, especially low, moist or cool, sandy woodlands, Nova Scotia to Ontario and Wisconsin, south to Georgia and Missouri. Flowers in May and usually a few days later than the white or red trilliums.

Nodding Wake-robin

Trillium cernuum Linnaeus

Plate 24b

Stems rather slender, 8 to 20 inches high; leaves pale green, broadly rhombic, acuminate at the apex, narrowed at the base, sessile or with very short petioles, peduncle one-half to $1\frac{1}{2}$ inches long, recurved beneath the leaves and bearing a single drooping flower about 1 to $1\frac{1}{4}$ inches broad, sepals lanceolate or ovate-lanceolate, acuminate, petals white or pinkish, ovate-lanceolate or oblong-lanceolate, rolled backward, wavy-margined, two-thirds to 1 inch long, as long or longer than the sepals; anthers about as long as the subulate filaments and overtopping the stout, recurved styles, ovary whitish, ripening into an ovoid reddish-purple berry.

In rich, usually low woodlands Newfoundland to Ontario and Manitoba, south to Georgia and Missouri. Flowering in May or in the extreme northern part of its range in June, usually about ten days later than the white or red trilliums.

Amaryllis Family

Amaryllidaceae

Yellow Star Grass

Hypoxis hirsuta (Linnaeus) Coville

Plate 25

A low, perennial herb with the leaves all basal, narrowly linear, one-eighth to one-fourth of an inch wide, more or less villous and mostly longer than the flowering stems, from an ovoid or globose corm, one-fourth to one-half of an inch in diameter; flowering stems erect, slender, villous above, usually glabrous below, 2 to 6 inches high, bearing at the summit an umbel of one to seven flowers; perianth six-parted, its segments narrowly oblong, spreading, equal or nearly so, obtuse, bright yellow within, greenish and villous without, one-fourth to one-half of an inch long; stamens somewhat unequal; the style rather shorter than the stamens and three-angled, the stigma decurrent on the angles; capsules in fruit about one-eighth of an inch in diameter, the black seeds angled.

In dry, especially sandy soil, in fields, thickets and open woods, Maine to Ontario, Assiniboia, Kansas, Florida and Texas. Flowering in May and June, but frequently putting up additional flowering scapes as late as August and September.

Iris Family

Iridaceae

Larger Blue Flag

Iris versicolor Linnaeus

Plate 26

Stems round and smooth, erect, sometimes flexuous, 2 to 3 feet tall, often branched above, leafy; leaves erect, shorter than and chiefly upon the lower part of the stem, somewhat glaucous, one-half to $1\frac{1}{4}$ inches wide; rootstock horizontal, thick, fleshy, covered with the fibrous roots. Flowers several, the perianth consisting of six, clawed segments united below into a tube, the three outer ones dilated, reflexed, violet-blue, variegated with yellow, green and white; crestless, spatulate, 2 to 3 inches long, and wider and longer than the three inner segments; the ovary below the perianth tube, in fruit becoming an oblong, obscurely three-lobed capsule, 1 to $1\frac{1}{2}$ inches long; divisions of the style petallike, arching over the stamens, bearing the stigmas immediately under their two-lobed tips.

In marshes, thickets and wet meadows, common along streams and ponds, Newfoundland to Manitoba, south to Florida and Arkansas.

Narrow Blue Flag; Poison Flagroot

Iris prismatica Pursh

Plate 27

More slender in every way than I r i s v e r s i c o l o r Linnaeus, with a tuberous-thickened rootstock; stem 1 to 3 feet tall, bearing two or three very narrow, almost grasslike leaves usually less than one-fourth of an inch wide; flowers one or two at summit of each stem, blue, veined with yellow on slender pedicels; outer perianth segments one-half to 2 inches long, smooth and devoid of a crest, the inner segments smaller and narrower; the perianth tube about one-fourth of an inch long above the ovary. Fruit a narrowly oblong capsule, acute at each end and sharply three-angled, 1 to $1\frac{1}{2}$ inches long.

Marshes, wet meadows and swamps, mainly near the coast from Nova Scotia to Pennsylvania and Georgia.   Flowering in May and June.

Pointed Blue-eyed Grass

Sisyrinchium angustifolium Miller

Plate 28a

Perennial and tufted, stems stiff and erect, pale green and glaucous, 4 to 18 inches high.   Leaves pointed, about half as long as the stems, about one-sixth of an inch or less wide.   Stem simple or rarely branched, winged, the edges minutely serrulate.   Flowers deep violet-blue, one-half of an inch broad, umbellate from a pair of erect, green or slightly purplish bracts (spathe), the outer bract rather less than twice the length of the inner one, the six spreading segments of the perianth oblong and aristulate at the tip.   Capsules subglobose, often purplish tinged, about one-fourth of an inch in diameter or less.

In fields and on hillsides, Newfoundland to Saskatchewan, British Columbia, Virginia, Nebraska, Colorado and Utah. Flowering from May to July.

There are four other species of blue-eyed grass in New York State: S. mucronatum Michaux, S. arenicola Bicknell, S. graminoides Bicknell and S. atlanticum Bicknell.

Orchid Family

Orchidaceae

The members of the Orchid family in New York State, of which several are described and illustrated here, constitute a very important number of our wild flowers and call for a description of the family.   They are all perennial herbs with corms, bulbs or tuberous roots and entire, sheathing leaves, in some species reduced to scales. Flowers perfect, irregular, solitary, spiked or racemed. Perianth consisting of six segments, the three outer (sepals) similar or nearly so, two of the inner ones (petals) lateral, alike; the third inner one (lip) unlike the other two, often markedly so, usually larger, often spurred. Stamens variously united with the style into an unsymmetrical column, usually one anther, sometimes two, each two-celled; the pollen in two to eight pear-shaped, usually stalked masses (pollinia), united by elastic threads, the masses waxy or powdery and attached at the base to a viscid disc (gland). Style often terminating in a beak (rostellum) at the base of the anther or between its sacs. Stigma a viscid surface, facing the lip beneath the rostellum, or the cavity between the anther sacs (clinandrium). Ovary inferior, usually long and sometimes twisted, three-angled, one-celled. Seeds very numerous and minute, usually spindle shaped.

Small White Lady's-slipper

Cypripedium candidum Willdenow

Plate 29

This is one of the rarer Lady's-slippers of the east, with rather stiffly erect stems 6 to 12 inches high. Leaves three to five, elliptic or lanceolate, pointed, 3 to 5 inches long, two-thirds to $1\frac{1}{2}$ inches wide; flowers solitary or very rarely two on a stem; sepals lanceolate, as long or longer than the lip, greenish, spotted with purple; petals somewhat longer and narrower than the sepals, wavy-twisted, greenish; lip white, striped with purple or magenta inside, about three-fourths of an inch long.

In marly bogs and low meadows, sometimes in sphagnum bogs, New York and New Jersey to Kentucky, Minnesota, Missouri and Nebraska. Flowering in June and July.

Showy Lady's-slipper

Cypripedium reginae Walter

Plate 30

The largest and most showy of our native orchids, with a stout, villous-hirsute stem, 1 to 3 feet high, leafy to the top. Leaves large, 3 to 8 inches long, 1 to 4 inches wide, elliptic in shape, acute. Flowers 1 to 3; sepals round-ovate, white, the lateral ones united for their entire length; petals somewhat narrower than the sepals, white, lip much inflated, 1 to 2 inches long, white, variegated with crimson and white stripes.

In swamps and open wet woods, Newfoundland to Ontario, Minnesota and Georgia. Flowering in June and July, more rarely in August in the far north. Known also as Whip-poor-will's Shoe.

It is doubtful if any wild flower surpasses this in beauty. It has been gathered so extensively for its flowers in some localities that it has become rather rare. It is one of the plants that above all others needs protection in the way of education that will lead lovers of wild flowers to admire its beauty where it grows, and to use caution in picking.

Yellow or Downy Lady's-slipper

Cypripedium pubescens Willdenow

Plate 31

Stems tall and leafy, $1\frac{1}{2}$ to $2\frac{1}{2}$ feet high; leaves oval or elliptic 3 to 6 inches long, $1\frac{1}{2}$ to 3 inches wide, pointed; sepals ovate-lanceolate, usually longer than the lip, yellowish or greenish yellow and striped with purple, petals narrower, usually twisted and elongated; lip much inflated, subglobose, 1 to 2 inches long, pale yellow to bright yellow and sometimes with purple lines, a tuft of white, jointed hairs inside at the top; sterile stamen triangular, the thick, somewhat triangular stigma incurved.

In rich woods and thickets, Nova Scotia to Ontario and Minnesota, Alabama and Nebraska. This species is usually regarded as a form of C y p r i p e d i u m p a r v i f l o r u m Salisbury, which has a small, laterally compressed lip one-half to three-fourths of an inch long. Since numerous intermediate forms occur it is probable that they represent forms of a single variable species.

Ram's-head Lady's-slipper

Criosanthes arietina (R. Brown) House

(*Cypripedium arietinum* R. Brown)

Plate 32b and Figure V

Stems 6 to 12 inches high, with three or four elliptic or lanceolate leaves 2 to 4 inches long, one-third to 3 inches wide, one-flowered; sepals

(Photograph by G. A. Bailey)

Figure V
Ram's-head Lady's-slipper
(Criosanthes arietina (R. Brown) House)

separate, lanceolate, one-half to seven-eighths of an inch long, longer than the lip; petals linear, greenish brown, about as long as the sepals; lip one-half to three-fourths of an inch long, red and white, veiny, prolonged at the apex into a long blunt spur, somewhat distorted at the upper end, which gives the plant its common name of Ram's-head Lady's-slipper.

A very rare species of cold and damp woods from Quebec to Manitoba, Massachusetts, New York and Minnesota. The colored illustration is made from a photograph taken in southern Herkimer county, New York, by Mr Edward H. Eames of Buffalo and the accompanying halftone from a photograph by Mr G. A. Bailey of Geneseo.

Moccasin Flower; Stemless Lady's-slipper

Fissipes acaulis (Aiton) Small

(*Cypripedium acaule* Aiton)

Plate 33 and Figure VI

A short-stemmed plant with only two large, basal, elliptic leaves, 6 to 8 inches long and 2 to 3 inches wide, thick and dark green. The single fragrant flower borne on a scape 6 to 15 inches high; sepals greenish purple, spreading, $1\frac{1}{2}$ to 2 inches long, lanceolate, the two lateral ones united; petals narrower and somewhat longer than the sepals; lip a large, drooping, inflated sac with a closed fissure down its whole length in front, $1\frac{1}{2}$ to $2\frac{1}{4}$ inches long, somewhat obovoid, pink with darker veins, rarely white, the upper part of the interior surface of the lip crested with long, white hairs. Fruit an ascending capsule, pointed at each end.

In sandy or rocky woods, Newfoundland to Manitoba, south to North Carolina, Tennessee and Minnesota. One of the few conspicuous wild flowers that appears to be equally at home in the pine lands of the northern coastal plain and the rocky woods of the central and northern part of New York. On Long Island it sometimes blooms in May but in the north it usually blooms in June.

(Photograph by E. A. Eames)

Figure VI
Moccasin Flower; Stemless Lady's-slipper
(F i s s i p e s a c a u l i s (Aiton) Small)

Small Round-leaved Orchis

Orchis rotundifolia Pursh

Figure VII

(Photograph by O. O. Nylander)

Figure VII
Small Round-leaved Orchis
(O r c h i s   r o t u n d i f o l i a   Pursh)

Along with the Calypso, this small orchis shares the distinction of being the rarest wild flower of New York. Its slender stem rises to a height of 6 to 10 inches and bears near the base a single oval or orbicular leaf, 1 to 3 inches long, with one or two scales sheathing the stem below the leaf. Flowers in a short terminal spike, usually five to ten in number, each flower subtended by a small green bract. Sepals and petals oval, rose-colored, the lateral sepals spreading and usually slightly shorter, but sometimes longer than the petals; lip white, beautifully spotted with purple, longer than the petals, three-lobed, the middle lobe larger, dilated and two-lobed or notched at the apex; spur slender, shorter than the lip or barely equalling it in length.

In damp, mossy woods, Greenland to the Rocky mountains, Maine, New York and Wisconsin. The records of its occurrence in New York are very few. It has been found in Oneida, Herkimer and Lewis counties, but not in recent years. Our illustration is from a photograph by Olaf O. Nylander, taken in Maine.

Showy Orchis

Galeorchis spectabilis (Linnaeus) Rydberg

(*Orchis spectabilis* Linnaeus)

Plate 34

Entire plant rather fleshy; stems short, five-angled, 4 to 12 inches high from a short rootstock provided with numerous fleshy roots. Leaves two, near the base of the stem, obovate, dark glossy green, 4 to 8 inches long and 2 to 4 inches wide, clammy to the touch; the three to ten flowers in a terminal spike, each flower about 1 inch long, violet-purple mixed with lighter purple and white, the subtending bracts sheathing the ovaries; sepals united above forming a hood; petals connivent under the sepals and more or less attached to them; lip whitish, wavy, produced into an obtuse spur, about as long as the petals; column short, scarcely extending above the base of the lip, violet on the back.

In rich woods, New Brunswick to Ontario, Dakota, Georgia, Kentucky, Missouri and Nebraska. Flowering in May and June or as late as July in the extreme northern part of its range.

Tall Leafy Green Orchis

Limnorchis hyperborea (Linnaeus) Rydberg

Plate 37a

A rather inconspicuous orchis with small flowers, the stem usually stout, 10 inches to 3 feet high. Leaves lanceolate, pointed, 3 to 10 inches long, one-half to $1\frac{3}{4}$ inches wide. Flowers numerous in a narrow terminal spike, small, greenish or greenish yellow; sepals and petals free and spreading, ovate, blunt; lip entire, lanceolate, blunt, about one-fourth of an inch long; spur about as long as the lip, blunt, slightly incurved or often thickened at the end (clavate).

In bogs, wet woods and swamps, Greenland to Alaska, New Jersey, Colorado and Oregon. Flowering in May and June or later in cold bogs and woods of the north.

The Tall White Bog Orchis (Limnorchis dilatata (Pursh) Rydberg) is usually more slender, with small white flowers; the ovate or lanceolate sepals nearly one-fourth of an inch long; petals lanceolate, pointed; lip entire, dilated or obtusely three-lobed at the base, blunt at the apex, about as long as the blunt and incurved spur. In similar situations, but southward only to Maine and New York.

Large Round-leaved Orchis

Lysias orbiculata (Pursh) Rydberg

Plate 35 and Figure VIII

Flowering scape rather stout, 1 to 2 feet high, with a few inconspicuous bracts, and at the base, spreading flat on the ground, two large orbicular or orbicular-elliptical, dark-green, shining leaves, silvery beneath, 4 to 8 inches in diameter. Flowers forming a loose raceme, each flower on a pedicel about one-half of an inch long, erect in fruit, greenish white; upper sepal short and rounded; lateral sepals spreading, falcate-ovate and blunt; one-third to one-half of an inch long; petals smaller and narrower; lip entire, oblong-linear, blunt, white, about one-half of an inch long; spur longer than the ovary, about $1\frac{1}{2}$ to 2 inches long.

In rich woods, Newfoundland to Minnesota, south to Pennsylvania. Flowering in June and July.

Plate 35 shows the flowers after they have begun to fade. The detail of the flowers is shown better in figure VIII. Oakes Ames regards the loose-flowered form with long spurs as Habenaria macrophylla Goldie, and restricts Lysias orbiculata to the form with dense inflorescence and spurs 1 to $1\frac{1}{4}$ inches long.

Hooker's Orchis

Lysias hookeriana (A. Gray) Rydberg

Plate 36

Stem or flowering scape 8 to 15 inches high, stout, smooth, without bracts, but with two fleshy, shining, dark-green, oval-orbicular or obovate, spreading or ascending leaves at the base, 3 to 6 inches long, rarely flat on the ground. Flowers in a rather loose raceme, 4 to 8 inches long, yellowish

Figure VIII

Flowers of Large Round-leaved Orchis (L y s i a s o r b i c u l a t a (Pursh)
Rydberg), left; and Large Coralroot (C o r a l l o r r h i z a m a c u l a t a
Rafinesque) at right

green; each flower about two-thirds of an inch long; lateral sepals greenish, lanceolate and spreading, about one-third of an inch long; petals narrowly linear; lip linear-lanceolate, pointed, one-third to nearly one-half of an inch long; spur slender, pointed, two-thirds of an inch or more long, as long or longer than the ovary.

In cool, moist woods, Nova Scotia to Minnesota, south to New Jersey, Pennsylvania and Iowa. Flowering in June and July or later, in the north.

Yellow-fringed Orchis

Blephariglottis ciliaris (Linnaeus) Rydberg

Plate 37b

Stem slender, 1 to $2\frac{1}{2}$ feet high. Leaves lanceolate, pointed, 4 to 8 inches long, one-half to $1\frac{1}{2}$ inches wide, the upper ones much smaller. Flowers orange or yellow, large and showy in a terminal, many-flowered spike, 3 to 6 inches long; sepals orbicular or broadly ovate, oblique at the base, the lateral ones mostly reflexed; petals much smaller, oblong or cuneate, usually toothed; lip oblong, about one-half of an inch long, copiously fringed more than halfway to the middle; spur 1 to $1\frac{1}{2}$ inches long and very slender.

In meadows and open places in woods, especially in sandy regions, Vermont and Ontario to Michigan, Missouri, Florida and Texas. In New York State it is rare and local north of the coastal plain, occurring on the Schenectady plains and several other places, especially on the Ontario lowlands, from Rome west to Lake Erie.

White-fringed Orchis

Blephariglottis blephariglottis (Willdenow) Rydberg

Plate 38

A plant similar to the Yellow-fringed Orchis, but with a densely or rather dense, many-flowered spike of pure-white flowers, the petals toothed or somewhat fringed at the apex, rarely entire, the lip copiously or sparingly fringed.

In bogs and swamps, Newfoundland to Minnesota, Florida and Mississippi. When growing with the Yellow-fringed Orchis, it blooms a few days earlier. It is found in nearly all the sphagnum bogs of northern New York and is not uncommon in moist depressions of the sandy coastal plain. Flowering from late June until early August in northern New York.

The Prairie White-fringed Orchis (Blephariglottis leucophaea (Nuttall) Farwell) has larger, white, fragrant flowers, sometimes tinged with green; the lip three-parted, the segments broadly wedge-shaped and copiously fringed. Most abundant westward but occurring eastward to New England.

Ragged or Green-fringed Orchis

Blephariglottis lacera (Michaux) Farwell

Plate 39b

Stems varying from slender and 1 foot or less high to stout and 2 to 3 feet high. Leaves firm, lanceolate, 3 to 8 inches long, two-thirds to $1\frac{3}{4}$ inches wide, decreasing in size upward. Flowers greenish yellow or greenish, in a loose spike, 2 to several inches long; petals linear, blunt, about as long as the sepals; lip three-parted, the segments narrow, deeply fringed or lacerate with a few threads about one-half of an inch long; spur one-half to three-fourths of an inch long, curved and thickened at the end, shorter than the ovary.

Common in swamps, low meadows and wet woods, Newfoundland to Minnesota, south to Georgia and Arkansas. Flowering in June and July. Forms frequently occur in which the fringe of the lip is very short.

Smaller Purple-fringed Orchis

Blephariglottis psycodes (Linnaeus) Rydberg

Plate 39a

Stem rather slender, 1 to 3 feet high. Leaves oval, elliptic or lanceolate, 3 to 10 inches long, two-thirds to 3 inches wide, becoming smaller above, dark green and glossy above. Flowers lilac-purple or rarely white, fragrant, in a dense, many-flowered terminal raceme, 2 to 8 inches long; petals oblong or oblanceolate, toothed on the upper margin; lip three-parted, one-fourth to one-half of an inch broad, the segments fan-shaped and copiously fringed, the fringe of the middle segment shorter than that of the lateral ones; spur somewhat thickened at the tip, about three-fourths of an inch long, and longer than the ovary.

In meadows, swamps and wet woods, Newfoundland to Minnesota, North Carolina and Tennessee. Flowering in July and August.

The Large or Early Purple-fringed Orchis (Blephariglottis grandiflora (Bigelow) Rydberg) has a large, dense raceme of lilac or purplish, fragrant flowers, the lower lip, three-parted, the segments broadly fan-shaped and copiously fringed to about the middle. The flowers average one-third or one-half larger than those of B. psycodes; otherwise they are very similar and this may be only a large-flowered race of that species. Growing in similar situations.

Rose Pogonia; Snakemouth

Pogonia ophioglossoides (Linnaeus) Ker

Plate 40

A slender plant with fibrous roots and stems 8 to 15 inches high, propagating by runners. Leaves one to three on each stem, one-half to 4 inches long, lanceolate or ovate, erect, pointed or rather blunt. Flowers solitary or sometimes in pairs with leaflike bracts, fragrant, pale rose-colored, slightly nodding, 1 to 2 inches broad; sepals and petals similar, two-thirds to 1 inch long; lip spatulate, crested and fringed with white.

In swamps, low meadows and boggy depressions, especially in sandy regions, Newfoundland to Ontario, Florida, Kansas and Texas. Flowering in June and July, and in the north sometimes in flower as late as August.

Whorled Pogonia

Isotria verticillata (Willdenow) Rafinesque

Figure IX

Stems 10 to 15 inches high, from long, perennial, horizontal, fleshy rootstocks, which give rise to new stems by buds. Stems bearing a whorl of five leaves at the summit. Leaves obovate, abruptly pointed at the

Figure IX
Whorled Pogonia
(Isotria verticillata (Willdenow) Rafinesque)

apex, sessile, 1 to 4 inches long, usually only partially developed at flowering time.   Flowers solitary, erect or declined, on a peduncle one-half to two-thirds of an inch long; sepals linear, dull reddish purple, spreading, $1\frac{1}{2}$ to 2 inches long and about one-twelfth of an inch wide; petals linear, erect, blunt, light green and arching above the lip, about five-sixths of an inch long; lip three-lobed at the end, middle lobe broadest, white and crenulate on the margin; two lateral lobes of the lip and the lateral margins tinged and veined with bright crimson-purple, most vivid at the apex of the two lateral lobes, crest of the lip green and papillose.   Capsule erect, 1 to $1\frac{1}{2}$ inches long.

In moist soil of woods and thickets, often around cold sphagnum bogs, Ontario and Massachusetts to Michigan, Indiana and Florida.   Flowering in May and June.

Arethusa; Dragon's-mouth; Wild Pink

Arethusa bulbosa Linnaeus

Plate 43ᵇ

A low, scapose, smooth plant, 5 to 10 inches high from a small bulb, stem bearing one to three loose sheathing bracts on the stem and a single linear leaf hidden at first in the upper bract and developing after the flower has faded.   The single flower arising at the top of the stem from between a pair of small unequal scales, rose-purple, 1 to 2 inches high; sepals and petals similar, linear to elliptic in shape, obtuse, connivent, hooded, and arching over the column; lip usually drooping beneath the sepals and petals, the apex broad, variegated with purplish blotches and crested down the face with three hairy ridges, the margin fringed or toothed.   Capsule about 1 inch long, ellipsoid, strongly six-ribbed.

In bogs, low meadows and mossy depressions or moist thickets, Newfoundland to Ontario and Minnesota, South Carolina and Indiana.   Flowering in May and June.   One of the most dainty and beautiful of our native orchids.

Grass Pink; Calopogon

Limodorum tuberosum Linnaeus

Plate 41a

Scape slender, 12 to 18 inches high from a round, solid bulb, arising from the bulb of the previous year, a single leaf appearing the first season, followed the next year by the flowering stem and a single linear-lanceolate leaf, 8 to 12 inches long, one-fourth to 1 inch wide. Flowers three to fifteen, forming a loose, terminal spike or raceme, each about 1 inch broad, purplish pink; sepals and petals nearly alike, separate, obliquely ovate-lanceolate, acute; lip broadly triangular and dilated at the apex, bearded along the face with yellow, orange and rose-colored hairs.

Common in bogs or boggy meadows. Newfoundland to Ontario and Minnesota, south to Florida and Missouri. Flowering in June and July.

Wide-leaved Ladies'-tresses

Ibidium plantagineum (Rafinesque) House

Plate 42a

A rather inconspicuous little orchid, 4 to 10 inches high with tuberous-fleshy roots. Leaves three to five to a stem, mostly near the base, lanceolate, 2 to 5 inches long. Flowers spreading in a dense, terminal spike, 1 to 2 inches long, one-third to one-half of an inch thick, each flower about one-fourth of an inch long; petals and sepals white, the lateral sepals free, narrowly lanceolate, the upper sepals somewhat united with the petals; lip pale yellow on the face, oblong, not contracted in the middle, the wavy apex rounded, crisped or fringed, the base short clawed, bearing mere traces of callosities at the base.

Moist banks, meadows and bogs, Nova Scotia to Minnesota, south to Virginia and Wisconsin. Flowers in June and July.

The most showy species of Ladies'-tresses is I b i d i u m c e r n u u m (Linnaeus) House (figure X), which is 6 to 24 inches high and pubescent above. Leaves mainly toward the base of the stem, linear-lanceolate or linear, 3 to 14 inches long; flowers very fragrant, white or yellowish, forming

Figure X
Showy Ladies'-tresses
(I b i d i u m c e r n u u m (Linnaeus) House)

a spike, 4 to 5 inches long and one-half to two-thirds of an inch thick; flowers spreading or nodding, each about five-twelfths of an inch long in three rows; lip oblong or ovate, rounded at the apex, crenulate or crisped on the margin. Flowering in late summer and autumn.

Another common species of Ladies'-tresses is I b i d i u m s t r i c t u m (Rydberg) House, perhaps only a race of I b i d - i u m r o m a n z o f f i a n u m, which has the sepals and petals coherent and connivent into a hood. It is common in bogs and swamps during July and August.

Southern Twayblade

(*Ophrys australis* (Lindley) House)

(*Listera australis* Lindley)

Figure XI

The Twayblades are among the smallest of our native orchids and require sharp eyes to detect them among the recesses of the forest or bogs. The Southern Twayblade is about 5 to 10 inches tall, with two ovate, rather pointed, smooth and shining sessile leaves slightly above the middle of the stem at the top of which is a loose raceme of six to fifteen small, yellowish green flowers; sepals and petals minute, the lip one-fourth to one-half of an inch long, and two-parted or split nearly to the base four to eight times as long as the tiny petals.

A rare plant of cold, sphagnous bogs in northern New York and locally southward except the coastal plain. In the Appalachian region south to Georgia, this is not a rare species.

Very similar to the Southern Twayblade is the Heart-leaved Twayblade (O p h r y s c o r d a t a Linnaeus) in which the two sessile leaves are rounded or slightly heart-shaped, and the lip of the flower only two or three times as long as the petals. It is not rare in the Adirondack region but on account of its small size is easily overlooked. It has also been found in deep cedar swamps in certain other portions of eastern states.

Downy Rattlesnake Plantain

Peramium pubescens (Willdenow) MacMillan

Figure XII

Flowering scape 6 to 20 inches high, densely glandular-pubescent,

(Photograph by E. A. Eames)

Figure XI

Southern Twayblade

(O p h r y s a u s t r a l i s (Lindley) House)

Figure XII
Downy Rattlesnake Plantain
Peramium pubescens (Willdenow)
(MacMillan)

bearing several lanceolate scales, from a branching, fleshy, perennial rootstock. Leaves all near the base of the scape, 1 to 3 inches long, two-thirds to 1 inch wide, pointed at the apex, rather abruptly contracted into short petioles, oval or ovate in shape, rather strongly reticulated with white along the principal veins on the upper surface, pale green beneath. Flowers white or tinged with green, forming a rather dense terminal spike which is not one-sided; each flower about one-fourth of an inch long or slightly less; lateral sepals ovate; upper sepals united with the petals to form an ovate hood (galea); lip saccate with a short broad blunt recurved or spreading tip.

In dry woods, Maine to Ontario and Minnesota, south to Florida and Tennessee. Flowering in July and August.

The Lesser Rattlesnake Plantain (Peramium ophioides (Fernald) Rydberg) is only about 6 to 10 inches high, with smaller, ovate, white-blotched leaves and small, greenish white flowers, one-eighth to one-sixth of an inch long in a one-sided spike. Frequent in woods.

Loddiges's Rattlesnake Plantain

Peramium tesselatum (Loddiges)
Heller

Plate 41b

Leaves oblong-ovate or ovate-lanceolate, 1 to 2 inches long, one-third to one-fourth of an inch wide, bright green, abruptly narrowed into the petioles which sheathe the base of the stem, more or less marked on the upper surface with white; stem 6 to 14 inches high, glandular-pubescent and scaly, bearing at the summit a loosely spiral spike of flowers 1 to 5 inches long; flowers whitish, lateral sepals free, the upper ones united with the petals to form a hood (galea), 2 to 3 lines long, broad and recurved at the tip; lip roundish-ovate, slightly saccate at the base, the long tip somewhat recurved.

In coniferous woods, more rarely in open places, Newfoundland to Ontario, Pennsylvania and Michigan. Flowering from July to September.

White Adder's-mouth

Malaxis monophylla (Linnaeus) Swartz

Figure XIII

Stem very slender, 4 to 8 inches high, smooth, bearing below the middle a single leaf which sheathes the stem,

Figure XIII
White Adder's-mouth
(M a l a x i s m o n o p h y l l a (Linnaeus)
(Swartz)

the blade 1 to 3 inches long, one-half to 1¾ inches wide. Flowers whitish, very small, in a slender raceme, 1 to 4 inches long; each flower about one-half of an inch long on a very short, nearly erect pedicel; lip triangular or ovate and long pointed.

In woods, thickets and recent clearings, Quebec to Manitoba, south to Pennsylvania and Nebraska. Flowering in July.

The Green Adder's-mouth (M a l a x i s u n i f o l i a Michaux) has the single leaf clasping the stem near the middle; flowers greenish on slender pedicels; lip broad and three-toothed at the apex. Small and inconspicuous as well as rather rare.

Large Twayblade
Liparis liliifolia (Linnaeus) L. C. Richard
Figure XIV

Scapes 4 to 10 inches high, striate and smooth from a perennial solid bulb, the base of the stem sheathed by several scales and two ovate or oval, blunt, shining, light-green leaves, 2 to 5 inches long, 1 to 2½ inches wide. Flowers yellow, numerous, rather showy, forming a loose terminal raceme; petals very narrow and threadlike; lip erect, large, fully one-half inch long, wedge-obovate in shape. Capsule club-shaped and about one-half inch long.

In moist woods, thickets and recent clearings, Maine to Minnesota, south to Georgia and Missouri. Flowering from latter part of May to July.

Fen Orchis; Loesel's Twayblade
Liparis loeselii (Linnaeus) L. C. Richard
Plate 42b

A low bog orchis with two light-green, shining, elliptic or elliptic-lanceolate leaves, 2 to 6 inches long, one-half to 2 inches wide and obtuse, arising with the short stem from a solitary bulb which, with the base of the stem, is sheathed by several scales and the remains of leaves of former seasons; flowers greenish yellow, about one-fourth of an inch long, in a

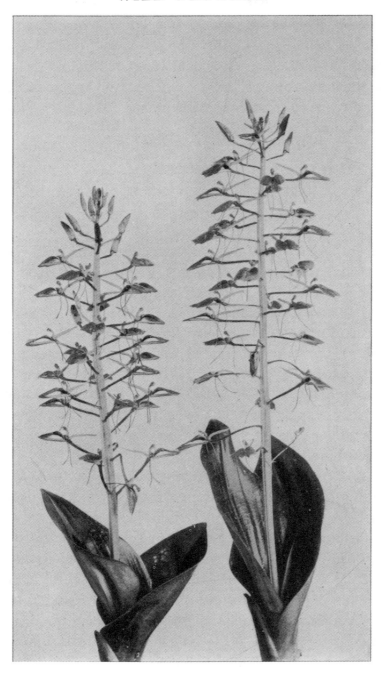

Figure XIV
Large Twayblade
(Liparis liliifolia (Linnaeus) L. C. Richard)

terminal, loosely flowered raceme; petals linear, somewhat reflexed; lip obovate, pointed, a little shorter than the petals and sepals, its tip incurved; capsules about one-half of an inch long, wing-angled.

In wet thickets, springy banks, and bogs or boggy meadows, Nova Scotia to Saskatchewan, south to Alabama and Missouri. Flowering from late May to July and sometimes later.

Calypso

Cytherea bulbosa (Linnaeus) House

(*Calypso borealis* Salisbury)

Plate 43a

Stem or scape 3 to 7 inches high from a perennial bulb one-half of an inch or less thick with coralloid roots. The scape bears two or three loose sheathing scales and at the base a single round-ovate leaf, 1 to 2 inches long, blunt or pointed at the apex and rounded or heart-shaped at the base, the petiole 1 to 2 inches long. Flower showy, solitary, 1 to 1½ inches broad, at the summit of the scape, variegated with purple, pink and yellow; petals and sepals similar, nearly equal, linear, erect or spreading, each with three longitudinal purple lines. Lip saccate, large, two-divided below, spreading or drooping, with a patch of yellow woolly hairs. Column erect, broadly ovate and petallike, shorter than the petals, bearing the lidlike anther just below the summit.

In bogs and cold Arbor Vitae swamps, Labrador to Alaska, south to Maine, New York, Michigan, California and in the Rocky mountains to Arizona and New Mexico. Also in Europe.

One of the rarest and at the same time most beautiful of our native Orchids, appearing much like a small Cypripedium (Lady's-slipper). In New York it has been found in several localities in southern Herkimer, in Lewis, Oswego and Onondaga counties. The writer found it several years ago in Lodi or Tamarack swamp near Syracuse, but the place has since been obliterated by the growth of the city. For the illustration used here we are indebted to Edward A. Eames of Buffalo.

Large Coralroot

Corallorrhiza maculata Rafinesque

Figure VIII, page 73

Stems stout or slender, 8 to 20 inches high, with a large mass of coral-like branching rootstocks, the stem purplish, clothed with several appressed scales, devoid of green leaves or green color. Flowers ten to thirty, forming a terminal raceme 2 to 8 inches long, purplish brown; sepals and petals linear-lanceolate, about one-fourth of an inch long; lip white, spotted and lined with crimson, oval or ovate in outline, deeply three-lobed, crenulate; spur yellowish. Fruiting capsules ovoid or oblong, one-half to two-thirds of an inch long and drooping.

In woods, Nova Scotia to British Columbia, south to Florida, Missouri, New Mexico and California. Flowering from July to September.

The Early Coralroot (Corallorrhiza corallorrhiza (Linnaeus) Karsten) blooms in May and June. It has smaller flowers of a dull-purple color; sepals and petals about one-fourth of an inch long and a whitish, oblong lip; spur reduced to a small protuberance adnate to the summit of the ovary. Common in moist woods.

The Small or Late Coralroot (Corallorrhiza odontorhiza (Willdenow) Nuttall) blooms from July to September. It is 6 to 15 inches high and very slender. Flowers purplish; sepals and petals about one-sixth of an inch long or less, marked with purple lines; lip entire or denticulate, whitish, spotted with purple. A rather rare plant of moist woods. All the species of Coralroot are devoid of green leaves or green coloring matter in the stems, because of their parasitic or saprophytic habit.

Lizard's-tail Family

Saururaceae

Lizard's-tail

Saururus cernuus Linnaeus

Plate 44

Stem 2 to 5 feet high from a slender rootstock, jointed, pubescent when young, becoming smooth. Leaves ovate, thin, palmately five to nine-ribbed, dark green, entire, deeply cordate at the base, acuminate, 3 to 6 inches long, 2 to 3½ inches wide; petioles sheathing the stem at the enlarged nodes; the stem terminating in one or two elongated white spikes, their tips drooping in flower. Flowers fragrant, small, white, without any perianth; stamens six to eight, white, spreading; ovary consisting of three or four carpels united at the base, becoming slightly fleshy and strongly wrinkled in fruit.

In swamps and shallow water, Rhode Island to Florida west to southern Ontario, Minnesota and Texas. Flowering from June to August.

Nettle Family

Urticaceae

False Nettle

Boehmeria cylindrica (Linnaeus) Swartz

Plate 45

A perennial, rough-pubescent or nearly smooth, erect plant, 1 to 3 feet tall, not provided with stinging hairs as are the true nettles. Leaves mostly opposite, thin, petioled, ovate to ovate-lanceolate, coarsely toothed, 1 to 4 inches long, one-half to 1½ inches wide. Flowers greenish, small and dioecious, that is, some of the axillary spikes containing only staminate flowers, and others only pistillate flowers, or some of the spikes containing both kinds of flowers (androgynous); the staminate spikes interrupted, the pistillate mostly continuous, one-fourth to 1½ inches long, often terminated by small leaves.

In moist soil and thickets, Quebec and Ontario to Minnesota, Florida, Texas and the West Indies. Flowering from July to September. Not an attractive plant but figured here as a representative of the Nettle family, none of our species having conspicuous flowers. The True or Stinging Nettle (Urtica dioica Linnaeus), naturalized in the eastern states from Europe, the Slender Wild Nettle (Urtica gracilis Aiton) and the Wood Nettle (Urticastrum divaricatum (Linnaeus) Kuntze) are all provided with stinging hairs and are most unpleasant plants to encounter unexpectedly in the woods.

Sandalwood Family
Santalaceae
Bastard Toadflax
Comandra umbellata (Linnaeus) Nuttall

Plate 28b

Stems numerous from a horizontal, branching rootstock, said to be parasitic on the roots of adjacent herbs, 6 to 18 inches tall, usually branched and very leafy. Leaves oblong or oblong-lanceolate, pale green, pointed at each end, sessile, one-half to $1\frac{1}{2}$ inches long, the lower ones smaller. Flowers numerous in terminal cymes, corymbose at the summit of the stem, or also axillary, their branches divergent or ascending, greenish white, white, or purplish, about one-fifth of an inch long, calyx usually five-lobed, corolla none. Fruit a globose drupe about one-fourth of an inch in diameter, crowned by the upper part of the calyx tube and its five oblong lobes.

In dry fields and thickets, especially sandy soil, Cape Breton Island to Ontario and Assiniboia, south to Georgia, Kansas and Arkansas. At Bergen swamp in Genesee county, New York, it grows in an open marl bog, which, however, is dry in certain seasons, in company with Arethusa bulbosa, Cypripedium candidum, Scirpus caespitosus, Anticlea chlorantha, Triantha glutinosa, Solidago houghtonii, and other bog plants, a habitat most unusual for this species.

Birthwort Family
Aristolochiaceae
Wild or Indian Ginger
Asarum canadense Linnaeus

Plate 46

Leaves clustered in pairs from a slender, branching, aromatic rootstock, having the flavor of ginger. Leaf blades long petioled, reniform, thin, short pointed at the apex, 3 to 7 inches broad, dark green, the base deeply cordate. Entire plant densely and finely pubescent. Flowers on a short, slender peduncle from between the bases of the petioles, often concealed or partly buried in old leaves on the ground, 1 inch or more broad, brownish purple; calyx ovoid, its tube completely adnate to the ovary, its three lobes inflexed in bud, ovate-lanceolate, acute or long-acuminate, spreading; stamens twelve in number, the stout, short filaments inserted on the inferior six-celled ovary.

In rich woods, New Brunswick to Manitoba, south to North Carolina, Missouri and Kansas. Flowering in April and May.

In southern New York occurs also the Short-lobed Wild Ginger (Asarum reflexum Bicknell) with smaller flowers, the calyx tube white within, and the triangular, acute lobes strongly reflexed.

Buckwheat Family

Polygonaceae

Swamp Smartweed

Persicaria muhlenbergii (S. Watson) Small

Plate 47a

Perennial by long rootstocks, rooting in the mud or in the water, stem erect, glabrous, or somewhat pubescent, enlarged at the nodes, 1 to 3 feet high. Leaves ovate-lanceolate or oblong-lanceolate, the upper ones often narrower, 2 to 8 inches long, acute or acuminate at the apex, rounded or cordate at the base, petioled, ocreae cylindric, becoming loose, not ciliate. Flowers in linear-oblong, dense, terminal racemes, 1 to 3 inches long; calyx dark rose-colored, five-parted; stamens five in number.

In swamps, marshes and moist soil, Ontario to British Columbia, Virginia, Louisiana and Mexico. Flowering from July to September.

Lady's-thumb; Heartweed

Persicaria persicaria (Linnaeus) Small

Plate 47b

Annual, smooth or somewhat puberulent, stems one-half to 2 feet high, erect or nearly so, simple or branched. Leaves lanceolate or linear-lanceolate, 2 to 6 inches long, nearly sessile, acuminate at both ends, conspicuously dotted, usually with a triangular or lunar dark blotch near the center; ocreae cylindric, fringed with short bristles. Flowers in dense, erect, ovoid or oblong racemes, one-half to 2 inches long, pink to dark purple; stamens usually six.

Native of Europe but naturalized and often an abundant weed in waste places throughout North America, except in the extreme north.

Arrow-leaved Tearthumb

Tracaulon sagittatum (Linnaeus) Small

Plate 48a

Stems slender, weak, annual, decumbent, or climbing over other plants by the numerous sharp, recurved prickles which arm its four prominent angles. Leaves lanceolate-sagittate or oblong-sagittate, 1 to 3 inches long, pointed at the apex, slightly rough margined, the lower leaves petioled, upper ones sessile or nearly so, prickly on the petioles and beneath on the midribs; ocreae oblique, not ciliate. Flowers in terminal heads or racemes, rose-colored or greenish; stamens usually eight in number; style three-parted.

In wet soil, Newfoundland and Nova Scotia to the Northwest Territory, south to Florida and Kansas. Flowering from July to September.

Halberd-leaved Tearthumb

Tracaulon arifolium (Linnaeus) Rafinesque

Plate 48b

Stems angled, reclining, 2 to 6 feet long from a perennial root, armed with recurved prickles. Leaves broadly hastate, long petioled, 1 to 8 inches long, pubescent or glabrous beneath, the apex and basal lobes sharp pointed; petioles and larger nerves prickly; peduncles and pedicels glandular; ocreae oblique, fringed at the summit with short bristles and at the base with slender prickles. Flowers in terminal and axillary heads or racemes, rose-colored or greenish, four parted. Stamens six; style two-parted.

In moist or wet soil and thickets, New Brunswick and Ontario to Minnesota, south to Georgia.   Flowering from July to September.

Climbing False Buckwheat

Bilderdykia scandens (Linnaeus) Greene

(*Polygonum scandens* Linnaeus)

Plate 15b

Stems slender or stout, glabrous, high climbing, 2 to 20 feet long from a perennial root, somewhat rough on the ridges which mark the stem. Leaves ovate, sharp pointed, cordate at the base, 1 to 6 inches long, or the upper ones smaller, finely dotted, ocreae oblique, smooth and glabrous. Flowers in numerous panicled racemes, 2 to 8 inches long, usually interrupted with small leaves, yellowish green or whitish; calyx five-parted; stamens eight; calyx in fruit about one-half of an inch long with crisped wings.

In woods, thickets and on banks and along fence rows, Nova Scotia to Ontario and British Columbia, south to Florida, Nebraska and Texas. Flowers in August and September.

Coast Jointweed

Polygonella articulata (Linnaeus) Meisner

Plate 49a

Stems slender, wiry, erect or somewhat diffusely spreading, annual, glaucous, simple or the larger ones often much branched, 4 to 12 inches high. Leaves linear or linear-subulate, with revolute margins, sessile, one-third to $1\frac{1}{2}$ inches long, jointed to the summits of the ocreae.   Flowers small, in numerous terminal racemes on reflexed pedicels; calyx five-parted, its segments white with a conspicuous purple midrib.

In sand near or on the seashore from Maine to Florida, and inland on the Schenectady plains, those east of Oneida lake, and along the Great Lakes.

Goosefoot Family

Chenopodiaceae

Slender or Jointed Glasswort; Saltwort

Salicornia europaea Linnaeus

Plate 49b

A fleshy, glabrous annual plant, 4 to 20 inches high, usually erect and much branched, with opposite, ascending branches, their joints two to four times as long as thick. Leaves reduced to mere scales. Fruiting spikes 1 to 3 inches long. Flowers three at each joint, the middle one as high as the lateral ones. Each flower consists of a fleshy, obpyramidal three-toothed calyx, two stamens and an ovoid ovary. Seed inclosed by the spongy fruiting calyx.

Common in salt marshes along the coast from Anticosti to Georgia, and at the head of Onondaga lake.

Pokeweed Family

Phytolaccaceae

Poke; Scoke; Pigeon Berry; Garget

Phytolacca americana Linnaeus

Plate 50

A tall, strong-smelling, succulent and glabrous plant with an erect herbaceous stem 3 to 10 feet tall, from a large, perennial, poisonous root, the pith of the stem divided into discs separated by lens-shaped cavities. Leaves oblong-lanceolate or ovate-lanceolate, pinnately veined, acute or acuminate at both ends, petioled, 5 to 12 inches long. Flowers in terminal racemes, which become opposite the leaves by continued growth of the stem. Each flower about one-fourth of an inch broad, consisting of four or five rounded, white sepals; ten stamens, slightly shorter than the sepals; and a ten-celled green ovary. Fruit a long raceme of dark-purple berries, each one-fourth to three-eighths of an inch in diameter.

In waste places, fields, woods and thickets, usually in moist soil, often in stony fields and frequently a troublesome weed. Distributed from Maine and Ontario to Minnesota, Arkansas, Florida, Mexico and Bermuda. Europe has contributed many weeds to America, but the Pokeweed or Scoke is one of the few American plants, often reckoned as a weed, which has become thoroughly naturalized in many parts of Europe.

Purslane Family
Portulacaceae
Narrow-leaved Spring Beauty
Claytonia virginica Linnaeus

Plate 51a

Stems 6 to 12 inches long, ascending or decumbent from a deep, tuberous, perennial root. Leaves linear or linear-lanceolate, glabrous and somewhat fleshy, blunt or pointed, narrowed below into a petiole, the lower leaves 3 to 7 inches long, one-eighth to one-half of an inch wide, the two-stem leaves opposite and shorter. Flowers one-half to seven-eighths of an inch broad, white or pink with darker pink veins, in a loose terminal raceme, often becoming 3 to 6 inches long. Sepals two, ovate, persistent; petals five, emarginate; pedicels slender, becoming recurved.

In moist woods, Nova Scotia to Saskatchewan, south to Georgia, Montana and Texas. Flowering in early spring. More frequently found in low woodlands and along streams in the northern part of its range, and not so frequent as the next species except near the coast.

Carolina or Wide-leaved Spring Beauty
Claytonia caroliniana Michaux

Plate 69a

Closely resembling the Narrow-leaved Spring Beauty, but usually more erect. Basal leaves ovate-lanceolate or oblong, 1 to 4 inches long, one-half to 1 inch wide, obtuse; stem leaves petioled; flowers fewer. The corm is usually thicker and depressed at the top.

In damp woods, Nova Scotia to Saskatchewan, Connecticut, south to North Carolina along the mountains, and to Ohio and Missouri. Rare or absent near the coast in New York, but very abundant in the interior where it occurs in almost every moist woodland. Flowering in the early spring.

Chickweed Family

Alsinaceae

Field or Meadow Chickweed

Cerastium arvense Linnaeus

Plate 63a

A densely matted or tufted perennial plant, usually more or less pubescent. Flowering stems 4 to 10 inches high, simple or sparingly branched. Lower leaves and those of the numerous sterile shoots linear-oblong, close together, slightly narrowed at the base. Leaves of the flowering stems more distant, linear or narrowly lanceolate, one-half to $1\frac{1}{2}$ inches long, one-eighth of an inch wide or slightly wider. Flowers white, one-half to three-fourths of an inch broad, several in a cymose inflorescence. Petals five, obcordate or deeply notched at the ends, much longer than the lanceolate, acute sepals. Fruit a small, cylindrical capsule, a little longer than the sepals and slightly oblique at its apex.

In dry, rocky places, stony fields or ledges, Labrador to Alaska, south to Georgia, Missouri, Nevada and California. Also found in Europe and Asia. Flowering from April to July. In New York usually in bloom during some part of May.

This is a much larger flowered and more attractive plant than the Mouse-ear Chickweed (Cerastium vulgatum Linnaeus), which is naturalized almost everywhere, especially in the stony or rocky places where the Field Chickweed is found.

Pink Family

Caryophyllaceae

Bladder Campion; White Ben

Silene latifolia (Miller) Britten & Rendel

Plate 52

Stems herbaceous, from a perennial root, glaucous and glabrous, or rarely pubescent, extensively branching from the base, 6 to 20 inches high.

Leaves opposite, ovate-lanceolate, pointed, variable in size, the lower ones often spatulate. Flowers white, two-thirds to seven-eighths of an inch broad, in loose cymose panicles, often drooping; calyx tubular-campanulate, becoming globose and much inflated, about one-half of an inch long, strongly veined, with five triangular, acute lobes; petals five, each two-cleft, with or without a small crown.

In fields, meadows and waste places, New Hampshire to Ontario, New Jersey and Missouri. Native of Europe and naturalized in this country. Flowering in July and August.

Wild Pink

Silene caroliniana Walter

Plate 53

Densely tufted and perennial from a stout root, 4 to 10 inches high, viscid-pubescent, especially above, often glabrous below. Basal and lower leaves spatulate or oblanceolate, pointed or blunt, 2 to 4 inches long; stem leaves sessile, shorter, oblong or lanceolate. Flowers pink, about 1 inch broad, in terminal cymes. Calyx narrow and tubular, much enlarged by the ripening pod, its teeth ovate, pointed; petals cuneate, emarginate, eroded or finely toothed at the apex, crowned at the base of the claw.

In dry, sandy or rocky soil, Maine to Georgia, west to central New York, Pennsylvania and Kentucky.

Cuckoo-flower; Ragged Robin

Lychnis flos-cuculi Linnaeus

Plate 54a

Stems slender, erect, 1 to 2 feet high, simple or branching, from a thick, perennial root, downy-pubescent below, slightly viscid above. Lower and basal leaves spatulate or oblanceolate, 2 to 4 inches long; upper leaves lanceolate or linear-lanceolate, opposite and sessile, the uppermost leaves reduced to small bracts; flowers pink, purplish, blue, or white, three-fourths to 1 inch broad, in many-flowered panicles at the summit of the stems; calyx one-fourth of an inch long, ten-nerved, cylindrical, becoming campanulate in fruit, its apex with five triangular, pointed teeth; petals five, narrowly clawed, the spreading limbs each cleft into four linear lobes, of which the middle pair is longest.

Moist meadows, fields and waste places, New Brunswick to New Jersey and Pennsylvania. Frequent in cultivation. A native of Europe but thoroughly naturalized in many places in the eastern states. Flowering in July and August.

Sacred Bean Family

Nelumbonaceae

American Nelumbo or Lotus

Nelumbo lutea (Willdenow) Persoon

Plate 55

Rootstock stout, nearly horizontal, tuberiferous, in mud beneath 2 to 6 feet of water. Leaves 1 to 2 feet broad, orbicular, or somewhat constricted in the middle, centrally peltate, floating or raised a foot or two out of the water, prominently veined, smooth and dark green above, more or less pubescent and finely scaly beneath; leaf petioles and flower stems 3 to 7 feet long, rigid and tough, with several large air canals. Flowers pale yellow, fragrant, 4 to 10 inches broad; petals concave, obovate, blunt, numerous, surrounded by four or five overlapping scales. Carpels numerous, contained in pits in the large convex receptacle which becomes 3 to 4 inches long and obconic in fruit. Seeds about one-half of an inch in diameter.

In rivers and lakes, locally distributed from Massachusetts to Minnesota, Nebraska, Louisiana and Cuba. Flowering in August at Sodus bay, New York, where a large colony of it exists. Tubers and seeds farinaceous and edible. The local distribution in the north may be due to introduction by the Indians. The Indian Lotus or Sacred Bean (Nelumbo nelumbo (Linnaeus) Karsten), with large pink flowers, is frequent in cultivation.

Water Lily Family
Nymphaeaceae
Large Yellow Pond Lily; Spatter-dock
Nymphaea advena Solander

Plate 56

Floating and emersed leaves 5 to 12 inches long and 5 to 9 inches broad, ovate or orbicular-oval, thick, with a sinus 2 to 5 inches deep and generally open; submerged leaves, when present, thin and membranous; petioles, peduncles and lower surfaces of the leaves usually pubescent. Flowers $1\frac{1}{2}$ to $2\frac{1}{2}$ inches broad, depressed, globose, yellow, usually tinged with purple within; sepals six, oblong; petals fleshy, oblong truncate, one-half to two-thirds of an inch long; stamens numerous in five to seven rows; carpels numerous, united into a compound pistil which is surmounted by an undulate, yellow or pale-red stigmatic disc with twelve to twenty-four rays, ripening into an ovoid, berrylike fruit, 1 to 2 inches long and about 1 inch thick, maintained at the surface of the water or above it.

In ponds, lakes, slow streams or often subterrestrial in boggy meadows, Labrador and Nova Scotia to the Rocky mountains, south to Florida, Texas and Utah. Flowering from May to September. Consists of several races or perhaps species, differing in the character of the pistil, stigmatic disc and leaf outline. In the lakes and ponds throughout the north the small Yellow Pond Lily (N y m p h a e a   m i c r o p h y l l a   Persoon) is also found, with flowers 1 inch broad or less, and small leaves 2 to 4 inches long and 1 to 3 inches broad. The northern form of the larger Yellow Pond Lily is described in some books under the name of N y m p h a e a   v a r i - e g a t a (Morong) Greene, and a hybrid between the two, N y m p h a e a   r u b r o d i s c a (Morong) Greene, is of frequent occurrence, having fewer stigmatic rays than N. v a r i e g a t a and spatulate petals. Our illustration is from a plant on Long Island.

Sweet-scented White Water Lily

Castalia odorata (Aiton) Woodville & Wood

Plate 57

Aquatic, with a thick, horizontal rootstock. Leaves floating, orbicular or nearly so, 4 to 12 inches in diameter, glabrous, green and shining above, purple and somewhat pubescent beneath, the sinus open or almost closed, petioles and peduncles slender with four main air channels. Flowers white or in some varieties pink or rose-colored, 3 to 6 inches broad, very fragrant, with four greenish sepals and numerous, narrowly oblong, blunt petals, the inner ones shorter and narrower and gradually passing into stamens; stamens numerous and yellow. Carpels numerous, united into a compound pistil with radiating, linear, projecting stigmas, becoming a globose, fleshy fruit and ripening beneath the surface of the water by the coiling of the peduncles.

In ponds, lakes and slow streams, Newfoundland to Manitoba, south to Florida, Louisiana and Kansas. Flowering from June to August.

Tuberous White Water Lily

Castalia tuberosa (Paine) Greene

Plate 58

Leaves orbicular, 5 to 12 inches in diameter, floating, green on both sides, sometimes slightly pubescent beneath, sinus open or closed. Rootstock thick, with numerous lateral tuberous-thickened branches which become detached and propagate the plant. Flowers white, 4 to 9 inches broad, slightly fragrant or inodorous; petals oblong, broader than those of C. o d o r a t a, obtuse. Fruit depressed-globose.

In shallow water of bays and protected coves, Lake Champlain, Lake George, Oneida lake and along the Great Lakes to Michigan, south to Delaware and eastern Nebraska and Arkansas. Flowering in July and August.

Crowfoot Family

Ranunculaceae

Marsh Marigold; Cowslip

Caltha palustris Linnaeus

Plate 59

A succulent, herbaceous plant with stout, glabrous, hollow stems, erect or ascending, 1 to 2 feet high, branching and bearing several or numerous bright-yellow flowers. Lower leaves long petioled, the blades cordate or reniform, 2 to 8 inches broad, with a narrow sinus, crenate, dentate, or nearly entire on the margin. Upper leaves smaller, with short petioles or sessile with nearly truncate bases. Flowers 1 to 1½ inches broad; sepals oval, obtuse, petallike. True petals none. Stamens numerous, obovoid. Carpels several, in fruit forming follicles which are slightly compressed, about one-half of an inch long, and slightly curved outward.

In swamps, wet meadows and marshes, Newfoundland to South Carolina, west to Saskatchewan and Nebraska. Flowering in May and June.

Goldenseal; Orange-root

Hydrastis canadensis Linnaeus

Figure XV

An erect, perennial herb with a thick yellow rootstock. Stems 10 to 15 inches high. Usually each plant with a single, long-petioled basal leaf which is 5 to 8 inches broad and palmately 5 to 9-lobed, the lobes broad, pointed, sharply and unequally toothed. Stem leaves two, borne at the summit of the stem, similar in shape but smaller than the basal leaf, the uppermost leaf just below the solitary, greenish white flower, which is one-third to one-half of an inch broad. Sepals three, petallike and falling away as the flower opens. Petals none. Stamens numerous, their filaments widened and about one-sixth of an inch long; anthers oblong, obtuse. Carpels several, ripening into an ovoid, crimson head of fruit about two-thirds of an inch long, each carpel in fruit tipped with a short recurved beak.

In moist or low woodlands, Connecticut to Minnesota, Ontario, Kansas and Missouri, south to Georgia.

Figure XV
Goldenseal or Orange-root
(H y d r a s t i s   c a n a d e n s i s   Linnaeus)

American Globeflower
Trollius laxus Salisbury

Plate 61

Stems few or several from a perennial fibrous root, erect or ascending, often slightly fleshy but weak, from a few inches to 2 feet long. Lower leaves long-stalked; upper ones short-stalked or sessile; blades 3 to 5 inches broad, parted into five to seven wedge-shaped, cleft or toothed segments, the blades small at flowering time, much enlarged later. Flowers 1 to 1½ inches broad, with five to seven spreading, yellowish green, petallike sepals; true petals minute, fifteen to twenty-five in number and much shorter than the numerous yellow stamens. Fruit about 1 inch broad, consisting of several small pods (follicles) each about one-fourth of an inch long and tipped with a straight, slender beak of about one-fourth its length.

A rare or local plant of low or swampy woodlands, New England to Delaware, central and western New York to Michigan. Flowering from April to June.

Goldthread

Coptis trifolia (Linnaeus) Salisbury

Plate 60a

A low, herbaceous plant with a slender or filiform bright-yellow, bitter rootstock. Leaves all basal, evergreen, long petioled, the blade reniform, 1 to 2 inches broad, divided to the petiole into three wedge-shaped, obtuse segments, dark green, shining above, paler beneath, sharply toothed. Scape one-flowered, slender; sepals five to seven, oblong, obtuse, white; petals small and club-shaped; carpels three to seven, spreading, about one-fourth of an inch long, on stalks of about their own length, tipped with a beak.

In damp, mossy woods and bogs, Newfoundland to Virginia and eastern Tennessee, Iowa, Minnesota and Alaska.

In the Memoirs of Bastram and Marshall, page 20, it is stated that John Ellis, the eminent naturalist, in a letter to Linnaeus, dated London, April 25, 1758, says: " Mr Colden of New York, has sent Dr Fothergill a new plant, described by his daughter (Miss Jane Colden). It is called Fibraurea, gold thread. This young lady merits your esteem and does honor to your system. She has drawn and described 400 plants in your method only. She uses the English terms. Her father has a plant called after him, Coldenia; suppose you should call this Coldenella, or any other name that might distinguish her among your genera." Linnaeus, however, referred the plant to his genus Helleborus, and when it was subsequently ascertained to be distinct, Salisbury, regardless alike of gallantry and justice, imposed on it the name of Coptis.

Red Baneberry; Black Cohosh
Actaea rubra (Aiton) Willdenow

Plate 62

Stems erect, 1 to 2 feet high, from a perennial root, pubescent or smooth. Leaves ternately divided, the divisions pinnate with the lower ultimate leaflets sometimes again compound; leaflets ovate or the terminal ones obovate, toothed or more or less cleft or incised with pointed or rounded teeth. Flowers small in a dense terminal, ovoid raceme; sepals three to five, petaloid and fugacious. Petals four to ten, spatulate, shorter than the numerous white stamens; pedicels slender, one-half to two-thirds of an inch long. Fruit consisting of a raceme of bright-red, oval or ellipsoid berries, each berry about one-half of an inch long.

In woods, thickets and shaded banks, Nova Scotia to New Jersey and Pennsylvania, west to South Dakota and Nebraska. Flowering from April to early June. A variety with red berries on slender pedicles (A c t a e a n e g l e c t a Gillman) is occasionally found.

White Baneberry; Snakeroot
Actaea alba (Linnaeus) Miller

Plate 63b

Resembling the Red Baneberry in general habit and aspect. Leaflets usually more cut and the teeth and lobes sharply pointed. Flowers in oblong racemes; petals truncate at the apex; fruiting pedicels as thick as the peduncle or in fruit even thicker, with swollen ends, often reddish; berries short-oval, white, sometimes purplish at the ends. A variety with berries on thickened pedicels is occasionally seen.

In rich woods, Nova Scotia to Georgia, west to Minnesota and Missouri. Flowering in April and May or as late as the middle of June.

Black Snakeroot; Black Cohosh

Cimicifuga racemosa (Linnaeus) Nuttall

Plate 64

Stems tall and slender, 3 to 8 feet high, leafy above, rootstock thick and perennial. Leaves ternate with pinnate divisions; leaflets ovate or oblong, the terminal ones usually obovate, pointed at the apex, truncate or narrowed at the base, margins coarsely toothed, cleft or divided, rather thick texture, smooth or nearly so. Flowers white, with a somewhat fetid odor, in tall, terminal, simple or compound racemes, 6 to 30 inches long, each flower about one-half of an inch broad; petals four to eight, two-cleft; stamens very numerous; pistils one or two, sessile. Fruiting follicles oval, about one-fourth of an inch long, minutely beaked.

In woods and shaded rocky places, Maine and Ontario to Wisconsin, south to Georgia and Missouri. Flowering in July and August.

Wild Columbine; Rock Bells

Aquilegia canadensis Linnaeus

Plate 65

Erect and branching, glabrous or somewhat pubescent, 1 to 2 feet high, from a perennial root. Leaves ternately decompound, the lower and basal leaves slender-petioled, 4 to 8 inches broad, the ultimate leaflets 1 to 2 inches broad, sessile or short stalked, obovate, obtuse, cuneate, obtusely lobed and toothed, pale beneath; leaves of the upper part of the stem lobed or divided. Flowers nodding, 1 to 2 inches long, scarlet or rarely white or yellow; sepals five, regular, petaloid; petals concave, produced backward between the sepals into hollow, nearly straight spurs, one-half to three-fourths of an inch long, thickened at the end; stamens numerous, with the styles long exserted. Fruit erect, consisting of five united carpels with slightly spreading filiform beaks.

In rocky woodlands and clearings, Nova Scotia to the Northwest Territory, south to Florida and Texas. Flowering from the latter part of April until June.

Known in many localities as Honeysuckle, a name which should more properly be applied to species of the genus Lonicera. The European Columbine (A q u i l e g i a   v u l g a r i s Linnaeus) with showy, blue, purple or white flowers is an occasional escape from gardens into woods and fields.

Tall Anemone; Thimbleweed

Anemone virginiana Linnaeus

Plate 66

Stem stout, hairy, 2 to 3 feet tall, branching above at the involucre which is composed of two to five, usually three, short-petioled leaves; the lateral peduncles often bearing secondary involucres of smaller leaves. Basal leaves long petioled, broader than long, three-parted, the divisions broadly cuneate-oblong, variously cleft and divided into acute, serrate lobes; those of the involucres similar. Flowers two-thirds to $1\frac{1}{2}$ inches broad, on peduncles 4 to 10 inches long; sepals five, white, obtuse; stamens numerous, shorter than the sepals. Carpels numerous, forming an oblong to subcylindric head, two-thirds to 1 inch long and about one-half as thick.

In woods, thickets and clearings, Nova Scotia to Alberta, south to South Carolina, Arkansas and Kansas. Flowering from May to July or August. Consists of several races, differing in size and color of flower, shape of fruit, and in the styles. Of these, the most distinct is A n e m o n e r i p a r i a Fernald, with smaller greenish flowers and pointed sepals.

The Slender-fruited Anemone (A n e m o n e   c y l i n d r i c a A. Gray), which is frequent in sandy woods and thickets in the eastern states has silky hairy stems and tufted basal leaves with narrower divisions, white or greenish flowers about three-fourths of an inch broad and the head of fruit cylindric, 1 inch long or often longer and one-fourth to one-third as thick.

Canada or Round-leaved Anemone

Anemone canadensis Linnaeus

Plate 67

Stems slender or stout, 1 to 2 feet tall, somewhat hairy, especially on the lower surfaces of the leaves, branching at the involucre. Basal leaves long petioled, broader than long, three to five-pointed, the divisions broad, oblong, acute, variously cleft or toothed, those of the primary and secondary involucres similar but sessile. Flowers 1 to 1½ inches broad; sepals white or sometimes tinged with pink, oblong, obtuse; head of fruit globose, consisting of numerous flattened, orbicular, pubescent achenes, tipped with stout, persistent styles.

Low grounds, along roadsides, railroads and in open woods, Labrador to Assiniboia, Massachusetts, Maryland, Illinois, Kansas and Colorado Very closely related to A n e m o n e   d i c h o t o m a of Siberia. Flowering from May to August, by the development of secondary involucres.

Windflower; Wood Anemone
Anemone quinquefolia Linnaeus

Plate 68a

Smallest of our wild anemones. Stems simple, glabrous, 4 to 10 inches high, from horizontal, perennial rootstocks. Basal leaves long petioled, usually developing after the flowering stem, five-parted, the divisions oblong, cuneate, dentate; those of the single involucre on slender petioles one-half to 1 inch long, three- to five-parted, the divisions about 1½ inches long, acute, variously cut and lobed. Flowers solitary, about 1 inch broad; sepals four to nine, obovate or oval, white or purplish without; head of fruit globose, inclined, consisting of several pubescent, oblong achenes, tipped with hooked styles.

Common in moist or low woodlands, Nova Scotia to Minnesota, south to Georgia and Tennessee. Flowering in April and May.

Round-lobed Hepatica or Liverleaf
Hepatica hepatica (Linnaeus) Karsten

Plate 51b

Leaves long petioled, arising with the flowering scapes directly from the fibrous roots, reniform, hairy, 2 to 2½ inches broad when mature, spreading on the ground, three-lobed (occasionally the lateral divisions again lobed), obtuse. Flowers blue, purple or white, one-half to 1 inch broad on hairy scapes 4 to 6 inches high. Each flower subtended by an involucre of three sessile, obtuse, oblong, small leaves immediately under the flowers. Sepals oval or oblong, obtuse, longer than the numerous stamens. Fruit consisting of several oblong, acute, hairy achenes.

In woods, often in large tufts. Nova Scotia to northern Florida, west to Manitoba, Iowa and Missouri. Also in Alaska, Europe and Asia. Flowering in earliest spring, with us usually early in April but sometimes in March, and even unseasonably warm spells in midwinter may find it in flower. The leaves of Hepatica hepatica in central Europe possess blunt lobes, while our form usually has perfectly rounded lobes.

Sharp-lobed Hepatica or Liverleaf

Hepatica acutiloba DeCandolle

Plate 69b

Resembling in most respects the Round-lobed Hepatica but the leaf lobes and the leaves of the involucre are pointed, the scapes usually a little longer, and the flowers somewhat larger. The flowers are often dioecious.

In woods, Maine, Quebec and Ontario; south in the Alleghanies to Georgia; west to Missouri and Minnesota. Rare or absent near the Atlantic coast.

Puzzling forms sometimes occur which are intermediate between this and the preceding species.

Rue Anemone

Syndesmon thalictroides (Linnaeus) Hoffmannsegg

Plate 68b

Stems slender and weak, glabrous, 4 to 10 inches high; the flowering stem appearing in early spring from a cluster of tuberous roots, the ternately compound basal leaves appearing later and resembling those of the Meadow Rue, but smaller. Leaves of the involucre similar, sessile, the leaflets long petioled. Flowers perfect, few or several forming a loose umbel immediately above the involucre, white or pinkish, one-half to 1 inch broad; sepals five to ten, thin and soon falling, longer than the numerous stamens.

In woods, New Hampshire and Massachusetts to Florida, Ontario, Minnesota and Kansas. Flowering in early spring, March to early June.

Swamp or Marsh Buttercup

Ranunculus septentrionalis (Linnaeus) Poiret

Plate 70

Stems branching, 1 to 2 feet long, or becoming longer in summer, ascending, the later branches procumbent and often rooting at the nodes. Roots simply fibrous; stems glabrous or pubescent. Leaves large, petioled, three-divided, the divisions mostly stalked, usually cuneate at the base, cleft into broad lobes; petioles of the lower leaves sometimes a foot long. Flowers bright yellow, 1 to $1\frac{1}{4}$ inches broad; petals five, obovate, twice as long as the spreading sepals. Stamens numerous. Fruit a globose or oval head of flat, strongly margined achenes, each achene tipped by the subulate, persistent, sword-shaped style.

Marshes, swamps, ditches and low meadows, New Brunswick to Manitoba, Georgia and Kansas. Flowering from April to July.

Hispid Buttercup

Ranunculus hispidus Michaux

Plate 60b

Plant usually hairy when young, sometimes merely appressed-pubescent or glabrate when old; stems ascending or spreading, usually several from a thickened, fibrous, perennial root; at flowering time the stems only a few inches long, later becoming 1 to 2 feet long, but not stoloniferous. Leaves pinnately three to five divided, the divisions ovate, oblong or obovate, narrowed or cuneate at the base, sharply cleft or lobed, usually thin; flowers one-half to $1\frac{1}{2}$ inches broad; petals usually five, oblong, about twice as long as the spreading sepals and entire or sometimes slightly notched at the apex; achenes of fruit oval, lenticular, narrowly margined, abruptly tipped by a subulate style of about one-half their length.

In dry woods and thickets, Vermont and Ontario to North Dakota, south to Georgia and Arkansas. Flowering from March to May.

Stiff White Water Crowfoot

Batrachium circinatum (Sibthorp) Reichenbach

Plate 79a

Plant entirely submerged, except the flowers. Stems branching, usually 1 foot long or longer. Leaves about 1 inch long, spreading nearly at right angles from the stem, only slightly or not at all collapsing when drawn from the water, repeatedly forked into capillary divisions. Flowers white, one-third of an inch broad on stout peduncles, 1 to 2 inches long opposite the leaves, flowering just above the surface of the water; sepals and petals five; petals oblong-oval and blunt. Fruit a small cluster of tiny, apiculate achenes.

In ponds and slow streams, Nova Scotia to British Columbia, south to North Carolina, also in Europe and Asia. Flowering from June to September.

The form illustrated here has the beak of the achenes about 1 mm long, so that it should be classed as Batrachium longirostre (Godron) F. Schultz.

Early Meadow Rue

Thalictrum dioicum Linnaeus

Plate 71

Stems glabrous, erect, 1 to 2 feet high, slender and leafy from brown perennial roots. Leaves three to four-ternate. Leaflets thin, pale beneath, orbicular or broader, often cordate and the terminal one somewhat cuneate five to nine-lobed. Flowers dioecious, greenish or greenish yellow, drooping or spreading; panicle elongated, of numerous lateral corymbs or umbels; sepals usually four, blunt; petals none; stamens numerous, filaments longer than the sepals; anthers linear, blunt, longer than the filaments. Achenes in fruit ovoid, sessile or minutely stipitate, strongly ribbed, much longer than the style.

In woods and on shaded banks, Maine to Alabama, Saskatchewan and Missouri.   Flowering in April and May.

Fall Meadow Rue

Thalictrum polygamum Muhlenberg

Plate 72

Stems stout, smooth or pubescent but not glandular or waxy, 3 to 10 feet high, branching.   Leaves three to four-ternate; leaflets thickish, light green above and pale beneath, oblong or orbicular with three main apical pointed or blunt lobes; panicle compound, leafy, a foot long or more. Flowers polygamous, white or purplish, usually the pistillate flowers purplish and the staminate flowers white; filaments broad, narrowly clavate; anthers oblong, short.   Fruiting achenes ovoid, sessile or short-stipulate, six to eight-winged, glabrous or pubescent.

Marshes, open sunny swamps and low meadows.   Newfoundland to Florida, Ontario and Ohio.   Flowering from July to September.

Virgin's Bower; Woodbine; Wild Clematis

Clematis virginiana Linnaeus

Figure XVI and Plate 73

A long vine, climbing over bushes in low woodlands, and along fences and watercourses.   Stems somewhat woody below but only the root perennial in the north at least.   Leaves opposite, glabrous, trifoliate; leaflets broadly ovate, acute at the apex, toothed or lobed, sometimes slightly cordate.   Flowers in leafy panicles, white, polygamo-dioecious, two-thirds to $1\frac{1}{4}$ inches broad when expanded.   Sepals usually four, spreading, petallike; petals none; stamens numerous, spreading; filaments glabrous; pistils numerous.   In fruit the styles become an inch long or more, plumose and persistent on the achenes (figure XVI).

Nova Scotia to Georgia, west to Manitoba and Tennessee.   Flowering in midsummer, July to September.

Figure XVI
Virgin's Bower (Clematis virginiana Linnaeus), in fruit

Purple Virgin's Bower

Atragene americana Sims

(*Clematis verticillaris* De Candolle)

Figure XVII

A trailing or partly climbing vine, somewhat woody and perennial below, glabrous or nearly so. Leaves trifoliate; leaflets thin, ovate, acute, toothed or entire and more or less cordate; petioles and petiolules slender. Flowers purplish blue, 2 to 4 inches broad, solitary on slender peduncles in the axils of the leaves or at the ends of the branches. Sepals four, thin and translucent, strongly veined, silky along the margins and veins; petals four, spatulate, one-half to two-thirds of an inch long; stamens very numerous, the outer ones usually with broadened filaments; styles long, persistent, plumose throughout and about 2 inches long in fruit.

Rocky woodlands and thickets, Hudson bay to Manitoba, south to Connecticut, Virginia and Minnesota. Flowering in May and June. One of our rarest wild flowers.

Erect Silky Leather Flower

Viorna ochroleuca (Aiton) Small

Plate 74

Stems erect, silky-hairy, 1 to 2 feet high and somewhat woody at the base from a thickened, woody, perennial root. Leaves opposite, simple, sessile, ovate or elliptical-ovate, blunt, smooth and glabrous above, silky and reticulate-veined beneath, entire or rarely somewhat lobed; each stem with a single terminal nodding flower about 1 inch long or less. Calyx rather broadly cylindric in shape, composed of four or five thick sepals, very silky without, their yellowish-green tips recurved; petals none. Stamens numerous, parallel with the sepals, their anthers very narrow. Pistils very numerous, their styles silky or plumose. In fruit the fleshy sepals fall away leaving an erect head of small achenes plumose with the long, yellowish-brown, persistent styles which are 1 to 2 inches long.

Figure XVII
Purple Virgin's Bower
(A t r a g e n e a m e r i c a n a Sims)

Sandy fields and thickets, Staten Island and Pennsylvania, south to Georgia. Flowering in late May and June. In the southern states several additional species of Leather Flower (Viorna) are found, but this is the only one which enters New York.

Barberry Family

Berberidaceae

Blue Cohosh

Caulophyllum thalictroides (Linnaeus) Michaux

Plate 75

Stems erect, glabrous and glaucous when young, 1 to 3 feet high from a thickened, perennial rootstock; the base of the stem with two or three large, sheathing bracts, near the top of the stem a single, large, triternate, nearly sessile leaf and usually a similar but smaller leaf near the base of the inflorescence. Leaflets thin, oval, oblong or obovate, 1 to 3 inches long when mature, usually only partly developed at flowering time, three to five-lobed at the apex. Flowers several in a loose terminal panicle, greenish purple, one-quarter to one-half of an inch broad; sepals six, oblong; petals six, smaller, cucullate and opposite the sepals; stamens six. Each flower contains a single pistil with two ovules, which ripens into a globose, blue, glaucous, berrylike fruit, about one-third of an inch in diameter. As the seed grows it ruptures the thin, transparent pericarp before maturity.

In woods and thickets, New Brunswick to South Carolina, west to Manitoba, Tennessee, Nebraska and Missouri. Flowering in April and May.

May Apple; Wild Mandrake

Podophyllum peltatum Linnaeus

Plate 76

Stems erect, 1 to 1½ feet high, from a perennial, horizontal, poisonous rootstock. Basal leaves centrally peltate, often nearly a foot in diameter, long petioled, deeply five to nine-lobed, glabrous or pubescent and light green on the lower surface, darker above; lobes two-cleft and toothed at the apex. Flowering stems appearing from different rootstocks, bearing one to three, usually two, similar leaves (rarely leaflets). Flowers $1\frac{1}{2}$ to 2 inches broad, white, fragrant, on stout, nodding peduncles one-half to 2 inches long, appearing from the base of the upper leaf or usually from the fork between the two leaves; sepals six, petallike and soon falling. Petals six to nine, flat, obovate, longer than the sepals; stamens twice as many as the petals. Ovary ovoid, forming in fruit a large, yellowish, ovoid, edible berry, $1\frac{1}{2}$ to 2 inches long, the numerous seeds inclosed in fleshy arils within the fruit.

In low woods, moist banks and clearings, western Quebec and southern Ontario to Minnesota, Kansas, Florida, Louisiana and Texas. Flowering in May and June.

The fruit is edible and harmless, although somewhat insipid and to many people its taste is disagreeable. Both foliage and root are said to be poisonous and serious results have followed the use of the leaves as greens. The root is a violent purgative, resembling jalap in its action. Its popular name, Mandrake, relates it in no way to the Mandrake or Mandragora of the ancients and, notwithstanding its poisonous character it is a very respectable herb in comparison with the traditions of the Mandrake of the ancients, described as flourishing best under a gallows, with a root resembling a man in shape, uttering terrible shrieks when it was torn from the ground, and possessing the power of transforming men and beasts.

Twin-leaf

Jeffersonia diphylla (Linnaeus) Persoon

Figure XVIII

A smooth, perennial, fibrous-rooted plant, 6 to 8 inches high when in flower, later becoming 10 to 18 inches high. Leaves and flowering stems arising from a scaly base. Leaves glaucous beneath, long petioled, cordate or reniform, 3 to 6 inches long, 2 to 4 inches wide when mature, parted longitudinally into two obliquely ovate, blunt, lobed or entire divisions; lobes rounded with sinuses sometimes three-fourths of an inch deep. At

Figure XVIII
Twin-leaf
(Jeffersonia diphylla (Linnaeus) Persoon)

flowering time the leaves are but partially developed. Flowering stems without leaves and one-flowered. Flowers white, about 1 inch broad; the calyx with four (sometimes three or five) caducous, petallike divisions. Petals eight, flat, oblong, longer than the sepals. Stamens eight with slender filaments. Fruit a short-stalked capsule about 1 inch long, opening at maturity near the summit by a half-circumscissle cleft.

In moist woods, New York, Ontario and Pennsylvania to Wisconsin, Iowa, Virginia and Tennessee. Flowering in April and May.

Poppy Family

Papaveraceae

Bloodroot; Puccoon-root

Sanguinaria canadensis Linnaeus

Plate 77

Leaves and stems glabrous, especially when young, from a stout, horizontal rootstock, one-half to 1 inch thick, densely clothed with thick, fibrous roots. Juice of the roots and stems red. Leaves basal on petioles 6 to 14 inches long, palmately five to nine-lobed, the lobes repand or cleft at the apex and palmately veined. Flowering scapes, one-flowered, at length overtopped by the mature leaves, but at flowering time longer than the partially unfolded immature leaves. Flowers white or sometimes pinkish, 1 to 1½ inches broad; sepals two, soon falling. Petals eight to sixteen, oblong-spatulate, arranged in two or three rows and soon falling; stamens numerous, yellow. Fruit a narrow, one-celled, two-valved capsule, pointed at both ends, about 1 inch long.

In rich woods and on shaded banks, Nova Scotia to Manitoba and Nebraska, south to Florida, Alabama and Arkansas. Flowering in April and May.

WILD FLOWERS

Fumewort Family

Fumariaceae

Dutchman's-breeches

Bicuculla cucullaria (Linnaeus) Millspaugh

Plate 78

A rather delicate, smooth and somewhat tufted herbaceous plant from a bulbous, perennial base. Leaves all basal, numerous and slender-stalked, pale beneath, finely divided into many narrow segments. Flowers nodding, fragrant, few or several on a slender stalk which rises above the leaves; each flower about one-half to two-thirds of an inch long, and somewhat broader than long across the spreading basal spurs, white or faintly pink, yellow at the summit; the four petals in two pairs, the outer pair oblong, concave, each with a divergent spur at the base and the tip spreading, the inner pair narrow and minutely crested. Fruit an oblong pod, opening into two parts to the base when mature.

In rich woods, Nova Scotia to North Carolina, west to Minnesota, Kansas and Missouri. Flowering in April and May.

The Squirrel Corn or Turkey Corn (B i c u c u l l a c a n a d e n s i s (Goldie) Millspaugh) is similar, but the spurs of the two outer petals are shorter, rounded and not divergent, the inner pair of petals is conspicuously crested and the roots have numerous small tubers. The Wild Bleeding Heart (B i c u c u l l a e x i m i a (Ker) Millspaugh) of the middle western states has pink flowers.

Mountain Fringe; Alleghany Vine

Adlumia fungosa (Aiton) Greene

Plate 79b

Stems weak, slender, climbing several feet over other plants by its slender petioles from a biennial root. Leaves two to three-pinnate, the leaflets slender stalked, lobed or entire, very thin, ovate or cuneate, about one-fourth of an inch long and pale beneath. Flowers numerous in axillary drooping cymes; petals four, united into a narrowly ovate-cordate, spongy corolla about one-half of an inch long and one-fourth of an inch broad at the base, four-lobed at the apex, greenish purple, or pink, usually rather persistent, dry and brownish with age; stamens six, united below and adherent to the petals. Fruiting capsule oblong, included in the persistent, dry corolla.

In moist woods, thickets and shaded cliffs, New Brunswick to Ontario and Michigan, south to North Carolina and Tennessee. Flowering from June to October. Frequent in cultivation.

Pink or Pale Corydalis

Capnoides sempervirens (Linnaeus) Borkhausen

Plate 80

Stems and leaves glabrous, glaucous, erect or ascending, 6 inches to 2 feet high and freely branching. Lower leaves 1 to 5 inches long, short petioled, the upper leaves sessile or nearly so, all divided into numerous obovate or cuneate segments, toothed or entire, obtuse. Flowers numerous, panicled, borne in cymose clusters at the ends of the branches. Each flower one-half to two-thirds of an inch long, pink or rarely white with a yellow tip; sepals two, small; corolla irregular, deciduous; petals four, erect-connivent, one of the outer pair with a spur at the base about one-eighth of an inch long, the inner pair narrower, keeled at the back. Capsules narrowly linear, erect, 1 to 2 inches long.

In rocky places, Nova Scotia to Alaska, Georgia, Minnesota, Montana and British Columbia. Flowering from May to September.

Two other species of this genus are found in the eastern states, both with low, diffusely spreading stems and with yellow flowers. They are the Yellow Corydalis (C a p n o i d e s   f l a v u l u m (Rafinesque) Kuntze) with flowers about one-fourth of an inch long and short spurred; and the Golden Corydalis (C .   a u r e u m (Willdenow) Kuntze) with flowers slightly more than one-half of an inch long and spurs one-half the length of the corolla.

Mustard Family

Cruciferae

Lyre-leaved Rock Cress

Arabis lyrata Linnaeus

Plate 54b

A low, tufted perennial or biennial plant with ascending or erect stems, 4 to 12 inches high, smooth above, pubescent below or glabrous throughout. Basal leaves lyrate-pinnatifid, 1 to 2 inches long, spatulate or oblanceolate, pubescent or glabrous; stem leaves entire or toothed, spatulate or linear, one-half to 1 inch long. Flowers white, one-fourth of an inch broad or less, several or numerous in a terminal raceme which elongates in fruit; pedicels ascending, about one-third of an inch long or longer in fruit; petals four, much longer than the four stamens. Fruit a linear, slightly flattened pod three-fourths to $1\frac{1}{4}$ inches long; seeds in one row, oblong and wingless.

Rocky and sandy places, Connecticut and Ontario west to Manitoba and Alaska, south to Virginia, Tennessee, Missouri and British Columbia. Flowering from April to September.

Bulbous Cress; Cuckoo-flower

Cardamine bulbosa (Schreber) Britton, Sterns & Poggenberg

Plate 90a

A slender, erect, herbaceous plant with smooth stems, 6 to 20 inches high from a perennial, tuber-bearing root, simple or rarely branched. Leaves of two sorts, those of the stem sessile and clasping or the lower ones very short petioled, rather distant from one another, oblong or lanceolate, blunt, toothed or entire, 1 to 2 inches long; the basal leaves oval or orbicular, one-half to 2 inches broad, often slightly heart-shaped, toothed or usually entire, with long, slender petioles. Flowers white, about one-half of an inch broad, in a terminal, several to many-flowered cluster; petals four, three to four times the length of the four sepals. Fruit a number of erect, very slender pods, narrowed at each end and about an inch long.

In low, wet woods, thickets and wet meadows, New Brunswick to Vermont, southern Ontario and Minnesota, south to Florida and Texas. Flowering in April and May, or in cool woods as late as early June.

The Purple Cress (C a r d a m i n e d o u g l a s s i i (Torrey) Britton) has leaves which are more angularly toothed and showy purple flowers often three-fourths of an inch broad. It is found in cold, springy places.

The True Water-cress (S i s y m b r i u m n a s t u r t i u m-a q u a-t i c u m Linnaeus) is a native of Europe, but is common in brooks and streams in many sections of the eastern states.

Cut-leaved Toothwort or Pepperroot

Dentaria laciniata Muhlenberg

Plate 81a

Stems erect, pubescent or glabrous, 8 to 15 inches high from a deep, perennial, tubercled, jointed rootstock, the joints easily separable. Leaves all petioled, 2 to 5 inches broad, those on the stem usually three and forming a whorl, rarely distant, three-parted nearly to the base, the divisions lanceolate, linear or oblong, the lateral ones often deeply cleft, all deeply toothed or lobed; basal leaves similar, usually developing later than the flowering stems. Flowers numerous in a stout, broad raceme, two-thirds to three-fourths of an inch broad, pink or white. The four petals longer than the sepals. Stamens six. Fruiting pod linear, ascending, 1 to 1½ inches long.

In moist or rich woods, Quebec to Florida, west to Minnesota, Kansas and Louisiana. Flowering in April and May.

Two-leaved Toothwort or Crinkleroot

Dentaria diphylla Michaux

Plate 81b

Stems stout, simple, glabrous, 6 to 14 inches high from a perennial, notched but continuous rootstock. Basal leaves long petioled, 4 to 5 inches broad, with three broadly ovate, dentate or somewhat lobed leaflets each about 2 inches long; stem leaves usually two, opposite or nearly so, short petioled and also three-divided, the leaflets often narrower than those of the basal leaves. Flowers white, one-half to two-thirds of an inch broad.

In rich woods, Nova Scotia and New Brunswick to Minnesota, south to South Carolina and Kentucky. Flowering usually in late April and in May.

The Large Toothwort (D e n t a r i a   m a x i m a Nuttall) has a jointed rootstock and three stem leaves (sometimes two or as many as five or six), alternate, with ovate and obovate toothed and cleft leaflets and large pale-purple flowers. It is rare and local in distribution.

The species of Dentaria are members of the Mustard family (Cruciferae) which contains a very large number of small-flowered, inconspicuous plants, many of them weeds, as well as a number of cultivated species which have become naturalized or established throughout the eastern states.

American Sea Rocket

Cakile edentula (Bigelow) Hooker

Plate 82a

Plant very fleshy throughout, bushy branched from a deep, annual root, the lower branches spreading or ascending, the center ones erect, a few inches to a foot high. Leaves oblanceolate or obovate, obtuse, lobed or toothed, narrowed at the base, the lower leaves 2 to 5 inches long, the upper leaves smaller. Flowers light purple, less than one-fourth of an inch broad, the four petals long-clawed, more than twice the length of the sepals; fruit one-half to 1 inch long, the upper joint slightly longer than the lower, ovoid, angled, flattened, narrowed above into a beak; lower joint obovoid, not flattened.

Sandy places along the seashore, Newfoundland to New Jersey and Florida, and along the Great Lakes, New York to Minnesota.

Pitcher Plant Family
Sarraceniaceae
Pitcher Plant; Sidesaddle Flower
Sarracenia purpurea Linnaeus

Plate 83

Leaves tufted, ascending, hollow, much inflated and trumpet-shaped, 4 to 12 inches long, with a broad, lateral wing and an erect terminal lid or lamina, glabrous except the inner side of the lamina and the inner surface of the pitchers, which are densely clothed with stiff, reflexed hairs, purple-veined or sometimes green, yellowish or reddish all over, narrowed into petioles below, persistent over winter. Roots large, stout and fibrous. Flowers solitary on slender scapes, 1 to 2 feet high, nodding, deep purple or rarely yellow, nearly globose, $1\frac{1}{2}$ to $2\frac{1}{4}$ inches broad; sepals five, green, with three or four bracts at the base; petals five, obovate, narrowed in the middle, incurved over the yellowish style. Style dilated at the apex into a peltate umbrellalike structure with five rays which terminate under its angles in hooked stigmas.

In peat bogs and wet sphagnous places, Labrador to the Canadian Rocky mountains, Florida, Kentucky and Iowa. Flowering in May and June. The pitcher-shaped leaves usually contain more or less water in which are numerous drowned insects which furnish food for the larvae of a fly which is instrumental in the cross-pollination of the flowers.

Sundew Family
Droseraceae
Spatulate-leaved Sundew
Drosera intermedia (Linnaeus) Hayne

Plate 84

A tufted bog plant with erect, flowering scapes, 2 to 8 inches high, and elongated rootstocks. Leaf blades ascending, spatulate, obtuse at the apex, one-fourth to three-fourths of an inch long, one-half to one-third as wide as long, clothed above with long, glandular hairs secreting a fluid which entraps insects, narrowed below into glabrous petioles one-half to $1\frac{1}{2}$ inches long; usually the entire foliage reddish or greenish red in color. Flowers several in one-sided racemes; petals five, white, slightly longer than the greenish sepals; the one-celled ovary surmounted by three styles, each deeply two-parted so as to appear like six.

In bogs and sphagnous places, Newfoundland to Saskatchewan, south to Florida and Louisiana, and also in northern Europe. Flowering from June to August.

The Spatulate-leaved Sundew is not so common as the Round-leaved Sundew (D r o s e r a r o t u n d i f o l i a Linnaeus), with orbicular leaf blades. Two additional Sundews may be looked for, namely the Oblong-leaved Sundew (D r o s e r a l o n g i f o l i a Linnaeus), with leaf blades elongated-spatulate, six to eight times as long as wide; and the Thread-leaved Sundew (D. f i l i f o r m i s (Linnaeus) Rafinesque), with linear leaves ten to fifteen times as long as wide and purple flowers. The last grows in wet sand near the coast, the others in bogs.

Virginia Stonecrop Family

Penthoraceae

Ditch or Virginia Stonecrop

Penthorum sedoides Linnaeus

Plate 87b

Stems erect, glabrous, often branched and angled above, 6 inches to 2 feet high, from a perennial root. Leaves alternate, sessile, lanceolate or narrowly elliptic, acuminate at each end, finely toothed, 2 to 4 inches long, one-half to 1 inch wide. Flowers perfect, yellowish green, in two or three forked, one-sided cymes, the branches 1 to 3 inches long. Each flower about one-fifth of an inch broad; calyx five-parted, the sepals triangular-ovate, pointed, shorter than the flattish capsule; stamens ten; petals often lacking, when present, linear or linear-spatulate. Fruit a depressed, five-lobed capsule with five divergent tips.

Common in ditches and swampy places, New Brunswick to Florida, west to Nebraska, Kansas and Texas. Flowering from July to September.

Not a very attractive plant, but the only American representative of the Penthoraceae (Virginia Stonecrop family), which is joined with the Saxifrage family by some authors and to the Orpine family by others.

Grass-of-Parnassus Family
Parnassiaceae
Carolina Grass-of-Parnassus
Parnassia caroliniana Michaux

Plate 85

Flowering scape 6 to 20 inches high, with a sessile, ovate, clasping leaf below the middle. Basal leaves very numerous, ovate, oval, or nearly orbicular, obtuse at the apex, rounded or slightly cordate at the base, or decurrent on the petiole, 1 to 2 inches long, on petioles 2 to 6 inches long. Flowers three-fourths to $1\frac{1}{2}$ inches broad; calyx lobes five, ovate-oblong, obtuse and much shorter than the five broadly oval, white, greenish veined petals; each petal with a set (usually three) of gland-tipped staminodia at the base which do not exceed the five fertile stamens in length, the latter alternate with the petals. Fruit a one-celled capsule about one-half of an inch long.

In swamps, low meadows and boggy places, New Brunswick to Manitoba, south to Virginia, Illinois and Iowa. Flowering from July to September, rarely earlier than July in our latitude. At Taberg growing on wet cliffs with the Yellow Mountain Saxifrage and Dwarf Canadian Primrose.

Saxifrage Family
Saxifragaceae
Yellow Mountain Saxifrage
Leptasea aizoides (Linnaeus) Haworth

Plate 82b

Stems tufted, forming loose or dense leafy mats, 2 to 7 inches high. Leaves alternate, linear, thick, fleshy, sharply pointed at the apex, sessile, one-third to three-fourths of an inch long, one-eighth of an inch wide or usually less, sometimes sparingly ciliate on the margins. Flowers several, corymbose, one-third to two-thirds of an inch broad on slender pedicels; petals five, oblong, yellow and often spotted with orange, longer than the ovate calyx lobes and alternate with them. Stamens ten; ovary almost superior, the two capsules united to above the middle.

On wet or dripping rocks, Newfoundland and Labrador to Vermont, northern and western New York, and west through Arctic America to the Rocky mountains. Also in Alpine and Arctic Europe and Asia. Flowering in July and August.

Early Saxifrage

Micranthes virginiensis (Linnaeus) Small

Plate 87a

Flowering stem 4 to 12 inches high, viscid-pubescent with whitish hairs, leafless or with a few green bracts at the base of the inflorescence. Leaves all basal, 1 to 3 inches long, obovate, or oval, toothed, blunt or pointed at the apex, spatulate at the base and narrowed into a margined petiole; inflorescence cymose, becoming paniculate by the elongation of the lower branches. Flowers white, less than one-fourth of an inch broad; calyx of five erect, triangular, pointed lobes; petals five, oblong-spatulate, obtuse, longer than the calyx; stamens ten, carpels of the fruit usually two, nearly separate, widely divergent when mature.

In dry or rocky woodlands, banks and ledges, New Brunswick to Minnesota, south to Georgia and Tennessee. Flowering from April until June.

Swamp Saxifrage

Micranthes pennsylvanica (Linnaeus) Haworth

Plate 86

Flowering scape stout, viscid-pubescent, 1 to $3\frac{1}{2}$ feet high, with green bracts at the inflorescence, otherwise leafless. Leaves all basal, large, oval, ovate, obovate or oblanceolate, pubescent or nearly glabrous, 4 to 10 inches long, obtuse at the apex, narrowed below into a broad petiole, the margins denticulate or repand. Flowers in elongated, loose, terminal panicles, greenish. Each flower about one-eighth of an inch broad or slightly broader; the obtuse calyx lobes reflected; petals five, lanceolate or linear-lanceolate, twice as long as the calyx.

Swamps, wet banks and wet woods, Maine to Ontario, Minnesota, Virginia, Iowa and Missouri. Flowering in May and June.

Foamflower; False Miterwort

Tiarella cordifolia Linnaeus

Plate 88

Flowering scapes 6 to 12 inches high, slender and pubescent, from a rather stout, perennial root. Leaves all basal, long petioled, broadly ovate or nearly orbicular, cordate at the base, three to seven-lobed, blunt or pointed at the apex, 2 to 4 inches long, margins crenate or dentate, pubescent above with scattered hairs, glabrate or downy along the veins beneath. Flowers white, forming a terminal raceme, 1 to 4 inches long. Each flower about one-fourth of an inch broad; petals five, oblong, entire or slightly toothed, somewhat longer than the five white calyx lobes; stamens ten, anthers reddish or yellowish. Fruit of two very unequal carpels, about one-fourth of an inch long, reflexed on slender pedicels.

In rich, moist woods, Nova Scotia to Ontario and Minnesota, south along the mountains to Georgia, and west to Indiana and Michigan. Flowering from April to June. Also known as Coolwort.

Alumroot

Heuchera americana Linnaeus

Plate 89

Flowering stem rather stout, $1\frac{1}{2}$ to 3 feet high, leafless, glandular, hirsute. Leaves basal, long petioled, 3 to 4 inches wide with seven to nine rounded, crenate-dentate lobes; the older leaves glabrous or with scattered hairs on the upper surfaces, new leaves usually somewhat pubescent. Flowers greenish yellow, in elongated panicles; calyx tube broadly campanulate, nearly regular, somewhat less than one-fourth of an inch long, five-lobed; petals five, very small, greenish and alternate with the lobes of the calyx which they do not exceed in length. Stamens five, projecting out from the calyx more than one-half their length, anthers orange.

In dry or rocky woods and banks, Ontario to Connecticut, west to Minnesota, south to Alabama and Louisiana. Flowering from May to August.

Two-leaved Bishop's Cap; Miterwort

Mitella diphylla Linnaeus

Plate 90b

Stems erect, often several together from a perennial root, 8 to 17 inches high, pubescent, each stem bearing a pair of opposite, sessile or nearly sessile leaves near or above its middle. Basal leaves broadly ovate, cordate at the base, acute or long pointed at the apex, three to five-lobed, toothed, rather rough-hairy on both sides, 1 to 2 inches long. Flowers small, white, rather distant from one another, in a very narrow, elongated, erect raceme, 3 to 8 inches long; calyx tube bell-shaped, five-lobed; petals five, finely pinnatifid. Fruiting capsules one-celled, two-valved at the apex, many seeded, somewhat flattened and broad, seeds smooth, black and shiny.

In rich woods, Quebec to Minnesota, North Carolina and Missouri. Flowering in April and May.

In the cold woods across the northern states and Canada occurs a smaller species of Miterwort, M i t e l l a n u d a Linnaeus, with reniform-orbicular, basal leaves and the stems usually without leaves; flowers greenish yellow. Another species, M. o p p o s i t i f o l i a Rydberg, has been described from central New York which differs from M. d i p h y l l a only in having long-petioled stem leaves, lanceolate calyx lobes and filiform divisions to the petals.

Rose Family

Rosaceae

Meadowsweet; Quaker Lady

Spiraea latifolia (Aiton) Borkhausen

Plate 93ᵃ

An erect shrub, 2 to 6 feet high, usually more or less branched above and smooth with reddish stems. Leaves short petioled, blades oblanceolate or obovate, glabrous or nearly so, coarsely toothed, 1 to 2 inches long, one-half to $1\frac{1}{2}$ inches wide, usually larger on young shoots, obtuse or slightly pointed at the apex, rounded or tapering at the base, pale beneath. Flowers white or pinkish, in dense terminal panicles, each flower about one-fourth of an inch broad or less; petals four or five, inserted on the calyx; stamens numerous. Pistils commonly five, alternate with the calyx lobes.

In moist or rocky places, in open woods, or in old meadows and along roadsides, Newfoundland to Saskatchewan, Virginia and western Pennsylvania. Flowering from June to August.

The Narrow-leaved Meadowsweet (Spiraea alba Du Roi) has yellowish brown branches, narrowly oblanceolate to oblong leaves and white flowers. It is much less abundant than Spiraea latifolia, and is found in wet soil, Ontario to New York, south to North Carolina, west to Indiana, Missouri and Saskatchewan.

Hardhack; Steeplebush

Spiraea tomentosa Linnaeus

Plate 94a

Erect, shrubby and perennial at least below, the tops usually dying back, 1 to 3 feet tall, usually simple; stems floccose-pubescent. Leaves short petioled, ovate or oval, 1 to 2 inches long, one-half to 1 inch wide, unequally toothed, blunt or pointed at the apex, narrowed or rounded at the base, smooth and dark green above, woolly-pubescent with whitish hairs beneath. Flowers pink or purplish, rarely white, in dense terminal panicles, each flower about one-fifth of an inch broad; divisions or follicles of the fruit pubescent.

In wet meadows, swamps and low ground, Nova Scotia to Manitoba south to Georgia and Kansas. Flowering from July to September.

The Corymbed Spiraea (S p i r a e a c o r y m b o s a Rafinesque), with oval, ovate or orbicular leaves, slightly cordate at the base, or rounded, and with small white flowers in dense terminal, often leafy corymbs, is found occasionally on rocky banks and in woods from New Jersey southward.

Indian Physic; Bowman's Root

Porteranthus trifoliatus (Linnaeus) Britton

Plate 91

Stems erect, herbaceous, 2 to 4 feet high, from a perennial root, usually branched, glabrous or slightly pubescent. Stipules small, one-eighth to one-fourth of an inch long, entire or toothed. Leaves sessile or nearly so, three-foliate; leaflets oval, ovate, lanceolate or slightly obovate, long pointed at the apex, narrowed at the base, 2 to 3 inches long, irregularly toothed. Flowers white or pinkish, one-half to two-thirds of an inch long on slender peduncles, in loose, terminal, leafy panicles; calyx reddish, five-toothed, ten nerved; petals five, linear-lanceolate, somewhat unequal.

In woods and thickets, Ontario and New York to Michigan, Georgia and Missouri. Flowers in June and July.

A closely related species, P o r t e r a n t h u s s t i p u l a t u s (Muhlenberg) Britton, has incised leaflets, broad, foliaceous, incised stipules and slightly smaller flowers. Its range is about the same.

Common Five-finger or Cinquefoil

Potentilla canadensis Linnaeus

Plate 92

Stems ascending, a few inches high, spreading by slender runners 3 inches to 1 or 2 feet long; the pubescence of the stem, petioles and peduncles spreading. Leaves petioled, digitately five-foliated; leaflets oblanceolate to oblong, blunt at the apex, narrowed at the base, one-half to 1 inch long, toothed. Flowers yellow, one-fourth to three-fourths of an inch broad on slender, axillary, one-flowered peduncles; the first flower appearing from the axil of the second stem leaf; petals five, broadly oval, slightly longer than the acute calyx lobes and the linear-lanceolate bractlets; stamens about twenty.

In dry soil of meadows and fields, New Brunswick to Georgia, Minnesota and Texas. Flowering from April to August.

The genus Potentilla contains a number of additional representatives, several of which are introduced species. Of these, the most common is the Rough Cinquefoil (Potentilla monspeliensis Linnaeus), with stout, erect, hairy stems and leaves, and yellow flowers in which the calyx lobes exceed the petals in length.

The Silvery Cinquefoil (Potentilla argentea Linnaeus) is a native species of dry soils or rocky places, with spreading or ascending, white, woolly-pubescent stems, leaflets green and smooth above and white-tomentose beneath, the margins revolute, and small yellow flowers.

Rough-fruited Cinquefoil

Potentilla recta Linnaeus

Plate 95

Stems erect, stout, branched above, villous-pubescent, 1 to 2 feet high from a stout, perennial root, with ovate-lanceolate stipules, the lower foliaceous and cut. Leaves digitately five to seven-foliate, petioled or the upper leaves nearly sessile; leaflets oblanceolate, blunt at the apex, narrowed at the base, pubescent with scattered hairs above, more densely pubescent beneath, sharply toothed, 1 to 3 inches long. Flowers numerous, bright or dull yellow, about three-fourths of an inch broad, in terminal, cymose clusters; stamens about twenty.

Roadsides, fields and waste places, Maine to Ontario, New York, Virginia and Michigan. Naturalized from Europe and Asia. Flowering from June to September.

Silverweed; Wild or Goose Tansy

Argentina anserina (Linnaeus) Rydberg

Plate 92b

Stems and leaves herbaceous and tufted from a perennial root; spreading by slender runners, 8 inches to 3 feet long. Leaves pinnate, 3 to 18 inches long; leaflets seven to twenty-five, oblong, oblanceolate or obovate, obtuse, the lower leaflets usually smaller, often with still smaller ones interspersed, all sharply toothed, nearly glabrous above, white or silky-pubescent beneath. Flowers yellow, three-fourths to $1\frac{1}{8}$ inches broad, solitary on erect axillary peduncles; petals five, broadly oval or obovate, longer than the five ovate, pointed sepals and the five oval bractlets; stamens about twenty, borne around the base of the hemispheric, villous receptacle.

Lake shores, sandy fields and salt meadows, New Jersey to Greenland, west to Nebraska, British Columbia and Alaska, south in the Rocky mountains to New Mexico and California; also in Europe and Asia. Flowering from May to September. Consists of several or numerous races, differing in the size and shape of the leaflets, and slightly in the achenes. Small northern plants have been referred to A . e g e d i i of Greenland, and a form from Oneida lake has been described as A. b a b-c o c k i a n a Rydberg.

Purple or Marsh Cinquefoil; Purplewort

Comarum palustre Linnaeus

Plate 96a

Stems decumbent, often rather long, somewhat woody and perennial at the base; pubescent above. Leaves pinnate, upper leaves three to five-foliate, nearly sessile, lower ones successively longer petioled, five to seven-foliate; leaflets oblong or oval, sharply toothed, blunt or pointed at the apex, narrowed at the base, 1 to 3 inches long; petioles sheathed at the base by large membranous stipules. Flowers conspicuous, three-fourths to $1\frac{1}{4}$ inches broad; calyx deeply five-lobed with five narrow bractlets, the calyx lobes ovate, acuminate, red or purple within, much exceeding the purple, ovate-lanceolate petals; pistils numerous, seated on an enlarged, pubescent receptacle which becomes spongy in fruit.

In swamps and peat bogs, Greenland and Labrador to New Jersey, Iowa, British Columbia, Wyoming, Alaska and California; also in northern Europe and Asia. Flowering from June to August.

Wild or Scarlet Strawberry
Fragaria virginiana (Linnaeus) Duchesne
Plate 97a

Plants tufted, usually several or many together, dark green, foliage villous-pubescent with spreading hairs. Leaves thick, with three broadly oval or obovate, coarsely toothed leaflets, the terminal one usually narrowed at the base; petioles 2 to 6 inches long. Flowering scapes as long or shorter than the leaves, bearing several white flowers on appressed-pubescent pedicels. Flowers one-half to three-fourths of an inch broad, white, petals obovate. Fruit red, ovoid, the achenes imbedded in pits.

In rather dry soil, fields, hillsides etc., Newfoundland to South Dakota, Florida and Oklahoma. Flowering in April and May.

The European Wood Strawberry (F r a g a r i a v e s c a Linnaeus) is a common escape everywhere in the east and frequently hybridizes with F. v i r g i n i a n a, so that some forms are difficult to classify. The American Wood Strawberry (F r a g a r i a a m e r i c a n a (Porter) Britton), with longer flowering scapes and elongated-conic fruit, with achenes borne on its shining, even surface and but slightly attached to it, is a common species in rocky woodlands. The Northern Wild Strawberry (F r a g a r i a c a n a d e n s i s Michaux) has a long, slender fruit with the achenes sunk in pits and oblong or narrowly obovate leaflets. It ranges across the northern states and Canada.

Shrubby Five-finger or Cinquefoil

Dasiphora fruticosa (Linnaeus) Rydberg

Plate 96b

A branching shrub with ascending or erect, leafy branches, 1 to 4 feet high. Leaves pinnate, leaflets five to seven, linear-oblong or oblanceolate, pointed at each end, one-half to 1 inch long, silky-pubescent, the margins entire and revolute; stipules membranous, ovate-lanceolate, entire and pointed. Flowers terminal, in dense or loose cymose clusters, or solitary, bright yellow, three-fourths to $1\frac{1}{4}$ inches broad; the five calyx lobes ovate, with five bractlets; petals five, nearly orbicular and longer than the calyx lobes. Achenes of the fruit covered with long straight hairs.

In swampy or marshy places, often in moist rocky places, Labrador and Greenland to Alaska, south to New Jersey, Illinois, Minnesota, Rocky mountains and California; also in northern Europe and Asia. In northern New England it is often a troublesome, bushy weed. Flowering from June to September.

American Great Burnet

Sanguisorba canadensis Linnaeus

Plate 94b

An erect, leafy, herbaceous plant from a thick, perennial root; stems sometimes decumbent at the base, glabrous or somewhat pubescent below, simple or branched above, 1 to 6 feet high. Leaves odd-pinnate, the lower leaves long petioled, sometimes 1 to $1\frac{1}{2}$ feet long; leaflets seven to fifteen, ovate, oblong or oval, blunt or pointed at the apex; pointed, blunt or even cordate at the base, sharply toothed. Flowers white, in dense terminal spikes, 1 to 6 inches long; petals none; calyx tube turbinate, constricted at the throat, four-winged, four-lobed, the lobes petallike, concave and deciduous; stamens four, their filaments long and white.

In swamps and low meadows, sometimes in bogs, Newfoundland to Michigan, south to Georgia. Flowering from July to September or even later.

Common Agrimony

Agrimonia striata Michaux

(*Agrimonia brittoniana* Bicknell)

Plate 98b

Stem rather stout and usually with some straight, nearly erect branches, 2 to 6 feet tall from a perennial fibrous root, pubescent with short, spreading, brownish hairs, somewhat appressed above. Leaves numerous, alternate, compound with seven to nine, or rarely eleven, oblique leaflets, tetragonal-elliptic to rhomboid-lanceolate, pointed and sharply toothed, rather thick and somewhat rough, dull green above, softly pubescent beneath, usually several pairs of small, interposed leaflets; stipules lanceolate, pointed and cut-toothed. Flowers numerous in long, erect or ascending racemes; each flower about one-fourth of an inch wide; petals five, bright yellow; calyx tube in fruit long-turbinate, about one-fourth of an inch long, deeply grooved, unmargined; the bristles numerous, often purplish, short, crowded, inflexed and connivent over the sepals.

Thickets, open woods and roadsides, Newfoundland to Saskatchewan, south to West Virginia, Nebraska and Mexico. Flowering from June to September.

Barren or Dry Strawberry

Waldsteinia fragarioides (Michaux) Trattinnick

Plate 99

A perennial, herbaceous plant resembling a strawberry, with creeping, rather stout rootstock. Leaves tufted, mainly basal, long petioled, glabrous or somewhat pubescent, three-foliate; leaflets obovate, obtuse at the apex, tapering at the base with crenate or sometimes incised margins, 1 to 2 inches long. Flowering scapes slender, erect, bracted, corymbosely three to eight-flowered; pedicels slender, often drooping; flowers yellow, one-half to two-thirds of an inch broad; petals five, obovate and longer than the five ovate-lanceolate, acute calyx lobes; stamens eight, inserted on the throat of the calyx; achenes of the fruit four to six, finely pubescent.

Rocky woods, shaded hillsides and banks, New Brunswick to Ontario, Minnesota, Michigan, Indiana and Oregon. Flowering in May and June.

Yellow Avens; Camproot

Geum strictum Aiton

Plate 98a

Stems erect or nearly so, pubescent, somewhat branched, 2 to 4 feet high, basal leaves lyrate-pinnate with five to seven obovate, cuneate, toothed or lobed leaflets, with a few smaller leaflets interspersed, terminal leaflets largest, broadly ovate or cuneate; stem leaves short petioled or sessile with three to five ovate or oblong, acute segments. Flowers yellow, several, terminal and short peduncled, one-half to three-fourths of an inch broad; petals obovate, exceeding the five calyx lobes. Stamens numerous.

In low, shaded ground, swamps and wet meadows, Newfoundland to British Columbia, south to New Jersey, Pennsylvania, Missouri and New Mexico. Flowering from June to August.

Purple or Water Avens

Geum rivale Linnaeus

Plate 100

Stems simple or nearly so, erect, pubescent, 1 to 3 feet high, from stout perennial roots. Basal leaves lyrately and interruptedly pinnate, petioled, the lateral segments generally few and small, the terminal one to three leaflets much larger, all sharply and irregularly lobed and toothed; stem leaves rather far apart, short petioled or sessile, simple or three-foliated. Flowers few, terminal, purple or purplish, nodding, three-fourths to 1 inch broad; petals obovate emarginate, abruptly narrowed into a claw; calyx lobes spreading, purple; head of the fruit stalked in the calyx; achenes pubescent, style jointed, plumose below, about one-fourth of an inch long.

In swamps and low grounds, Newfoundland to British Columbia, New Jersey, Pennsylvania, Michigan and Colorado; also in northern Europe and Asia. Flowering from early June until the latter part of July.

There are several other Avens of which all except G. r i v a l e have reflexed calyx lobes. G. v i r g i n i a n u m Linnaeus and G. c a n a-d e n s e Jacquin have white flowers. G. v e r n u m (Rafinesque) Torrey & Gray; G. s t r i c t u m Aiton (described above), and G. m e y e r i a n u m Rydberg, have yellow flowers. G. m a c r o p h y l l u m Willdenow, a boreal species found across the northern states and Canada, also has yellow flowers. For complete descriptions of these additional species the student should refer to Gray's Manual or Britton and Brown's Illustrated Flora.

Purple-flowering Raspberry; Thimbleberry

Rubus odoratus Linnaeus

Plate 101

Shrubby, erect and branched, perennial; new growth glandular-pubescent and somewhat bristly but not prickly, 3 to 5 feet high. Leaves simple, petioled, large, 5 to 10 inches broad, three to five-lobed, cordate at the base, pubescent, especially on the veins beneath, the lobes long pointed, the middle lobe usually longer than the others; flowers rather numerous in corymbose, terminal clusters, purple, 1 to 2 inches broad; calyx lobes tipped with long, slender appendages; petals five; fruit red when ripe, broad and thin, scarcely edible.

In rocky woods and thickets, Nova Scotia to Ontario and Michigan, south to Georgia and Tennessee. Flowering from June to August.

There are numerous other species of native raspberries and blackberries. The principal species of Raspberries are R. s t r i g o s u s Michaux (red); R. n e g l e c t u s Peck (purple), and R. o c c i d e n t a l i s Linnaeus (Black Raspberry). The Blackberries are R. t r i f l o r u s Richards (Dwarf Red Blackberry), R. c a n a d e n s i s Linnaeus (Northern Blackberry), R. a l l e g h e n i e n s i s Porter (Mountain Blackberry), R. a r g u t u s Link (Tall Blackberry), and also the Dewberries. See Britton and Brown's Illustrated Flora for complete descriptions.

Dewberry; Low Running Blackberry
Rubus procumbens Muhlenberg

Plate 93b

Stems trailing, shrubby and perennial, often several feet long, armed with numerous or very few prickles. Branches erect, 4 to 12 inches long, slightly pubescent, often prickly and glandular. Leaves three to seven-foliate, usually three-foliate; leaflets ovate or ovate-lanceolate, thin, pointed at the apex, rounded or narrowed at the base, sharply toothed. Flowers few in terminal racemes, white, about 1 inch broad; the five petals usually as long or slightly longer than the calyx lobes. Fruit black, usually at least one-half of an inch long and sometimes 1 inch long, fine flavored but with large seeds.

In dry soil, especially in sandy sections, Nova Scotia to Ontario and Michigan, south to Virginia, Louisiana and Oklahoma. Flowering in May and June. Fruit ripe in June and July.

A similar species, R u b u s   h i s p i d u s Linnaeus (Hispid or Running Swamp Blackberry), with the stems densely beset with weak, retrorse bristles, is also common in swamps and low grounds throughout our area.

Dalibarda; Dewdrop or False Violet
Dalibarda repens Linnaeus

Plate 97b

Stems very slender, much tufted, several inches long. Leaves downy-pubescent on both sides, three-fourths to 2 inches broad, long petioled, ovate-orbicular, cordate, the margin with low, blunt or sometimes mucronulate crenations; stipules setaceous. The scapelike peduncles 1 to 5 inches long, bearing one or two large, perfect white flowers, each flower about one-half of an inch broad; calyx deeply five or six-parted, three of the divisions larger than the other two or three; petals five; stamens numerous. Fruit composed of five to ten nearly dry drupelets, inclosed by the calyx segments. Stems also have short, recurved peduncles bearing several or numerous small cleistogamous flowers.

In rich woods, Nova Scotia to Minnesota, south to Pennsylvania, southern New Jersey, North Carolina, Ohio and Michigan. Flowering from June to September.

Low or Pasture Rose

Rosa virginiana Miller

Plate 102

A bushy shrub, a few inches to 3 or 4 feet high, sometimes higher; the stems armed with slender or stout, straight or curved infrastipular spines, and more or less prickly. Stipules entire. Leaves alternate with five or sometimes seven rather thin ovate-oval or obovate leaflets, dull green or somewhat shiny, coarsely toothed, one-half to 2 inches long, usually pointed at the end, glabrous or pubescent beneath. Flowers few or solitary, 2 to 3 inches broad; pedicels and calyx usually glandular; calyx five-lobed, the segments lanceolate, long pointed, sometimes dilated toward the end, spreading and deciduous; petals five, obcordate, rose or pink, fading after opening. Fruit globose or depressed-globose, glandular-hispid, about one-third of an inch high.

In dry or rocky soil, Newfoundland to Ontario and Wisconsin, south to Georgia, Louisiana and Missouri. Flowering from May to July. The Swamp Wild Rose (R o s a c a r o l i n a Linnaeus) is frequent in open or wooded swamps and marshes.

Apple Family

M a l a c e a e

Black Chokeberry

Aronia melanocarpa (Michaux) Britton

Plate 103

An extensively branching shrub, 3 to 8 feet high. Leaves obovate to oval, the apex varying from blunt to pointed, narrowed or cuneate at the base, short petioled, the margins crenulate, dark green above, paler beneath, glabrous or nearly so when mature. Flowers numerous in terminal, compound, leafy cymes; each flower about one-half of an inch broad; calyx and pedicels glabrous or nearly so; calyx lobes glandular; petals five, concave, white or tinged with pink, spreading; stamens numerous, filaments rose-colored to white; anthers black or dark red. Fruit globose or oval, nearly black, or purplish black, about one-quarter of an inch in diameter.

In low grounds, swamps or open woods, sometimes in drier situations, Nova Scotia to western Ontario, south to Florida and Michigan. Flowers in April and May. Fruit ripe in August and September.

The Red Chokeberry (A. a r b u t i f o l i a (Linnaeus) Elliott) has the cymes and lower surface of the leaves woolly and the mature fruit is bright red. The Purple-fruited Chokeberry (A. a t r o p u r p u r e a Britton) also has the cymes and lower leaf surfaces woolly but the mature fruit is purple-black.

Senna Family

C a e s a l p i n i a c e a e

Wild or American Senna

Cassia marilandica Linnaeus

Plate 104

Stems 3 to 7 feet high, sparingly branched or simple, glabrous or with scant pubescence, from a perennial root. Leaves evenly pinnate, not sensitive to the touch, petioled and with a club-shaped gland near the base of the petiole; leaflets twelve to twenty, oblong, blunt but mucronate at the apex, rounded at the base, ciliate, 1 to 2 inches long, one-fourth to two-thirds of an inch wide. Flowers yellow, about two-thirds to three-fourths of an inch broad, numerous, in pubescent axillary racemes on the upper part of the plant. Calyx lobes five, nearly equal, ovate or oblong, obtuse; corolla nearly regular, of five spreading, nearly equal, clawed petals; stamens ten, the upper three imperfect. Fruit a flat linear pod, 3 to 4 inches long and about one-fourth of an inch wide, curved, pubescent, containing flat, suborbicular seeds. The segments of the pod are about as long as broad.

In moist meadows, marshes and swamps, sometimes on springy hillsides, Massachusetts to central New York, Ohio, Tennessee and North

Carolina. Rather rare and local in New York, frequently seen along the Hudson River valley and up the Mohawk, northward along West Canada creek to Newport in Herkimer county, which appears to be the northern limit of its range. Flowering in July and August.

Sensitive Pea; Wild Sensitive Plant

Chamaecrista nictitans (Linnaeus) Moenchhausen

Plate 105a

An annual plant, 5 to 16 inches high with erect or decumbent, branching and somewhat pubescent stems. Leaves evenly pinnate, sensitive to the touch, bearing a small gland near the base of the petiole; leaflets twelve to forty, linear-oblong, blunt and mucronate at the apex, rounded and oblique at the base, inequilateral, one-fourth to two-thirds of an inch long, about one-fourth as wide. Flowers two or three together in the axils, one-fourth of an inch broad or less; calyx lobes five, pointed; corolla yellow, somewhat irregular, three of the five petals smaller than the others; stamens five, all perfect. Fruit a small, linear, pubescent or smooth pod, 1 to $1\frac{1}{2}$ inches long.

In dry and sandy soil, Maine to Georgia, west to Indiana, Kansas and Texas. Flowering from July to September.

Partridge Pea; Large-flowered Sensitive Pea

Chamaecrista fasciculata (Michaux) Greene

Plate 105b

Stems annual, rather widely branched and pubescent with spreading hairs or nearly smooth, 1 to 2 feet high. Leaves with a sessile gland on the petiole, sensitive, similar to the preceding species but the twenty to thirty leaflets somewhat larger. Flowers two to four together in the axils, 1 to $1\frac{1}{2}$ inches broad and slender-pediceled; calyx lobes long pointed; petals yellow, sometimes purple spotted; stamens ten, all perfect; four of the anthers yellow, six of them purple. Fruit a linear, pubescent, or glabrous flattened pod, $1\frac{1}{2}$ to $2\frac{1}{2}$ inches long and one-fourth of an inch wide or less.

In dry or sandy soil, Massachusetts to Florida, Minnesota, Texas and Mexico. Flowering from July to September.

Pea Family
F a b a c e a e
Wild Indigo; Horsefly Weed
Baptisia tinctoria (Linnaeus) R. Brown
Plate 107a

Stems glabrous, erect, much branched, 2 to 4 feet high from a perennial root, blackening in dying. Leaves petioled, three-foliate, alternate; leaflets obovate, one-half to $1\frac{1}{2}$ inches long, nearly sessile, blunt, tapering at the base, entire. Flowers bright yellow, rather showy, in numerous, few-flowered, terminal racemes. Each flower about one-half of an inch long; calyx campanulate, the upper two lobes united into a lobe larger than the other three; corolla consisting of a standard (upper petal), two wings (lateral petals), and a keel (two lower petals); stamens ten, distinct; fruit a short ovoid or nearly globose pod, one-fourth to one-half of an inch long, and tipped with the subulate style.

In dry or sandy soil, Maine to Vermont, Ontario, Minnesota, Florida and Louisiana. Flowering from June to September.

The Blue Wild or Blue False Indigo, B a p t i s i a a u s t r a l i s (Linnaeus) R. Brown, has indigo blue flowers nearly an inch long and is naturalized in eastern and southern New York from the south.

Wild or Perennial Lupine
Lupinus perennis Linnaeus
Figure XIX and Plate 106

Stems 8 to 24 inches high, erect, pubescent and often branched, from a perennial root. Leaves digitately compound with seven to eleven (usually about eight), oblanceolate, sessile leaflets, blunt and mucronate at the apex, tapering to the base, 1 to 2 inches long, one-fourth to one-half of an inch wide, appressed-pubescent or glabrate; flowers blue, rarely white or pink, in terminal racemes; each flower one-half to two-thirds of an inch long, on pedicels one-fourth to one-half of an inch long; calyx two-lipped; standard (upper petal) orbicular with reflexed margins, wings (two lateral petals) obovate; stamens monadelphous, with two forms of anthers. Fruit a linear-oblong, very hairy pod, 1½ to 2 inches long and about one-fourth of an inch wide, with three to six seeds; the two valves of the pod coiling when it dehisces.

In dry, sandy soil, Maine and Ontario to Minnesota, Florida, Missouri and Louisiana. Flowering in May and June. This is the only native species of Lupine in New York, although there are about fifty species in the western states.

Figure XIX
Wild or Perennial Lupine
(Lupinus perennis Linnaeus)

Rabbit-foot, Old Field, or Stone Clover

Trifolium arvense Linnaeus

Plate 108a

An erect, usually much-branched annual, 5 to 18 inches high, silky-pubescent. Leaves very short petioled, three-foliate, oblanceolate or linear, minutely toothed, blunt and sometimes notched at the apex, narrowed at the base, one-half to 1 inch long. Flowers sessile in dense, terminal, peduncled, oblong or cylindric heads, one-half to 1 inch long; calyx very silky; corolla whitish, shorter than the elongated, slender, plumose calyx lobes. Fruiting pod very small.

In waste places, dry and sandy fields, roadsides etc., Quebec and Ontario to South Carolina, Florida, Tennessee and Missouri. Naturalized from Europe. Flowering from May to September.

The only Clover native to New York is the Buffalo Clover (T r i f o l i u m   r e f l e x u m   Linnaeus), which occurs from the western part of the State westward and southward. Our flora contains a large number of introduced species of clovers and related plants. Among them are the following:

Yellow or Hop Clover	T r i f o l i u m	a g r a r i u m
Low or Smaller Hop Clover	"	p r o c u m b e n s
Crimson Clover	"	i n c a r n a t u m
Red or Meadow Clover	"	p r a t e n s e
Alsike or Alsatian Clover	"	h y b r i d u m
White Clover	"	r e p e n s
Alfalfa	M e d i c a g o	s a t i v a
Black or Hop Medic	"	l u p u l i n a
White Sweet Clover	M e l i l o t u s	a l b a
Yellow Sweet Clover	"	o f f i c i n a l i s
Bird's-foot Trefoil	L o t u s	c o r n i c u l a t u s

Goat's-rue; Wild Sweet Pea

Cracca virginiana Linnaeus

Plate 108b

Stems from a few inches to nearly 2 feet high, few or many in a dense cluster, erect or nearly so, from a stout, perennial root which is elongated, tough and fibrous. Stems and leaves silky with whitish hairs. Leaves odd-pinnate, short petioled; leaflets nine to twenty-five, oblong, linear-oblong or the terminal one oblanceolate, narrowed at the base, rounded and mucronate at the apex or sometimes notched, three-fourths to 1 inch long and one-eighth to one-third of an inch wide. Flowers crowded in a terminal, often compound and nearly sessile racemelike cluster; each flower one-half to three-fourths of an inch long on a short pedicel. Calyx with five nearly equal teeth; petals clawed, the standard rounded, yellow and conspicuous, wings and keel reddish or purplish. Fruiting pod narrow, densely hairy, 1 to 2 inches long.

In dry and sandy soil, Maine to Minnesota, Arkansas, Florida, Louisiana and Northern Mexico. Flowering in June and July or sometimes as late as August in the north.

Coronilla; Axseed; Axwort

Coronilla varia Linnaeus

Plate 109

Stems ascending or straggling, glabrous and usually much branched, 1 to 3 feet long from perennial roots. Leaves sessile; odd-pinnate; leaflets eleven to twenty-five, oblong or obovate, blunt and mucronate at the apex, narrowed or rounded at the base, one-half to three-fourths of an inch long, one-eighth to one-fourth of an inch wide. Flowers numerous in dense umbels terminating peduncles several inches in length; each flower one-third to one-half of an inch long on very short pedicels; standard (upper petal) pink, wings (lateral petals) white or purple-tipped. Fruit pod coriaceous, linear, four-angled, with two or three joints, each about one-fourth of an inch long or slightly longer.

Waste places, fields and roadsides, Massachusetts to southern New York, Maryland and Missouri. Adventive or naturalized from Europe. Flowering from June to August.

THE TICK TREFOILS
Meibomia

The Tick Trefoils are all perennial herbs, often with stout roots, erect, ascending or trailing stems and three-foliolate leaves. The flowers are usually rather small, purplish in terminal or axillary, compound or simple racemes or panicles. Calyx two-lipped, the upper lip two-toothed, the lower lip with three acute or attenuate teeth. Stamens monadelphous or diadelphous (nine and one); anthers all alike. Fruit (loment) flat, sessile or stalked with several joints which are easily separable at maturity.

A large genus of plants with about sixteen representatives in the northeastern states. The following key is given as an aid in placing the various species not fully described and illustrated here.

Loment not constricted above, deeply constricted below, long-stalked; leaflets broad
    Panicle terminal on the leafy stem
        Leaves crowded at the base of the panicle...............M. grandiflora
        Leaves scattered along the stem........................M. pauciflora
    Panicle arising from the base of the plant, its stalk usually leafless...............
                                              M. nudiflora
Loment constricted on both margins, more deeply below than above
    Stems trailing or reclining
        Leaflets orbicular, 1 to 2 inches long and pubescent.........M. michauxii
        Leaflets ovate or oval, dull green...........................M. glabella
    Stems erect or ascending
        Leaves sessile or nearly so; leaflets linear or lanceolate.....M. sessilifolia
        Leaves petioled
            Joints of the loment notably longer than broad
                Leaflets obtuse, yellowish green, rough-pubescent....M. canescens
                Leaflets long-acuminate.........................M. bracteosa
           Joints of the loment little longer than broad
                Loment distinctly long-stalked in the calyx

Plants glabrous or nearly so (except varieties of M. p a n i c u l a t a)
 Leaflets lanceolate or oblong............M. p a n i c u l a t a
 Leaflets broadly ovate or oval, glaucous beneath............
           M. l a e v i g a t a
Plants pubescent
 Leaves velvety-pubescent beneath, thick and coriaceous.......
          M. v i r i d i f l o r a
 Leaves appressed-pubescent or villous beneath and scarcely
  coriaceous............................M. d i l l e n i i
Loment sessile in the calyx or nearly so
 Loment joints four to seven, flowers showy; leaflets not coriaceous..
         M. c a n a d e n s i s
Loment joints one to three
 Leaflets scabrous, 1 to 2 inches long...........M. r i g i d a
 Leaflets not scabrous, one-half to 1 inch long
  Plant nearly glabrous throughout..M. m a r y l a n d i c a
  Stem pubescent; leaflets and petioles ciliate.M. o b t u s a

Prostrate Tick Trefoil

Meibomia michauxii Vail

Plate 110

Stems prostrate, 2 to several feet long, softly pubescent or villous. Leaves petioled; leaflets nearly orbicular, pubescent, 1 to 2 inches long; stipules triangular-ovate, persistent, pointed, striate. Flowers in loose terminal and axillary panicles, purple, one-fourth to one-half of an inch long; calyx lobes ciliated. Loment about 1 inch long, three to five-jointed, the joints obliquely rhomboid below, slightly concave above, pubescent with hooked hairs, on a stipe about equaling the calyx lobes or slightly longer.

Dry or sandy woods, New England and Ontario to Minnesota, Florida, Missouri and Louisiana. Flowering from July to September.

Large-bracted Tick Trefoil

Meibomia bracteosa (Michaux) Kuntze

Plate 111

Stems erect, 2 to 6 feet high, glabrous or pubescent below, finely pubescent above in the panicle. Leaflets 2 to 8 inches long, longer than the petioles, ovate or ovate-lanceolate, long pointed, smooth or nearly so above, usually pubescent beneath; stipules lanceolate, sharp pointed. Flowers large, purple, one-third to one-half of an inch long with cuspidate, striate, deciduous bracts; calyx deeply two-lipped, the upper lip two-toothed. Loment 1 to 3 inches long, three to seven-jointed, the joints obliquely oblong, about twice as long as wide, pubescent with hooked hairs, on a stipe about as long as the lower calyx lobes.

In open woods and thickets, Maine to Ontario, Minnesota, Florida, Missouri, Arkansas and Texas. Flowering in August and September.

Dillen's Tick Trefoil

Meibomia dillenii (Darlington) Kuntze

Plate 112

Stems erect, pubescent with scattered hairs, 2 to 3 feet high. Leaflets rather thin, oval or oblong-ovate, blunt, $1\frac{1}{2}$ to 4 inches long, one-half to $1\frac{1}{2}$ inches wide, sparingly pubescent or glabrous above, softly pubescent beneath; petioles much shorter than the leaflets. Flowers one-fourth to one-third of an inch long, purple, in loose, terminal, compound racemes with small, deciduous bracts. Loment 1 to 2 inches long, two to four-jointed, the joints nearly triangular, about one-fourth of an inch long, slightly convex on the back, pubescent with hooked hairs, with a stipe shorter than the calyx lobes.

In woods and thickets, Maine to Ontario, Minnesota, Alabama, Tennessee, Missouri and Texas. Flowering from the last of June to September.

THE BUSH CLOVERS

Lespedeza

Herbs, often with perennial roots and erect or ascending stems. In a few species the stems trailing. Leaves three-foliolate. Flowers small, purple or whitish, in axillary clusters, heads or panicles. Frequently the flowers are of two kinds intermixed, one petaliferous but sterile, the other minute, apetalous and fertile. Calyx lobes nearly equal, those of the petaliferous flowers usually longer than those of the apetalous flowers. Upper petal (standard) obovate or oblong, the lower petals forming an incurved keel. Stamens usually diadelphous (nine and one); anthers all alike. Ovary one-ovuled, ripening into a flat, indehiscent, reticulated, mostly one-jointed and one-seeded pod.

Key to the Commoner Species of Lespedeza

Corolla purple or purplish; plants bearing both petaliferous and apetalous flowers

    Stems prostrate or trailing

        Foliage glabrous or somewhat appressed-pubescent...............L. r e p e n s

        Foliage downy-pubescent or tomentose..................L. p r o c u m b e n s

    Stems erect or ascending

        Peduncles distinct and mostly longer than the leaves

            Bushy-branched; petaliferous flowers paniculate...........L. v i o l a c e a

            Stems simple or little branched; flowers racemose or subspicate

                Stems tomentose; leaves tomentose beneath..........L. b r i t t o n i i

                Stems and leaves glabrate or appressed-pubescent; leaflets oval to

                    suborbicular.................................L. n u t t a l l i i

        Peduncles shorter than the leaves or the flower clusters sessile

            Leaflets densely tomentose beneath; calyx of the petaliferous flowers less

            than one-half as long as the pod........................L. s t u v e i

            Leaflets appressed pubescent beneath or glabrate

                Calyx of petaliferous flowers less than one-half as long as the pod;

                  leaflets oval to oblong......................L. f r u t e s c e n s

                Calyx of the petaliferous flowers two-thirds as long as the pod or more;

                  leaflets silvery-pubescent beneath.................L. s i m u l a t a

Corolla whitish or yellowish; flowers all complete; pod included or scarcely exserted from
the calyx

Leaflets oblong, ovate-oblong, or nearly orbicular

Peduncles mostly exceeding the leaves. . . . . .L. h i r t a

Peduncles shorter than the leaves. . . . . .L. c a p i t a t a

Stuve's Bush Clover

Lespedeza stuvei Nuttall

Plate 113b

Stems erect or nearly so, simple and wandlike or slightly branched, densely velvety or downy-pubescent all over, 2 to 4 feet high; petioles as long as the leaves or usually shorter; leaflets oval, oblong or suborbicular, blunt or retuse at the apex, one-half to 1 inch long. Flowers of both kinds in nearly sessile, axillary clusters; corolla violet-purple, one-fourth of an inch long or less. Pod oblong-ovate to orbicular, pointed, about one-fourth of an inch long or less, downy-pubescent, much longer than the calyx.

In dry or sandy soil, Vermont and Massachusetts to Virginia, Alabama, Michigan, Arkansas and Texas. Flowering in August and September.

Wandlike Bush Clover

Lespedeza frutescens (Linnaeus) Britton

Plate 114

Stems erect, 1 to 3 feet high, simple or somewhat branched, finely pubescent or nearly smooth; petioles as long as the leaflets or shorter; leaflets oval, oblong or elliptic, blunt, truncate or notched at the apex, narrowed or rounded at the base, one-half to $1\frac{1}{2}$ inches long, smooth and dark green above, paler and pubescent beneath. Flowers of both kinds in short-stalked axillary clusters which are more or less crowded toward the summit of the stem; corolla violet-purple, about one-fourth of an inch long; pod ovate, pointed, pubescent, about one-fifth of an inch long.

Dry soil in open woods, old fields, etc., Maine to Ontario, Minnesota, Florida, Illinois and Texas. Flowering in August and September.

Hairy Bush Clover

Lespedeza hirta (Linnaeus) Hornemann

Plate 113a

Stems rather stiff, erect and usually stout, simple or branched above, densely hairy or softly pubescent, 2 to 5 feet high. Leaflets three, oval or suborbicular, blunt at each end, or often notched at the apex, one-half to 2 inches long; the petioles shorter than the leaflets. Flowers in oblong-cylindric, rather dense heads on stalks which are much longer than the leaves; flowers all complete; corolla yellowish white, usually the standard with a purple spot near its base. Fruiting pod oval, pointed, hairy and about as long as the slender calyx lobes.

In dry or sandy soil, Maine to Ontario and Minnesota, south to Florida, Louisiana and Texas. Flowering from August to October.

The Round-headed Bush Clover (Lespedeza capitata Michaux) is similar but the stalks bearing the flower clusters are shorter than the leaves, forming a more compact inflorescence. Its range and period of flowering are about the same.

Beach Pea; Seaside Pea

Lathyrus maritimus (Linnaeus) Bigelow

Plate 115

Root perennial, stem glabrous or nearly so, stout, somewhat fleshy and slightly glaucous, angled, decumbent, 1 to 2 feet long with broad foliaceous, hastate, pointed stipules 1 to 2 inches long. Leaves nearly sessile, pinnate, the rachis terminating in a slender, forked tendril; leaflets six to twelve, oblong, oval or obovate, blunt and mucronulate at the apex, usually narrowed at the base, 1 to $2\frac{1}{2}$ inches long, one-half to three-fourths of an inch wide. Flowers six to ten on peduncles 3 to 4 inches long, purple, three-fourths to 1 inch long; calyx teeth often ciliate. Fruit a sessile, linear-oblong, nearly glabrous, veined pod, $1\frac{1}{2}$ to 3 inches long and about one-half of an inch wide.

Sea beaches and sandy fields near the coast, New Jersey to Arctic America, also Oneida lake, Great Lakes, Pacific coast and in northern Europe and Asia. Flowering from May to August.

Myrtle-leaved Marsh Pea

Lathyrus myrtifolius Muhlenberg

Plate 116

Stems very slender, smooth, angled but not winged, weak, 1 to 3 feet long with obliquely ovate or half-sagittate stipules, one-half to 1 inch long, one-third to one-half of an inch wide and toothed; leaflets usually six, varying from four to eight, oval or ovate, pointed and mucronate at the apex, narrowed at the base, three-fourths to 2 inches long, one-fourth to two-thirds of an inch wide, the rachis terminating in a forked tendril. Flowering peduncles as long as the leaves or shorter, with three to nine flowers, yellowish in bud but turning purple as the flower opens; each flower about one-half of an inch long. Fruit a narrow, smooth pod without visible stalk, 1 to 2 inches long and somewhat less than one-fourth of an inch wide.

In moist thickets, wet ground, swamps and shores, New Brunswick to Manitoba, south to North Carolina and Tennessee. Flowering from late in May until June or July.

The members of the genus Lathyrus are often called Vetchlings, because of their close relationship to the true Vetches (genus Vicia), most of which are cultivated or naturalized species in New York. Another native Vetchling is the Marsh Vetchling (L a t h y r u s p a l u s t r i s Linnaeus), a boreal species found in the northern part of the State. It has linear leaflets and the stems are usually winged. The flowers are purple. The Cream-colored Vetchling (L a t h y r u s o c h r o l e u c u s Hooker) with rather large cream-colored flowers, and broadly oval, acute leaflets, occurs from western Quebec and central New York westward.

Groundnut; Wild Bean

Glycine apios Linnaeus

Plate 117

Stems slender, hairy or nearly smooth, with milky juice, climbing over herbs and bushes to a height of several feet, from a perennial rootstock of several necklace-shaped, edible tubers. Leaves pinnately compound, five- to seven-foliolate; leaflets ovate to ovate-lanceolate, pointed at the apex, rounded at the base, 1 to 3 inches long. Flowers brownish purple, fragrant, about one-half of an inch long, in axillary racemes; peduncles shorter than the leaves; rachis of the inflorescence knobby; calyx two-lipped, the two lateral teeth very small, the two upper united and short, the lower one long and acute; standard ovate or orbicular and reflexed, wings obliquely obovate, adherent to the elongated, incurved and at length twisted keel; pod narrow, straight or slightly curved, 2 to $4\frac{1}{2}$ inches long and about one-fourth of an inch wide or less, many-seeded and rather thick in texture.

Moist thickets along streams, bottomlands, or low woods. New Brunswick to Florida, west to Ontario, Minnesota, Nebraska, Kansas and Texas. Flowering from July to September.

Wild or Hog Peanut

Falcata comosa (Linnaeus) Kuntze

Plate 118a

Stems very slender, simple or somewhat branched, twining and climbing over herbs and shrubs, 1 to 6 feet long, more or less pubescent. Leaves with three rhombic-ovate or broadly ovate leaflets pointed at the apex, rounded at the base, 1 to 3 inches long. Flowers purplish or nearly white in axillary, slender-stalked clusters or racemes. In the lower axils are solitary, apetalous, fertile flowers. Calyx of the petaliferous flowers four to five-toothed, tubular; the oblong wings of the corolla curved and adherent to the recurved, blunt keel and inclosed by the erect, obovate standard; pods oblong-lanceolate, pointed and hairy, about 1 inch long.

In moist, shaded places, New Brunswick to Florida, west to Manitoba, Nebraska and Louisiana. Flowering from early in August until late in September.

Falcata pitcheri (Torrey & Gray) Kuntze, very closely related to the preceding species, has leaves of a firmer texture and the stems, petioles and flowering stalks villous-pubescent with conspicuous brown hairs.

Trailing Wild Bean

Strophostyles helvola (Linnaeus) Britton

Plate 118b

A twining or trailing and climbing, herbaceous, rough-pubescent vine. Stems more or less branched below, 2 to 7 feet long, or dwarfed and almost erect, from an annual root. Leaves pinnately three-foliolate; leaflets ovate, pointed or blunt at the apex, the base rounded, thickish in texture, usually bluntly lobed, 1 to 2 inches long, the two lower leaves unequal at the base. Flowers greenish purple, about one-half of an inch long, three to twelve together in dense, capitate clusters at the ends of long, axillary stalks which are longer than the leaves; keel of the corolla strongly curved and slender. Fruiting pod round in cross-section, somewhat hairy, linear and without a stalk, 1½ to 3 inches long.

In sandy fields and thickets, mainly near the coast, Quebec to Massachusetts and Florida, less frequent westward through Ontario to South Dakota and Kansas. Flowering from the latter part of July to September and October.

A closely related species of Long Island and southward, S. umbellata (Muhlenberg) Britton, has shorter pods, slightly larger flowers, entire leaflets and perennial roots.

Geranium Family

Geraniaceae

Herb Robert; Red Robin

Robertiella robertiana (Linnaeus) Hanks

(*Geranium robertianum* Linnaeus)

Plate 119

Roots mostly biennial, sometimes annual, giving rise to one or several ascending or nearly erect, glandular-pubescent stems 5 to 18 inches high. Entire plant with a strong, disagreeable odor. Leaves rounded-ovate in outline, the divisions deeply cleft or lobed, the margins with oblong, mucronate teeth. Flowers reddish purple, about one-half of an inch broad, two on each stalk; sepals five, each tipped with an awn. Petals five, each with a slender claw and an obovate, rounded blade. Stamens ten; ovary five-lobed and five-celled. Fruiting capsule about 1 inch long, awn-tipped, separating at maturity into five carpels, the bodies deciduous from the styles at maturity, each with two fibrous appendages near the top.

In rich soil of rocky woodlands, Nova Scotia to Manitoba south to Pennsylvania and Missouri; also in Europe and Northern Africa. Flowering from May to September.

Wild Geranium; Wild or Spotted Crane's-bill

Geranium maculatum Linnaeus

Plate 120

Stems mainly simple from a stout, perennial rootstock, often much branched above, hairy, 10 to 20 inches high. The basal leaves nearly orbicular, broadly heart-shaped, on long leaf-stalks; the blades 3 to 5 inches wide, deeply three to five-lobed with wedge-shaped divisions, the margins cleft or toothed; leaves of the stem two, opposite, short-stalked, similar to the basal leaves. Flowers rose-purple, 1 to $1\frac{1}{2}$ inches broad, terminal in two to five-flowered, loose, leafy-bracted umbels; sepals sharp pointed; petals five, woolly at the base, thin, broad and overlapping one another. Fruit an elongated capsule tipped with the persistent compound style, which in fruit is 1 or more inches long; carpels of the fruit permanently attached to the styles, separating from the base and curved upward in dehiscence.

In rich or moist woodlands, Maine and Ontario west to Manitoba, south to Georgia and Alabama. Flowering from late in April to June or July.

There are several other species of Geranium in our flora, most of them small-flowered, introduced species. Of the native ones, Bicknell's Geranium (Geranium bicknellii Britton) is an annual with small, purple flowers, somewhat less than one-half of an inch broad in a loose cluster, on two-flowered peduncles, with the beak of the fruit long pointed. The Carolina Geranium (Geranium carolinianum Linnaeus) has a more compact inflorescence and a short-pointed fruit.

Wood Sorrel Family
Oxalidaceae
White or True Wood Sorrel; Alleluia
Oxalis acetosella Linnaeus
Plate 107b

Rootstock perennial, slender, scaly and little branched. Leaves basal, three to eight together, each 2 to 6 inches high, pubescent; petioles broadened at the base and jointed. Leaflets three, obcordate, wider than long, one-half to 1 inch wide. Flowers one-half to three-fourths of an inch broad, solitary on stalks as long or longer than the leaves; petals white or pink with deep pink veins, three or four times longer than the calyx; stamens ten. Fruit a subglobose, cylindric capsule about one-sixth of an inch long. At the base of the leaves are also found short-stalked flowers.

In cool, damp woods, or shaded mossy banks, Nova Scotia to the north shore of Lake Superior, south to North Carolina. Also in Europe, Asia and northern Africa. Flowering from May to July.

Violet Wood Sorrel

Ionoxalis violacea (Linnaeus) Small

Plate 121a

Flowering stalks and leaves smooth, 3 to 8 inches tall, arising from a perennial, brownish, scaly bulb. Leaves few or several, slender-stemmed, one-half to $1\frac{1}{4}$ inches wide. Leaflets three, broader than long, notched at the apex. Flowers three to ten, or rarely more on each stalk, forming a loose, umbellate inflorescence at the summit, which is taller than the leaves. Each flower two-thirds to three-fourths of an inch long on a short, slender pedicel; sepals blunt, five in number, with tubercles at the apex; petals five, rose-purple, lighter toward the base, blunt, about three times as long as the sepals; stamens ten; capsule ovoid, about one-fifth of an inch in diameter.

In open, usually rather dry woodlands, shaded hillsides and thickets; sometimes in open, recently cleared land, Massachusetts to Florida and Texas, west to Minnesota. Flowering in May and June.

Tall Yellow Wood Sorrel

Xanthoxalis cymosa Small

Plate 121b

Stems ascending or erect, branched above, 6 inches to 3 or 4 feet high and frequently reclining on surrounding vegetation, usually hairy, reddish or brown. Leaves bright green, three-fourths to $1\frac{1}{2}$ inches broad on petioles 1 to 3 inches long; leaflets broader than long, sharply notched. Flowers yellow, in forking cymes; each flower on a pedicel one-fourth to one-third of an inch long, which is more or less hairy and erect or ascending. Sepals five, lanceolate or narrowly elliptic, one-sixth to one-fourth of an inch long, spreading in fruit; petals five, obtuse or notched at the apex, one-third to nearly one-half of an inch long. Fruit a slender, columnar, erect capsule, about one-half of an inch long, gradually narrowed to the summit; seeds obovoid-oblong with nearly continuous ridges.

In fields, thickets and woods, Ontario to Michigan, south to Florida and Texas. Flowering from May to October.

There are several closely related species of Yellow Sorrel. Those of the northeastern states are illustrated and described by Britton & Brown (Illus. Flora, 2: 432–35, ed. 2) (X. s t r i c t a, X. b u s h i i, X. r u f a and X. b r i t t o n i a e).

Jewelweed Family

B a l s a m i n a c e a e

Spotted or Wild Touch-me-not

Impatiens biflora Walter

Plate 122a

A tall, glabrous annual, 2 to 6 feet high and much branched, more or less purplish. Leaves alternate, thin, ovate and elliptic, glaucous beneath, 1 to 3 inches long, blunt, the margins toothed. Flowers horizontal, orange-yellow, mottled with reddish brown, or rarely nearly white and not mottled, three-fourths to 1 inch long, on slender, pendent stalks. Sepals three, the two lateral ones small, green, nerved, the other one large, conic, petallike, saccate and spurred, longer than broad, contracted into a slender incurved spur, two-toothed at the apex. Petals three, with two of them two-cleft into dissimilar lobes; stamens five. Fruit an oblong capsule, violently and elastically dehiscent at maturity into five spirally coiled valves, expelling the oblong, ridged seeds. Also developing small, cleistogamous flowers later in the season.

Low grounds, thickets, ditches, along streams and low, moist woodlands, Newfoundland to Saskatchewan, south to Florida and Nebraska. Flowering from July to September.

Pale Touch-me-not; Jewelweed

Impatiens pallida Nuttall

Plate 122b

Resembling the Spotted Touch-me-not, but usually stouter and higher. Flowers pale yellow, sparingly spotted with reddish brown or without spots, 1 to $1\frac{1}{2}$ inches long, the saccate sepal dilated-conic, as broad as long, abruptly contracted into a short, scarcely incurved spur, which is less than one-third the length of the saccate sepal.

In situations similar to the preceding species but more common northward, Nova Scotia to Saskatchewan, south to Georgia and Kansas. Flowering from July to September.

Milkwort Family

Polygalaceae

A family of small herbs (our species) with alternate, opposite or whorled leaves. Flowers racemose, spicate or capitate, rarely solitary and axillary, sometimes also with cleistogamous and subterranean flowers. Sepals very unequal, the two lateral ones large and petallike. Petals three, united into a tube which is split on the back, and more or less adnate to the stamens. Stamens eight or six, monadelphous below, or diadelphous. Capsule membranaceous, compressed, dehiscent along the margin. Seeds one in each cavity of the capsule and usually hairy.

Our species all belong to Polygala, a very large genus of plants, containing about sixty species in North America, of which about eleven are found in New York State. The following key may be of service in identifying them.

Flowers orange-yellow in a dense oblong spike; basal leaves spatulate.......1 P. l u t e a

Flowers rose or purple, distinctly racemose.........................2 P. p o l y g a m a

Flowers rose-purple to white, one to four in number, axillary, but apparently terminal....

3 P. p a u c i f o l i a

Flowers in terminal, more or less elongated spikes, or if the spikes oblong, flowers not yellow and no basal leaves

Leaves at least the lower, verticillate, spikes 4 to 9 lines thick, blunt; flowers purple to greenish white

Spikes sessile or nearly so; wings deltoid....................4 P. c r u c i a t a

Spikes peduncled; wings lanceolate-ovate.................5 P. b r e v i f o l i a

Leaves verticillate and alternate; spikes 2 to 3 lines thick and acute

Verticillate leaves predominating; spikes dense; flowers green to purplish........

6 P. v e r t i c i l l a t a

Alternate leaves predominating; spikes loose; flowers more purple.............

7 P. a m b i g u a

Leaves all alternate

    Petals united into a tube which is cleft and about one-fourth of an inch long; flowers pink. . . . . .8 P. i n c a r n a t a

    Petals not conspicuously united into a tube

        Spikes ovoid to globose; bracts persistent; flowers rose-purple to white. . . . . . 9 P. v i r i d e s c e n s

      Spikes cylindric

        Leaves oblanceolate to linear, 2 to 6 lines long; flowers greenish to purplish. . . . . .10 P. n u t t a l l i i

        Leaves lanceolate, 1 to 2 inches long; flowers white to greenish. . . . . 11 P. s e n e g a

Orange Milkwort; Wild Bachelor's-button

Polygala lutea Linnaeus

Plate 123a

Stems annual, smooth, tufted from fibrous roots, erect or ascending, sometimes becoming branched, 6 to 12 inches high. Stem leaves oblong-lanceolate, pointed or blunt, three-fourths to $1\frac{1}{2}$ inches long, one-fourth of an inch wide or less, entire; basal leaves broader and usually larger, obovate or spatulate, blunt. Flowers in terminal, blunt, spikelike racemes which are dense and ovoid or oblong in shape, one-half to $1\frac{1}{2}$ inches long, one-half to three-fourths of an inch thick. Individual flowers about one-fourth of an inch long, orange-yellow, preserving their color in drying; wings oblong-ovate, abruptly pointed; crest of the corolla tube minute; caruncle lobes linear, about equaling the hairy seed, or shorter.

In pine-barren depressions and swamps, Long Island to New Jersey and eastern Pennsylvania to Florida and Louisiana. Flowering from June to August or September.

Cross-leaved or Marsh Milkwort

Polygala cruciata Linnaeus

Plate 123b

A small annual, 3 to 15 inches tall, with three or four alternate branches above, the stems angled or square. Leaves all on the stem and mostly verticillate in fours, oblanceolate or linear-lanceolate, one-half to $1\frac{1}{2}$ inches long and about one-eighth of an inch wide, entire, blunt and mucronulate at the apex. Flowers in short-stalked, oval, blunt racemes, about one-third to one-half of an inch thick, purplish green or nearly white; wings triangular-ovate, sessile, somewhat heart-shaped, pointed or awned, one-fourth of an inch long or less, longer than the pods; crest of the corolla minute; seeds oblong and somewhat hairy.

In low grounds and marshes along the coast and sandy swamps inland, Maine to Florida west to Michigan, Minnesota, Nebraska and Louisiana. Flowering from July to September.

Field or Purple Milkwort

Polygala viridescens Linnaeus

Plate 124a

Stems leafy, branched above, annual, smooth and somewhat angled, 5 to 15 inches high. Leaves all on the stem, oblong to linear-oblong in shape, three-fourths to $1\frac{1}{2}$ inches long, one-eighth or one-sixteenth of an inch wide, pointed and mucronulate. Flowers purplish, greenish purple, whitish or greenish in terminal, globose, blunt heads about one-half of an inch thick, becoming oval; wings of the flowers sessile, ovate, often slightly cordate, longer than the pod, bracts usually persistent on the elongating axis as the lower flowers fall away.

In meadows, fields and sandy depressions, Nova Scotia to Ontario and Minnesota, south to North Carolina, Kansas and Arkansas. Flowering from June to September.

Seneca Snakeroot; Mountain Flax

Polygala senega Linnaeus

Plate 125a

Stems usually several from a perennial, woody rootstock, ascending or erect, 5 to 18 inches high, usually simple, occasionally branched above, glabrous or nearly so. Leaves alternate, the lowest ones very small, closer together and scalelike, the upper ones oblong-lanceolate or ovate, sometimes lanceolate, sessile, 1 to 2 inches long, about one-fourth to one-third of an inch wide, minutely toothed. Flowers white, sometimes tinged with green, in dense, terminal, pointed spikes, 1 to 2 inches long. Each flower about one-eighth of an inch long; wings of the flower orbicular-obovate, concave; crest of the corolla short and few-lobed.

In dry or rocky woodlands, New Brunswick to Hudson bay and Alberta, south along the mountains to North Carolina and west to Missouri and Arkansas. Flowering in May and June.

Racemed Milkwort

Polygala polygama Walter

Plate 124b

Stems usually several or many from a deep, slender, perennial root, smooth and simple, 4 to 15 inches high. Leaves crowded along the stems, oblong or broadly lanceolate, blunt, mucronulate, two-thirds to 1 inch long and about one-sixth of an inch wide or less, the lower leaves usually smaller. Flowers purple, rarely whitish, in a loose, terminal raceme, 1 to 3 inches long or less; wings of the flower broadly ovate; crest of the corolla large and fringed; stamens eight. Numerous cleistogamous flowers are developed upon conspicuous, whitish subterranean branches which rise from the base of the stems.

In dry or sandy fields and meadows, Nova Scotia to Manitoba, south to Florida, Texas and Michigan. Flowering in June and July.

Fringed Milkwort; Flowering Wintergreen

Polygala paucifolia Willdenow

Plate 125b

Flowering and leaf-bearing stems smooth, ascending or erect, 3 to 7 inches high from slender, prostrate, perennial stems and rootstocks which are often several inches in length. Leaves few, clustered at the summit of the stems, ovate or oblong, 1 to 1½ inches long, two-thirds to 1 inch wide, pointed at each end, rough-margined. Flowers one to five on a stem, axillary to the upper leaves, rose-purple or rarely white, two-thirds to

1 inch long on slender, short flower stalks; wings of the flower obovate; crest of the corolla beautifully fringed. The base of the stems and root-stocks bear numerous cleistogamous flowers on short, lateral, subterranean branches.

In rich, moist woods, New Brunswick to Saskatchewan south to Georgia, Illinois and Minnesota. Flowering in May and June.

Buckthorn Family

Rhamnaceae

New Jersey Tea; Redroot

Ceanothus americanus Linnaeus

Plate 126

A low shrub with several or many ascending stems from a deep reddish root. Leaves alternate, ovate or oblong-ovate, 1 to 3 inches long, one-half to $1\frac{1}{2}$ inches wide, pointed at the apex, blunt or slightly heart-shaped at the base, pubescent, especially beneath, the margins finely toothed, the blade conspicuously three-nerved; petioles usually less than one-half of an inch long. Flowers small and white, in dense, oblong clusters on terminal or elongated axillary stalks; limb of the calyx tube five-lobed; petals five, with narrow claws and bearded blades; stamens five, their filaments slender and elongated. Fruit dark colored or nearly black when mature, three-lobed, about one-sixth of an inch long.

In sandy or dry open woods and fields, Maine to Ontario and Manitoba south to Florida and Texas. Flowering from the latter part of May to July.

Mallow Family

Malvaceae

Marsh Mallow; Wymote

Althaea officinalis Linnaeus

Plate 127

An introduced plant, well established in certain salt marshes along the coast, with erect, herbaceous stems, 2 to 6 feet high from perennial roots, densely velvety-pubescent all over. Leaves ovate, pointed or blunt at the apex, toothed and usually somewhat three-lobed, the lower leaves usually cordate, veins conspicuously raised on the lower surfaces. Flowers pink or nearly white, about 1½ inches broad in terminal and axillary leafy clusters. Calyx segments five, ovate-lanceolate, subtended by six to nine linear bractlets; petals five; stamens numerous, forming a central column around the pistil and united with the bases of the petals; styles united below. Carpels fifteen to twenty, each one-seeded, arranged in a circle around the axis of the fruit.

Flowering in June and July. The photograph for the illustration of this species was taken near Port Washington, Long Island.

Musk Mallow; Musk Plant

Malva moschata Linnaeus

Plate 128

Stems erect, 1 to 2½ feet high, more or less branching and hairy, from a perennial root. Leaves orbicular in outline, 3 to 4 inches broad with several broad, rounded, toothed lobes; stem leaves deeply cut into narrow segments. Flowers 1½ to 2 inches broad, pink or white, slightly musk-scented, clustered in leafy racemes at the summits of the stems and branches; petals five, notched at the apex, several times longer than the pointed, triangular-ovate calyx lobes; stamens numerous, forming a column in the center of the flower; carpels of the fruit fifteen to twenty in number, densely hairy, rounded at the back.

Roadsides, fields and waste places throughout the eastern states. Native of Europe and thoroughly naturalized in many places. Flowering from July to September.

Other Mallows, native of the Old World and adventive or naturalized in the eastern states, are the High Mallow (Malva sylvestris Linnaeus), the Low, Dwarf or Running Mallow, also known as Cheeses (Malva rotundifolia Linnaeus), the Whorled Mallow or Curled Mallow (Malva verticillata Linnaeus) and the Vervain Mallow

(Malva alcea Linnaeus). Descriptions of these may be found in the current floras or manuals of botany of the northeastern states.

Swamp Rose Mallow; Mallow Rose

Hibiscus moscheutos Linnaeus

Plate 129

Stems tall and canelike from a perennial root, 3 to 6 feet high. Leaves ovate-lanceolate or ovate, blunt or rounded and often slightly heart-shaped at the base, pointed or blunt at the apex, 3 to 5 inches long, the lower ones sometimes lobed, all conspicuously palmately veined, toothed, densely hairy with white stellate hairs beneath, green and finely hairy or nearly smooth above. Flowers 4 to 7 inches broad, pink, clustered at the top of the plant; calyx lobes five, ovate, pointed, subtended by several narrow bractlets; petals five, broadly obovate; stamens numerous in a column surrounding the style which is five-cleft at the summit with five stigmas. Fruit a five-chambered pod about 1 inch long, blunt or slightly pointed.

In marshes along the ocean or near the coast from eastern Massachusetts to Florida and in saline situations and marshy lake shores inland, especially throughout the Great Lakes region. Flowering in August and September.

The Crimson-eye Rose Mallow (Hibiscus oculiroseus Britton) is similar, but the flower is white with a dark-crimson center and the fruit pod is long pointed. It is found on Long Island, Staten Island and in New Jersey.

Saint John's-wort Family

Hypericaceae

A family containing about sixteen species in New York State, mostly herbs, some of them shrubs, chiefly with opposite leaves and yellow or rarely reddish flowers in terminal clusters. In many of them the foliage is pellucid-punctate or dotted. Flowers regular and perfect. Sepals four or five. Petals four or five. Stamens numerous or few, often in three or five sets.

Key to the More Common Species of the Saint John's-wort Family

Sepals four, in unequal pairs; petals also four

Stems erect, 1 to 2 feet high; leaves clasping, styles three to four...................

1 A s c y r u m   s t a n s

Stems diffusely branched, 5 to 10 inches high; leaves sessile; styles two.............

2 A s c y r u m   h y p e r i c o i d e s

Sepals and petals usually five

Petals pink or greenish purple, imbricated in the bud; leaves sessile; capsules red-

purple..................................3 T r i a d e n u m   v i r g i n i c u m

Petals yellow, convolute in the bud

Leaves reduced to minute appressed scales...4 S a r o t h r a   g e n t i a n o i d e s

Leaves normal

Styles five, large perennials

Flowers 1 to 2 inches broad; capsules three-fourths of an inch long.....

5 H y p e r i c u m   a s c y r o n

Flowers one-half to 1 inch broad; capsules about one-half of an inch

long........................6 H y p e r i c u m   k a l m i a n u m

Styles three or rarely four

Tall leafy shrubs with numerous flowers

Flowers one-half to three-fourths of an inch broad; pods one-third

to one-half of an inch long...7 H y p e r i c u m   p r o l i f i c u m

Flowers one-third to one-half of an inch broad; pods one-sixth to

one-fourth of an inch long...8 H y p e r i c u m   d e n s i f l o r u m

Herbaceous perennials, or woody at the base only

Stamens numerous (fifteen to forty); flowers one-fourth to 1 inch

broad

Capsules one-celled or incompletely three to four-celled

Capsules incompletely three to four-celled by the pro-

jecting placentae; leaves oblong.....................

9 H y p e r i c u m   a d p r e s s u m

Capsules strictly one-celled; placentae parietal; styles

united into a beak, separate above; leaves elliptic......

10 H y p e r i c u m   e l l i p t i c u m

Capsules completely three-celled; styles separate

Leaves linear or oblong; sepals lanceolate.   Introduced

from Europe.....11 H y p e r i c u m   p e r f o r a t u m

Leaves broadly oblong, oval or ovate-lanceolate, native; sepals ovate to ovate-lanceolate, acute................

12 H y p e r i c u m   p u n c t a t u m

Stamens few (five to twelve); flowers one-tenth to one-fourth of an inch broad

Cyme leafy-bracted ....13 H y p e r i c u m   b o r e a l e

Cymes subulate-bracted

Leaves ovate, oval or oblong; capsules one-twelfth to five-twelfths of an inch long........................

14 H y p e r i c u m   m u t i l u m

Leaves lanceolate or oblong-lanceolate; capsule one-third to one-half of an inch long........................

15 H y p e r i c u m   m a j u s

Leaves linear, blunt, three-nerved.....................

16 H y p e r i c u m   c a n a d e n s e

Great or Giant Saint John's-wort

Hypericum ascyron Linnaeus

Plate 130a

Stems herbaceous, 2 to 5 feet tall from a perennial root, angled, branching and smooth. Leaves sessile, ovate-oblong to ovate-lanceolate, 2 to 5 inches long and three-fourths to $1\frac{1}{2}$ inches wide, clasping the stem. Flowers bright yellow, showy, 1 to 2 inches broad, few or several in a loose, terminal cluster. Sepals five, ovate-lanceolate, about one-half of an inch long, pointed; petals five, obovate or oblanceolate; stamens numerous, united into five sets. Styles usually five in number, united below, the stigmas capitate. Fruit pod ovoid in shape, three-fourths to seven-eighths of an inch long.

Chiefly along streams, Quebec to Vermont and Manitoba south to Connecticut, Pennsylvania, Illinois and Missouri. Flowering in July and August.

The St Peter's-wort (A s c y r u m   s t a n s   Michaux) and the St Andrew's Cross (A s c y r u m   h y p e r i c o i d e s   Linnaeus), two small, leafy, shrubby species of the coastal region, differ from the species of

Hypericum by having four instead of five petals, as pointed out above in the key to the species of the family.

Elliptic-leaved or Pale Saint John's-wort

Hypericum ellipticum Hooker

Plate 130b

Stems herbaceous, slightly four-angled, mainly simple or with a few branches, erect, 6 to 20 inches high from a perennial root. Leaves oval or elliptic, sessile, spreading, thin in texture, three-fourths to $1\frac{1}{4}$ inches long and one-fourth to one-half of an inch wide, blunt at the apex. Flowers pale yellow, few or several in terminal cymes, each flower about one-half of an inch broad, central flower of each cluster opening first, the lateral branches of the cluster developing later; sepals slightly shorter than the petals; styles three, united below; capsules or fruit ovoid-globose, about one-eighth of an inch long and one-celled. Sepals and petals occasionally four instead of five.

In low grounds, swamps and along streams, Nova Scotia to Manitoba, south to New Jersey, Maryland and Minnesota. Flowering in July and August. Our illustration was made from plants just beginning to flower, before the lateral branches of the cyme were developed.

Common Saint John's-wort

Hypericum perforatum Linnaeus

Plate 131a

Stems herbaceous, smooth, slender, 1 to 2 feet high from a perennial root, usually much branched and with several barren shoots at the base. Leaves sessile, linear or oblong, one-half to 1 inch long, one-tenth to one-third of an inch wide, blunt, black dotted. Flowers three-fourths to 1 inch broad, bright yellow, several or many in terminal cymes; petals five, black dotted, longer than the lanceolate pointed sepals; stamens numerous, united by their base into three sets; styles three; fruit pod or capsule ovoid, about one-fourth of an inch long or less, three-celled.

Native of Europe and naturalized as a weed in fields and waste places throughout the East.

Rockrose Family

Cistaceae

Frostweed; Rockrose

Crocanthemum canadense (Linnaeus) Britton

Plate 131b

Stems erect or diffuse from a perennial root, 5 to 20 inches high, finely canescent and becoming branched. Leaves nearly sessile, linear-oblong to oblanceolate, one-half to $1\frac{1}{2}$ inches long, one-third of an inch wide or less, green above, canescent beneath. Flowers bright yellow, usually one or two, 1 to $1\frac{1}{2}$ inches broad; sepals five, the two outer ones much smaller; petals five, broadly obovate, soon withering and falling; capsule ovoid, about one-third of an inch long. After the petaliferous flowers fade and fall, the axillary branches elongate and bear numerous apetalous sessile flowers, which develop fruiting capsules about one-sixth of an inch in diameter.

In sandy fields or rocky soil, Maine to Ontario and Wisconsin, south to North Carolina and Mississippi. Flowering from May to July.

A closely related species of similar situations, C r o c a n t h e m u m m a j u s (Linnaeus) Britton, is more canescent, the primary flowers clustered at the summit of the stem and not surpassed by the branches; the secondary or apetalous flowers very small and producing capsules which are only about one-twelfth of an inch in diameter.

Woolly Hudsonia; False Heather

Hudsonia tomentosa Nuttall

Plate 132a

A diffusely branched, low-tufted or matted perennial, somewhat woody, 3 to 8 inches high, pale and hoary-pubescent, the branches stout and ascending. Leaves small and scalelike, about one-tenth or one-twelfth of an inch long, overlapping one another and appressed to the stem. Flowers numerous, almost sessile or on short, stout stalks less than one-fourth of an inch long, yellow, about one-fourth of an inch broad or slightly less; petals five, obovate-oblong; stamens numerous, nine to eighteen in number; sepals blunt. Fruit a small, ovoid, smooth and one-seeded capsule.

In sandy pine barrens and sandy shores along the coast, New Brunswick to Virginia and inland on sand hills and lake and river shores, west to Manitoba and North Dakota. Flowering from May to July.

Violet Family
Violaceae

Because of their abundance and beauty, the violets take rank with the favorites among our native flowers. Our species of violets are all low herbs, either leafy-stemmed or stemless, that is, the leaves and flowers arising directly from the rootstock. The flowers possess five stamens, the two lowest with appendages that project into the spur or nectar sac of the lower and odd petal. Only these two stamens are developed in the apetalous flowers which come after the petaliferous flowers in most stemless species except the Bird's-foot Violet. The petaliferous flowers are somewhat irregular, the lower petal extended into a spur or sac back of the flower, the lateral petals usually narrower than the two upper petals, and usually only the spur and lateral petals adorned at the base in some species with hairs.

Allied species of some groups freely hybridize when growing together. The hybrids commonly display characters more or less intermediate to those of the parent species, and show marked vegetative vigor, but very often also impaired fertility. These violets of hybrid origin are frequently unlike the mother plant and unlike one another, reverting variously in succeeding generations to the characters of the two original species.

Two cultivated species of violets are common in the east, and sometimes escape from cultivation. They are the English, Marsh or Sweet Violet (Viola odorata Linnaeus), and the Pansy or Heartsease (Viola tricolor Linnaeus) with variously colored flowers. The original form, and the one which the cultivated forms revert to sooner or later, has violet or purple flowers. The large Garden Pansy is the product

of various crosses of V i o l a t r i c o l o r with allied species of the
Old World.   In addition to these, there are about thirty-four native species
of violets in the eastern states, beside the many natural hybrids.   The
following key to the native species may be useful in determining certain
species not illustrated here.

1 Stemless; the leaves and scapes directly from a rootstock or from runners
    Petals bright yellow; leaves orbicular......................1 V. r o t u n d i f o l i a
    Petals violet, purple or white
        Cleistogamous flowers wanting; petals all beardless; leaves divided............
                                    2 V. p e d a t a
        Cleistogamous flowers present, at least later in the season
            Rootstock thick, often stout, without stolons; lateral petals bearded
                Cleistogamous flowers ovoid on short prostrate peduncles; their capsules
                    mostly purplish
                    Leaves except rarely the earliest, palmately five- to eleven-lobed
                      or parted; foliage villous-pubescent
                        Leaf-lobes blunt, lateral ones broad........3 V. p a l m a t a
                        Leaf-lobes acuminate, lateral ones linear...4 V. p e r p e n s a
                  Early and late leaves uncut; others three- to seven-lobed or parted
                        5 V. t r i l o b a
                  Leaves all uncut; blades ovate to reniform, cordate, crenate-
                    serrate
                    Plants nearly or quite glabrous; petals violet-purple; seeds
                    brown
                      Petioles smooth; plants of moist soil....................
                        6 V. p a p i l i o n a c e a
                      Petioles glandular roughened; plants of dry soil..........
                        7 V. l a t i u s c u l a
                  Leaves very hairy, especially beneath and on the petioles;
                  seeds dark brown......................8 V. s o r o r i a
                  Leaves hirsutulous above, otherwise smooth; seeds buff.......
                      9 V. h i r s u t u l a
             Cleistogamous flowers ovoid on ascending peduncles, soon elongated
                Leaves pubescent beneath and on the petioles; sepals and their
                  auricles ciliolate; blades broadly ovate, cordate................
                    10 V. s e p t e n t r i o n a l i s

Leaves glabrous beneath and on the petioles......11 V. a f f i n i s
Cleistogamous flowers on erect peduncles, their capsules green
Leaves broadly ovate, blunt at the apex; sepals obtuse
Cleistogamous flowers ovoid; spurred petal villous..........
12 V. n e p h r o p h y l l a
Cleistogamous flowers long and slender, spurred petal glabrous
13 V. c u c u l l a t a
Leaves lobed or the margins sharply incised or toothed toward the
subcordate or truncate base; spurred petal villous, lateral ones
with capillary beard
Blade of the mature leaves ovate-oblong, ciliate, finely pubes-
cent; petioles short...............14 V. f i m b r i a t u l a
Blade of the mature leaves lanceolate, usually smooth; petioles
long...............................15 V. s a g i t t a t a
Blade of the mature leaves broadly ovate or deltoid
Margin coarsely toothed near the base; blades sometimes
lobed......................16 V. e m a r g i n a t a
Margin sharply toothed toward the base and more or less
pectinately incised.............17 V. p e c t i n a t a
Blade of mature leaves primarily three-lobed or three-parted,
the segments two to three-cleft into linear or oblanceolate
lobes.........................18 V. b r i t t o n i a n a
Rootstock slender (or thicker and scaly with age); plants usually from
stolons
Petals pale violet; leaves minutely hairy on the upper surface; spur
large, 3 lines long.........................19 V. s e l k i r k i i
Petals white, with dark purple lines on the lower three
Cleistogamous capsules ovoid, usually purplish; woodland plants
Leaves reniform, lateral petals beardless; stolons short.......
20 V. r e n i f o l i a
Leaves broadly ovate, acute; lateral petals bearded; seeds
obtuse at the base.................21 V. i n c o g n i t a
Leaves ovate, acute or acuminate; lateral petals beardless;
seeds acute at base.....................22 V. b l a n d a
Cleistogamous capsules ellipsoid; always green; peduncles erect;
bog and wet meadow species

Leaves broadly ovate or orbicular, cordate, obtuse...........
23 V. p a l l e n s

Leaves oblong to ovate, the base slightly cordate to tapering
24 V. p r i m u l i f o l i a

Leaves lanceolate to elliptical.........25 V. l a n c e o l a t a

2 Leafy-stemmed; the flowers axillary

Style capitate, beakless, bearded near the summit, spur short; stipules nearly entire, soon scarious

Petals yellow

Sparingly pubescent; root-leaves usually one to three...26 V. e r i o c a r p a

Markedly pubescent; root-leaves usually wanting.....27 V. p u b e s c e n s

Inner face of the petals white with yellow base, outer face usually violet; leaves usually broadly ovate, acuminate, subglabrous.........28 V. c a n a d e n s i s

Style not capitate; spur long; stipules bristly toothed, herbaceous

Spur 2 to 4 lines long; lateral petals bearded; styles bent at tip, with short beard

Petals white or cream-colored..........................29 V. s t r i a t a

Petals violet-blue

Herbage glabrous or nearly so; leaves orbicular or suborbicular

Stipules ovate-lanceolate, bristly serrate; leaves often $1\frac{3}{4}$ inches wide.................................30 V. c o n s p e r s a

Stipules linear, entire except at base; leaves not over three-fourths of an inch wide; alpine...............31 V. l a b r a d o r i c a

Herbage puberulent; stems ascending; blades mostly ovate...........
32 V. a d u n c a

Spur 4 to 6 lines long, lateral petals beardless; style straight and smooth........
33 V. r o s t r a t a

Style much enlarged upward into a globose, hollow summit; stipules large, leaflike, pectinate at base; upper leaves and middle lobe of stipules entire or nearly so; dry sandy places..34 V. r a f i n e s q u i i

Bird's-foot Violet

Viola pedata Linnaeus

Plate 133

Leaves nearly smooth from a short, stout, erect rootstock, three-divided, the lateral divisions pedately three to five-parted or cleft, the segments linear to spatulate, often two to four-cleft or toothed near the apex. Early leaves usually smaller and less deeply dissected. Corolla two-thirds to $1\frac{1}{2}$ inches broad, the upper petals dark violet, the lower three lilac-purple, or as in the common northern variety (var. lineariloba DeCandolle) here illustrated, all the petals lilac-purple, all beardless, the orange tips of the stamens large and conspicuous in the center of the flower. Seed pods smooth, green; seeds copper-colored.

Apetalous or cleistogamous flowers are never formed in this species, but petaliferous flowers are frequent in late summer and autumn.

Common in dry or sandy fields and open woods from Massachusetts to Florida and Louisiana, less abundant or locally common inland to Minnesota. Flowering in May and June.

Early Blue or Palmate-leaved Violet

Viola palmata Linnaeus

Plate 134a

Leaves palmately five to eleven-lobed or parted, erect or nearly so, from a thick, usually oblique, simple or branched rootstock, the leaf segments variously toothed or cleft, the middle segment usually the widest, more or less villous beneath, especially on the veins and on the petioles, the upper surface of the leaves often smooth; early leaves smaller and usually less divided than the later ones. Flowers on stalks about as long as the leaves, two-thirds to 1 inch broad, violet-purple; sepals blunt; cleistogamous flowers on prostrate peduncles; seeds brown.

In woods and thickets, rarely in open fields and most abundant in rather dry, rich soil on wooded hills, Massachusetts to Minnesota, south to Florida. Flowering from April to June. Like several of the other blue-flowered violets it is locally known as Johnny-jump-up.

Among its close relatives in the east is Viola triloba Schweinitz, in which the earliest leaves and those put forth in late summer are usually with uncut, reniform, cordate blades, the summer leaf blades 4 to 6 inches wide, densely villous beneath and on the petioles, three-lobed or three-parted.

Viola perpensa Greene, of the Great Lakes region, possesses linear, acuminate lateral leaf lobes.

Coast or Britton's Violet

Viola brittoniana Pollard

Plate 136b

Early leaves reniform to ovate in outline, entire or incised, from a thick, erect rootstock; mature leaves three-parted and the segments two to four-cleft into linear or oblanceolate, acute lobes, the middle lobe somewhat the widest; smooth except for minute pubescence on the upper surface and margin. Flowering scapes as long or longer than the leaves. Flowers large, 1 to 1½ inches broad, rich purple with a conspicuous white throat. Sepals linear-lanceolate, acuminate.

In peaty or moist, sandy soil along the coast, southern Maine to Virginia. Flowering in May and June. Next to Viola pedata, one of the most showy of our native species of violet.

Woolly Blue Violet; Sister Violet

Viola sororia Willdenow

Plate 135a

Leaves ovate to orbicular from a stout, simple or branched rootstock; petioles and under surfaces of the young leaves, and often the scapes, villous-pubescent; leaf blades blunt or pointed, heart-shaped, the margins crenate-serrate, sometimes becoming 4 inches wide when mature. Corolla violet to lavender, and occasionally white; sepals broad, usually blunt, finely ciliate below the middle; petals rather broad, the lower and lateral ones densely bearded with white toward the center of the flower. Cleistogamous flowers ovoid on short, horizontal peduncles, usually underground, but lengthening and ascending as the capsule ripens; capsules green, mottled with brown; seeds dark brown.

In rocky or rich woodlands, moist meadows and on shady ledges, Quebec to Minnesota, south to North Carolina. Flowering in April and May.

Quite as abundant is the Meadow or Hooded Blue Violet (V i o l a p a p i l i o n a c e a Pursh) with nearly glabrous foliage, very large leaf blades which are reniform or ovate, deep-blue flowers, the odd petal often narrow and boat-shaped, usually beardless; capsules ellipsoid, green or dark purple. Common in moist fields and groves, frequently about dwellings.

The Broad-leaved Wood Violet (V i o l a l a t i u s c u l a Greene) possesses broadly ovate-deltoid leaf blades, the earliest ones blunt and tinged with purple beneath; petioles glandular-roughened; flowers violet-purple. In dry, open woods in sand or gravel.

The Southern Wood Violet (V i o l a h i r s u t u l a Brainerd) enters our range only in southern New York. It is a small species with leaves lying close to the ground, the blades orbicular to reniform, purplish beneath, silvery pubescent above; flowers reddish purple.

The Northern Wood Violet (V i o l a s e p t e n t r i o n a l i s Greene) is common in moist, open woodlands south to Connecticut and Pennsylvania. The foliage, except the earliest leaves, is hirsutulous. The leaf blades are ovate to reniform, heart-shaped, ciliate and blunt; sepals blunt, closely ciliolate nearly to the tip; flowers deep violet to pale lilac.

LeConte's Violet

Viola affinis LeConte

Plate 135b

Foliage nearly or quite smooth; rootstocks slender, branching, or the plants growing in matted clusters. Early leaves narrowly ovate and heart-shaped, more or less long pointed toward the apex, the margins crenate-serrate; petioles slender and smooth. Flowers violet with a conspicuous white center; the cleistogamous flowers small, on ascending stalks.

Common in moist meadows, low woodlands and shady borders of streams, New England to Wisconsin, south to Georgia and Alabama. Flowering from April until June. The mature leaves of midsummer are about 2 inches wide.

The Northern Bog Violet (V i o l a n e p h r o p h y l l a Greene) resembles LeConte's Violet in some respects, but the leaves are broader and more blunt. It occurs in cold, mossy bogs and sometimes along borders of streams and lakes from Quebec to British Columbia south to Connecticut and Wisconsin. It appears to be abundant in a bog in Bergen swamp, Genesee county, New York.

Marsh Blue Violet

Viola cucullata Aiton

Plate 138b

Leaves and stems smooth or nearly so; leaf blades, except the earliest, broadly ovate to reniform, heart-shaped at the base, the margins strongly cucullate (rolled inward) when the leaves are young, the apex pointed, margins crenate-serrate; when mature 2 to 4 inches broad. Flowering stalks much longer than the leaves. Flowers violet-blue with a dark-blue throat or center, or sometimes entirely white; lateral petals bearded, the lower or spur petal smooth and usually shorter than the lateral ones. Cleistogamous flowers on long, slender, erect stalks, their capsules green; seeds nearly black.

In moist meadows, springy places in woodlands and along streams, Quebec to Georgia. Flowering from late in April until June.

Ovate-leaved Violet

Viola fimbriatula J. E. Smith

Plate 137a

Rootstock long and stout, sometimes branching. The earliest leaf blades ovate and blunt; the later ones oblong-ovate, acute, finely pubescent, especially beneath, the margins crenulate toward the apex, the bases usually somewhat heart-shaped or truncate and sharply toothed, incised or auriculate. Flowering stalks about as long as the leaves when first in bloom or longer than the leaves in later flowers; the corolla violet-purple. Capsules green; seeds brown. Cleistogamous flowers on erect peduncles.

Dry fields and hillsides, throughout the eastern states and south to Georgia. Flowering in May and June.

Arrow-leaved Violet

Viola sagittata Aiton

Plate 137b

Leaves erect from a stout rootstock, smooth, or sometimes ciliate or finely pubescent; their petioles longer than the blades which are lanceolate or oblong-lanceolate, 1 to 4 inches long, truncate or heart-shaped at the base and blunt or pointed at the apex, the base hastately or sagittately toothed or cleft, the earliest leaves often deltoid-ovate, blunt, and merely crenate at the base. Flowers on stalks about as long as the leaves, the corolla violet-purple.

Moist banks, fields and wet meadows, Massachusetts to Minnesota, south to Georgia and Louisiana. Flowering in May and June. The smooth form appears to be the commoner on the coastal plain, while around the Great Lakes region and eastward to the Hudson River valley occurs a form with pubescent foliage.

Triangle-leaved Violet

Viola emarginata (Nuttall) LeConte

Plate 136a

Foliage glabrous, succulent, frequently in dense tufts from stout or matted rootstocks. Leaf blades at flowering time narrowly ovate or triangular, slightly heart-shaped; the later ones broadly ovate or deltoid, 1 to 3 inches wide, often as broad as long, the base truncate or slightly heart-shaped, coarsely toothed or incised toward the base. Flowering scapes usually longer than the leaves; flowers violet-blue, the petals often notched at the ends.

Dry woods, hillsides and fields, southern New York southward. Flowering in April and May.

Viola emarginata acutiloba Brainerd, found on Staten Island, possesses leaf blades (of mature leaves) which are five-cleft or five-parted, the middle lobe long and narrow, the lateral ones shorter and narrower than the middle lobe.

Closely related to the Triangle-leaved Violet is the Cut-leaved Violet (Viola pectinata Bicknell) in which the blades of the mature leaves are ovate-deltoid, wider than long, the margin deeply dentate or pectinate with numerous small linear acute, entire lobes. Low meadows and edges of salt meadows near the coast.

Great-spurred or Selkirk's Violet

Viola selkirkii Pursh

Plate 139a

Leaves and scapes 2 to 4 inches high from a slender rootstock or stolon. Leaf blades thin, crenate margined, ovate to suborbicular, deeply heart-shaped, the basal lobes converging or overlapping; leaves small at flowering time, when mature 1 to 2½ inches wide, smooth except for minute, spreading hairs on the upper surface of the leaves. Flowers pale violet, not bearded, the spur 2½ to 4 lines long and much enlarged toward the rounded end.

In shaded ravines and cool mountain forests, New Brunswick to Pennsylvania and Minnesota, north to Greenland. In central New York its favorite habitat is the moss-covered rocks and boulders beneath limestone cliffs and shaded by dense forests of mixed hardwoods and hemlock. Flowering in April and May.

Large-leaved White Violet

Viola incognita Brainerd

Plate 139b

Foliage somewhat pubescent with soft, white hairs, especially when young, upper leaf surfaces smooth. Leaves ascending from slender rootstocks. Leaf blades at flowering time orbicular or reniform, two-thirds to 2 inches wide, abruptly short pointed at the apex, cordate at the base; summer leaves with large, somewhat roughened blades, broadly ovate, cordate with an open sinus, acute, 2 to 4 inches wide or larger. Flowers white, on stalks as long as the leaves at flowering time, the lateral petals bearded, the upper pair obovate; seeds brown. In summer the plants produce numerous filiform runners.

Mountainous and low, moist woodlands, Newfoundland to Dakota and south to Tennessee.

The Kidney-leaved White Violet (V i o l a r e n i f o l i a A. Gray) is densely pubescent throughout, with reniform leaf blades which are distantly crenate-serrate on the margins and rounded at the apex; petals white, all beardless, the three lower with brownish veins. In Arbor Vitae swamps and cold woods, Newfoundland to Mackenzie river, south to Pennsylvania and Minnesota and along the Rocky mountains to Colorado.

The Sweet White Violet (Viola blanda Willdenow) has the petioles and scapes smooth and often tinged with red; smaller leaves, longer flowering stalks with very fragrant white flowers; lateral petals beardless, the upper pair of petals often long, narrow and strongly reflexed or sometimes twisted; seeds dark brown and minutely roughened.

The Northern White Violet (Viola pallens (Banks) Brainerd) has small, broadly ovate or orbicular, smooth, pale-green leaves; scapes much longer than the leaves, bearing white, slightly fragrant flowers. Common in mossy bogs and wet meadows.

Primrose-leaved Violet

Viola primulifolia Linnaeus

Plate 140a

Leaf blades oblong to ovate, obscurely crenate-serrate on the margins, smooth or somewhat hairy, especially toward the base of the petioles; the leaves and flower stalks arising from slender rootstocks or stolons. Flowering scapes 2 to 10 inches high, usually longer than the leaves. Flowers white, the three lower petals purple-veined, the lateral ones slightly or not at all bearded; capsules green; seeds reddish brown. Numerous leafy stolons are developed in late summer.

A frequent violet of moist, open, especially sandy soil near the coast from New Brunswick to Florida and Louisiana. Flowering in May and June.

Lance-leaved or Water Violet

Viola lanceolata Linnaeus

Plate 140b

Foliage smooth and plants usually profusely stoloniferous in late summer, the stolons rooting at the nodes and bearing numerous apetalous flowers; the rootstocks slender. Flowering stalks 2 to 4 inches high or higher; mature leaves lanceolate or elliptical in shape, the blade 2 to 6 inches long and one-eighth to three-fourths of an inch wide, tapering gradually below into the margined reddish petiole; margins of the leaves obscurely crenulate. Flowers white, the three lower petals striped with purplish veins. Fruiting capsules green; seeds dark brown.

Open bogs, marshes and moist meadows, Nova Scotia to Minnesota and southward. Flowering in May and June or sometimes as early as the latter part of April.

The Round-leaved Yellow Violet (Viola rotundifolia Michaux) possesses oval or orbicular, blunt leaves, heart-shaped with repand-crenulate margins; at flowering time about 1 inch wide; in mid-summer 2 to 4 inches wide and flat upon the ground; flowers bright yellow, the three lower petals with brown lines. In cold woods, Maine to Ontario, south to Georgia. Very common in the Adirondack and Catskill mountains.

Smoothish Yellow Violet

Viola eriocarpa Schweinitz

Plate 134b

Commonly with two to four ascending stems from a single rootstock. Basal leaves often several, long petioled with ovate to reniform blades, smooth except for minute pubescence on the upper part of the stem and on the lower leaf surfaces along the veins; the stems bearing one to three short-petioled leaves, each broadly ovate, slightly heart-shaped at the base and long pointed at the apex, the uppermost ones smaller and nearly sessile. Flowers in the upper axils, yellow, the lateral petals bearded. Fruiting capsules ovoid, woolly white or rarely nearly smooth; seeds brown.

In low, open, moist woods, Nova Scotia to Manitoba, south to Georgia and Texas. Flowering in May and June.

The closely related Hairy or Downy Yellow Violet (Viola pubescens Aiton) is softly pubescent throughout; stems usually but one from a rootstock; usually without basal leaves, but bearing one to three leaves on the stem, which are broadly ovate or reniform. In dry, rich woods, Nova Scotia to Dakota, south to Virginia and Missouri.

Canada Violet

Viola canadensis Linnaeus

Plate 141

Stems 6 to 18 inches high, usually several or many together from a perennial root, smooth or nearly so. Leaves broadly ovate, heart-shaped, pointed at the apex, the margins toothed. Basal leaves numerous on long petioles. Flowers in the axils of the stem leaves, often appearing throughout the season from May to July, whitish with a bright-yellow eye, the upper petals more or less tinged with violet on the outside, the lower petal striped with fine, dark lines.

In upland and mountainous forests, New Brunswick to Saskatchewan, south to South Carolina and Alabama.

The Pale or Striped Violet (Viola striata Aiton) possesses less ascending and more angular stems than V. canadensis, 6 to 12 inches high when in flower; the flowers white or cream-colored, densely bearded in the center. In low and shaded places, New York to Minnesota, south to Georgia.

American Dog Violet

Viola conspersa Reichenbach

Plate 142b

Usually several stems ascending from an oblique, branched rootstock, 3 to 6 inches long at flowering time. Leaf blades orbicular, heart-shaped, crenate-serrate on the margins, blunt, one-half to 2 inches wide, the upper ones smaller and more pointed. Flowers numerous, usually pale violet or rarely white, raised above the leaves on axillary stalks, 2 to 3 inches long.

Common in low ground or moist, shaded woods, Quebec to Minnesota, south to Georgia. Flowering from early spring until late in May.

Closely related, but more dwarfed, with small, orbicular blades and deep violet flowers is the Alpine Dog Violet (Viola labradorica Schrank) occurring in New York only on the higher mountains of the Adirondacks.

The Sand Violet (Viola adunca J. E. Smith; V. subvestita Greene) is finely puberulent, the stems only 2 to 6 inches long; leaf blades ovate, one-half to 1 inch long, crenulate, blunt, subcordate; flowers deep violet, with a straight, blunt spur about 3 lines long. Rather local in sandy or sterile soil or on dry stony ridges, Quebec to Maine and westward.

Long-spurred Violet

Viola rostrata Pursh

Plate 142a

Stems usually numerous from an elongated, jointed rootstock, 4 to 8 inches high. Leaves orbicular to broadly ovate, heart-shaped, nearly or quite smooth, serrate on the margins, the upper ones pointed, the lower and basal leaves blunt. Petaliferous flowers on long, slender stalks, violet with a dark purple-violet center, not bearded, the spur slender and one-half of an inch long or longer.

Shady hillsides and moist woods in leaf mold, Quebec to Michigan, south to Georgia. Flowering in May and June.

The Field Pansy (V i o l a   r a f i n e s q u i i Greene) is an annual plant with slender, smooth, erect stems, 3 to 8 inches high, sometimes branched. Leaves small, somewhat rounded on slender petioles; their stipules large, conspicuous and deeply cut or fringed. Flowers small, bluish white to cream-colored. In fields and open woods, southern New York to Michigan and southward to Georgia and Texas. Flowering in April and May.

Loosestrife Family

S a l i c a r i a c e a e

(Lythraceae)

The Swamp Loosestrife and the Spiked or Purple Loosestrife belong to this family, which in addition to these two species illustrated here, is represented in this State by two smaller flowered species of Lythrum (L y t h r u m   h y s s o p i f o l i a Linnaeus and L. a l a t u m Pursh) and the Clammy Cuphea or Blue Waxweed (P a r s o n s i a   p e t i o l a t a (Linnaeus) Rusby).

Swamp Loosestrife; Willow-herb

Decodon verticillatus (Linnaeus) Elliott

Plate 143a

An herblike perennial growing usually in swamps or shallow water. Although appearing like an herbaceous plant it is more or less shrubby. The stems are angular, recurved, smooth and somewhat woody below, 3 to 10 feet long, often rooting at the tip when they reach the soil or mud. Leaves lanceolate, opposite or verticillate, 2 to 5 inches long, one-third to 1 inch wide, smooth above, somewhat hairy beneath, pointed at both ends, on very short petioles. Flowers numerous in cymelike axillary clusters; calyx broadly campanulate; corolla about an inch or less broad, petals cuneate at the base, pink-purple, the slender filaments of the stamens projecting from the flower. Fruiting capsule about one-fourth of an inch in diameter or slightly less.

In swamps, shallow water around the edges of lakes and ponds, or along slow streams, often forming thickets, Maine to Florida, west to Minnesota, Tennessee and Louisiana. Flowering in June and July. Also known as peatweed or slink-weed, wild oleander and grass poly.

Spiked or Purple Loosestrife

Lythrum salicaria Linnaeus

Plate 143b

Stems four-angled, 2 to 4 feet high or sometimes taller from a perennial root, smooth or somewhat pubescent or tomentose above and more or less branched. Leaves opposite or sometimes in threes, sessile, lanceolate, clasping and heart-shaped at the base 2 to 3 inches long, one-fourth to one-half of an inch wide. Flowers purple, one-half to two-thirds of an inch long and half as broad, in dense, terminal, branched racemes interspersed with numerous small leaves; petals four or five, usually five; stamens eight or ten, the longer ones scarcely projecting beyond the flower.

Native of Europe but thoroughly naturalized and common in wet places and swamps throughout the east. Very common along the Hudson river from Albany to New York. Flowering in July and August.

Meadow Beauty Family

Melastomaceae

Meadow Beauty; Deer Grass

Rhexia virginica Linnaeus

Plate 138a

Stems square, 8 to 18 inches high, the angles of the stem usually slightly winged, hairy or nearly smooth; roots perennial and fibrous with a few small tubers. Leaves opposite, sessile or nearly so, ascending, ovate or elliptical-ovate, pointed at the apex, narrowed or rounded at the base, 1 to 2 inches long, one-half to 1 inch wide, with a few scattered hairs on both surfaces, conspicuously three to five-nerved, the margins ciliate-serrulate. Flowers bright purple, 1 to 1½ inches broad, few or several in terminal clusters; calyx-tube urn-shaped, constricted above with four triangular-pointed lobes, and like the stalk of the flower glandular-pubescent; petals four, broadly obovate; stamens eight, equal; anthers yellow, linear, curved and minutely spurred on the back. Fruit a four-celled, four-valved capsule with numerous small rough, bent seeds.

In moist, sandy meadows and marshes, Maine to northern New York, Ontario and Iowa, south to Florida, Louisiana and Missouri. Flowering from July to September. Common on the coastal plain, but rare or local inland, except east and north of Oneida lake, where it is very abundant in certain places.

The Maryland Meadow Beauty (R h e x i a m a r i a n a Linnaeus) occurs from Long Island southward. It is more densely hairy, the stems are not angled and the leaves are narrower and more spreading.

Sand dunes, woodland, marsh and shallow water habitats along the eastern end of Lake Ontario, north of Montario Point, Oswego county, New York. In such localities one may find in a limited area a great variety of rare and interesting land and water plants

Marly bog in the center of Bergen swamp, Genesee county, New York, the home of several rare wild flowers including the False Asphodel, Glaucous Anticlea, Small White Lady's-slipper, Rose Pogonia, Arethusa, Calopogon, Shrubby Cinquefoil, Wild Rosemary and Houghton's Goldenrod

Evening Primrose Family

Epilobiaceae

(Onagraceae)

Seedbox; Rattlebox

Ludwigia alternifolia Linnaeus

Plate 144b

Stems erect or nearly erect, branching, $1\frac{1}{2}$ to 3 feet high, from a perennial root which often bears small tubers; the stems smooth or minutely pubescent and more or less angled. Leaves alternate, lanceolate or linear-lanceolate, pointed at both ends, on very short petioles, $1\frac{1}{2}$ to 4 inches long. Flowers solitary in the axils of the leaves, each flower one-half to two-thirds of an inch broad, on short stalks; the calyx tube short, rounded at the base with four ovate, long-pointed lobes about as long as the four yellow petals which fall away very easily when the plant is disturbed. Fruiting capsule smooth and slightly wing-angled, about one-fourth of an inch high, opening by an apical pore but finally also dehiscent; many seeded.

In marshes, swamps and wet meadows, New Hampshire to Ontario, Michigan and Kansas, south to Florida and Texas. Flowering from the latter part of June to September.

Fireweed; Great or Spiked Willow-herb

Chamaenerion angustifolium (Linnaeus) Scopoli

Plate 144b

Stems slender or rather stout, 2 to 7 feet high, from a perennial root, smooth below, usually finely pubescent above. Leaves alternate, lanceolate, finely toothed or entire, 2 to 7 inches long, one-third to 1 inch wide, the upper ones smaller, all on very short petioles, long pointed at the apex, thin, the lateral veins joining one another in marginal loops. Flowers purple, rarely white, three-fourths to $1\frac{1}{2}$ inches broad in elongated, terminal, spikelike racemes; calyx tube cylindric, inclosing the ovary, four-lobed at the apex; petals four, obovate; stamens eight; capsules or fruit 2 to 3 inches long and about one-eighth of an inch thick, finely canescent; seeds numerous, small, with a long, whitish tuft of hairs.

In dry soil, usually on recently cleared or burned-over woodlands, Greenland to Alaska, south to North Carolina, Indiana, Kansas, Rocky mountains and California. Also in Europe and Asia. Flowering from July to September.

Great Hairy Willow-herb

Epilobium hirsutum Linnaeus

Plate 144a

Stems stout and softly hairy, 2 to 5 feet high from perennial roots, propagating by underground shoots. Leaves usually opposite, sometimes alternate, oblong-lanceolate to lanceolate, sessile or even clasping the stem at the base, pointed at the apex, sharply but finely toothed on the margins, 1 to 4 inches long, one-third to one-half of an inch wide, thin and pubescent. Flowers rose-purple, three-fourths to 1 inch broad, in the axils of the upper leaves; calyx tube linear with four deciduous lobes or sepals at its summit; petals broadly obovate and notched at the apex, pubescent within at the base. Stigma deeply four-lobed; stamens eight. Fruiting capsule 2 to 3 inches long and very slender, with numerous small seeds each provided with a tuft of whitish hairs.

A native of Europe which, like the Purple Loosestrife, is thoroughly naturalized in marshes, swamps and ditches throughout the eastern states, especially about the larger cities, towns and ports. Flowering from July to September.

The other species of Epilobium in our flora are chiefly inconspicuous, small-flowered marsh herbs, two of them very rare Alpine species of the higher Adirondacks, the other four being inhabitants of swamps and bogs at lower altitudes. Of these, the commonest in most localities is the Northern Willow-herb (E p i l o b i u m a d e n o c a u l o n Haussknecht).

Common Evening Primrose

Oenothera biennis Linnaeus

Plate 145a

Stems stout, wandlike and simple or somewhat branched, 1 to 6 feet high from a biennial root. Stems and leaves somewhat hairy. Leaves lanceolate to ovate-lanceolate, sessile, 2 to 6 inches long, the lower ones with petioles, the upper ones much reduced in size; margins with low, distant teeth. Flowers in the axils of the reduced upper leaves (or bracts), bright yellow, 1 to 2 inches broad in terminal spikes, opening in the evening; calyx tube slender, two or three times longer than the ovary, its four slender lobes reflexed; petals four, broadly obovate; stamens eight, equal in length, the linear anthers on threadlike filaments. Fruiting capsules oblong, narrowed toward the apex, three-fourths to $1\frac{1}{2}$ inches long and longer than the upper leaves (or bracts), one-eighth to one-fourth of an inch thick.

Dry or sandy soil in fields, waste ground and along roadsides, Labrador to Minnesota, south to Florida and Texas. Flowering from the latter part of June until autumn. Often appearing like a weed.

The Evening Primrose is a variable species and consists of several races or mutants which have been regarded as valid species. There are also two other closely related species in addition to the next one which is described. They are the Small-flowered Evening Primrose (O e n o t h e r a c r u c i a t a Nuttall), with linear-lanceolate calyx segments and linear petals, one-fourth to one-half of an inch long, found usually in sandy soil from Maine and Massachusetts to northern New York; and Oakes's Evening Primrose (O e n o t h e r a o a k e s i a n a Robbins), a dull-green plant covered with a soft, appressed pubescence, rather large flowers with linear-lanceolate calyx segments and obovate petals one-half to three-fourths of an inch long. Frequent in sandy soil in southern New England, Long Island and Eastern New York.

Northern Evening Primrose

Oenothera muricata Linnaeus

Plate 146

A slender plant resembling the common Evening Primrose but usually
less branched and more slender-stemmed, 2 to 3 feet high, the stem puberulent and covered with scattered hairs which are enlarged at the base.
Leaves lanceolate, mostly narrower than those of O e n o t h e r a
b i e n n i s, slightly repand-denticulate or entire. Flowers light yellow,
1 to 2 inches broad; petals rhombic-obovate and blunt at the apex. Capsules hairy, narrowly oblong-cylindric, about 1 inch long, slightly curved
and shorter than the persistent leaflike bracts which subtend them.

Sandy or gravelly soil, Newfoundland to southeastern New York and
New Jersey. Flowering from July to September.

Common Sundrops

Kneiffia fruticosa (Linnaeus) Raimann

Plate 147a

Stems erect, 1 to 3 feet high and usually more or less branched, hairy
or nearly smooth. Leaves lanceolate or broader, sometimes oval-lanceolate,
usually pointed at the apex and narrowed at the sessile base, or the lower
leaves petioled, the margins repand-denticulate or nearly entire, 1 to 4
inches long. Flowers bright yellow, diurnal, 1 to 2 inches broad, in terminal
leafy-bracted clusters; calyx segments lanceolate, spreading, the tube
mostly longer than the ovary; petals four, obcordate or slightly notched
at the ends. Fruiting capsules sessile or short stalked, oblong and
prominently winged, smooth or pubescent, one-fourth to one-third of an
inch long; stamens eight, the alternate ones longer.

In dry or sandy soil, New Hampshire to Minnesota, south to Georgia
and Louisiana. Flowering from June to August.

Among the closely related species are K n e i f f i a l o n g i p ed-
u n c u l a t a Small, with club-shaped fruit pods on stalks longer than
the body of the pod; leaves narrow but flowers conspicuous; K n e i f f i a

linearis (Michaux) Spach, with pedicels of the fruit shorter than the capsule; leaves very narrow, and Kneiffia pumila (Linnaeus) Spach, with small flowers one-half to 1 inch broad and almost sessile club-shaped fruit pods.

Biennial Gaura

Gaura biennis Linnaeus

Plate 148

Stems slender, erect, 2 to 5 feet high, branched, especially above, and downy or softly hairy. Leaves alternate, sessile, narrow, pointed at both ends, remotely toothed on the margins, 2 to 4 inches long and one-sixth to one-half of an inch wide. Flowers white or whitish, turning pink with age, very numerous in spikes terminating the stems and branches; each flower somewhat less than one-half of an inch broad; calyx tube with four reflexed lobes; petals four, oblanceolate, somewhat unequal; stamens eight, declined, each slender filament with a small scale at the base; stigma four-lobed, surrounded by a cuplike border. Fruit nutlike, sessile, one-fourth to one-third of an inch long, narrowed at each end, four-ribbed and hairy.

In dry, sandy or waste soil, Quebec to Minnesota, south to Connecticut, Georgia and Arkansas. Flowering from July to September.

Ginseng Family

Araliaceae

Dwarf Ginseng or Groundnut

Panax trifolium Linnaeus

Plate 132b

A small, smooth herb, 3 to 6 inches high from a deep-seated, globose, perennial tuber, one-half of an inch or less in diameter and very pungent to the taste. Leaves three, at the summit of the slender stem on petioles one-half to 2 inches long; each leaf with three to five oval or oblanceolate, sessile, blunt leaflets, 1 to 2 inches long and one-fourth to two-thirds of an inch wide, finely toothed on the margins. Flowers white, fifteen to twenty-five together in a solitary, stalked umbel; each flower about one-eighth of an inch broad or less.   Petals five, spreading; stamens eight, alternate with the petals, styles usually three.   Fruit a small, three-angled, yellow drupe about one-eighth of an inch broad (when the styles are only two-lobed, as is sometimes the case, the fruit is also two-lobed).

In woods and thickets, usually where the soil is moist, Nova Scotia to Wisconsin and Iowa, south to Georgia.   Flowering in April and May or until early June.

The True Ginseng (P a n a x   q u i n q u e f o l i u m Linnaeus) is much larger, 8 to 16 inches high, with a deep, simple compound or lobed tuberous root; leaflets 2 to 5 inches long, and the fruit, which is usually two-lobed, is bright crimson in color and nearly one-half of an inch broad.

Carrot Family

A m m i a c e a e

Hemlock Water Parsnip

Sium cicutaefolium Schrank

Plate 149

A perennial, smooth marsh herb with stout, erect, branching hollow stem, 2 to 6 feet high.   Lower and basal leaves long petioled, finely divided; petioles sheathing the stem at their bases; segments of the leaves seven to seventeen in number, linear or lanceolate, $1\frac{1}{2}$ to 5 inches long, one-eighth to 1 inch wide, long pointed at the apex, margins sharply toothed.   Flowers white in large compound umbels, 2 to 3 inches broad; primary rays of the umbel eight to twenty in number, one-half to $1\frac{1}{2}$ inches long; involucral bracts small and narrow; calyx teeth minute; petals inflexed at the apex. Fruit ovate, compressed, about one-eighth of an inch long, the ribs prominent.

In marshy places, Nova Scotia to British Columbia, south to Florida, Louisiana and California.   Flowering from July to October.

Plate 1

BROAD-LEAVED ARROWHEAD
Sagittaria latifolia

Plate 2

B. CAROLINA YELLOW-EYED GRASS.
Xyris caroliniana

A. SHEATHED COTTON GRASS

Plate 3

JACK-IN-THE-PULPIT; INDIAN TURNIP
Arisaema triphyllum

Plate 4

WILD CALLA; WATER ARUM

Plate 5

SKUNK CABBAGE
Spathyema foetida

Plate 6

B. ASIATIC DAYFLOWER

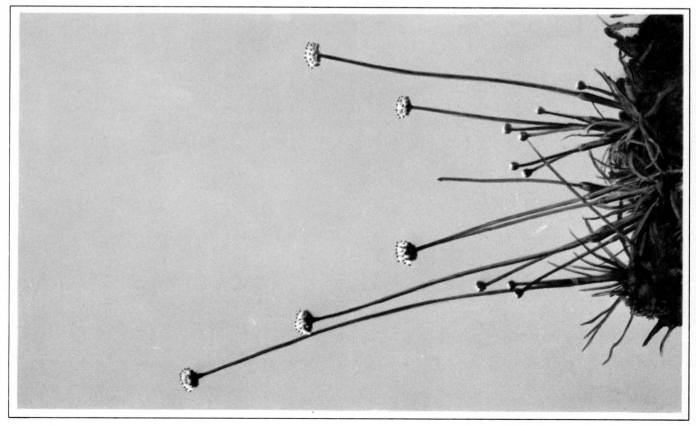

A. SEVEN-ANGLED PIPEWORT

Plate 7

SPIDER LILY; SPIDERWORT
Tradescantia virginiana

Plate 8

PICKEREL WEED
Pontederia cordata

Plate 9

A. GLAUCOUS ANTICLEA
Anticlea chlorantha

B. GLUTINOUS TRIANTHA; FALSE ASPHODEL
Triantha glutinosa

Plate 10

BUNCHFLOWER
Melanthium virginicum

Plate 11

AMERICAN WHITE HELLEBORE; INDIAN POKE
Veratrum viride

Plate 12

Plate 13

RED, WOOD OR PHILADELPHIA LILY
Lilium philadelphicum

Plate 14

WILD YELLOW LILY; CANADA OR NODDING LILY
Lilium canadense

Plate 15

A.   YELLOW ADDER'S-TONGUE; DOG'S-TOOTH VIOLET
Erythronium americanum

B. CLIMBING FALSE BUCKWHEAT
Bylderdykia scandens

Plate 16

AGUE OR COLICROOT; STAR GRASS
Aletris farinosa

Plate 17

YELLOW CLINTONIA; DOGBERRY
Clintonia borealis

Plate 18

WILD OR FALSE SPIKENARD; FALSE SOLOMON'S-SEAL
Vagnera racemosa

Plate 19

FALSE OR WILD LILY OF THE VALLEY; TWO-LEAVED SOLOMON'S-SEAL
Unifolium canadense

Plate 20

B. LARGE-FLOWERED BELLWORT
Uvularia grandiflora

A. SESSILE-LEAVED BELLWORT
Uvularia sessilifolia

Plate 21

HAIRY SOLOMON'S-SEAL
Polygonatum biflorum

Plate 22

INDIAN CUCUMBER ROOT
Medeola virginiana

Plate 23

A. RED TRILLIUM: WAKE-ROBIN OR BIRTHROOT
Trillium erectum

B. WHITE TRILLIUM; LARGE-FLOWERED WAKE-ROBIN
Trillium grandiflorum

Plate 24

A. PAINTED WAKE-ROBIN

B. NODDING WAKE-ROBIN

Plate 25

YELLOW STAR GRASS
Hypoxis hirsuta

Plate 26

LARGER BLUE FLAG
Iris versicolor

Plate 27

NARROW BLUE FLAG; POISON FLAGROOT
Iris prismatica

Plate 28

B. BASTARD TOADFLAX

A. POINTED BLUE-EYED GRASS

Plate 29

SMALL WHITE LADY'S-SLIPPER
Cypripedium candidum

Plate 30

SHOWY LADY'S-SLIPPER

Plate 31

YELLOW OR DOWNY LADY'S-SLIPPER
Cypripedium pubescens

Plate 32

(Photograph and Autochrome by Edward A. Eames)

Plate 33

MOCCASIN FLOWER; STEMLESS LADY'S-SLIPPER
Fissipes acaulis

Plate 34

SHOWY ORCHIS
Galeorchis spectabilis

Plate 35

LARGE ROUND-LEAVED ORCHIS
Lysias orbiculata

Plate 36

HOOKER'S ORCHIS
Lysias hookeriana

Plate 37

A. TALL LEAFY GREEN ORCHIS
Limnorchis hyperborea

B. YELLOW-FRINGED ORCHIS
Blephariglottis ciliaris

Plate 38

WHITE-FRINGED ORCHIS
Blephariglottis blephariglottis

Plate 39

A. SMALLER PURPLE-FRINGED ORCHIS
Blephariglottis psycodes

B. RAGGED OR GREEN-FRINGED ORCHIS
Blephariglottis lacera

Plate 40

ROSE POGONIA; SNAKEMOUTH
Pogonia ophioglossoides

Plate 41

A. GRASS PINK; CALOPOGON
Limodorum tuberosum

B. LODDIGES'S RATTLESNAKE PLANTAIN
Peramium tesselatum

Plate 42

B. FEN ORCHIS; LOESEL'S TWAYBLADE

A. WIDE-LEAVED LADIES'-TRESSES

Plate 43

B. ARETHUSA; DRAGON'S-MOUTH; WILD PINK
Arethusa bulbosa

(Autochrome by Edward A. Eames)

A. CALYPSO
Cytherea bulbosa

Plate 44

LIZARD'S-TAIL
Saururus cernuus

Plate 45

FALSE NETTLE
Boehmeria cylindrica

Plate 46

WILD OR INDIAN GINGER
Asarum canadense

Plate 47

A. SWAMP SMARTWEED
Persicaria muhlenbergii

B. LADY'S-THUMB; HEARTWEED
Persicaria persicaria

Plate 48

B. HALBERD-LEAVED TEARTHUMB

A. ARROW-LEAVED TEARTHUMB

Plate 49

B. SLENDER OR JOINTED GLASSWORT; SALTWORT
Salicornia europaea

A. COAST JOINTWEED
Polygonella articulata

Plate 50

POKE; SCOKE; PIGEON BERRY; GARGET
Phytolacca americana

Plate 51

A. NARROW-LEAVED SPRING BEAUTY
Claytonia virginica

B. ROUND-LOBED HEPATICA OR LIVERLEAF
Hepatica hepatica

Plate 52

BLADDER CAMPION; WHITE BEN
Silene latifolia

Plate 53

WILD PINK
Silene caroliniana

Plate 54

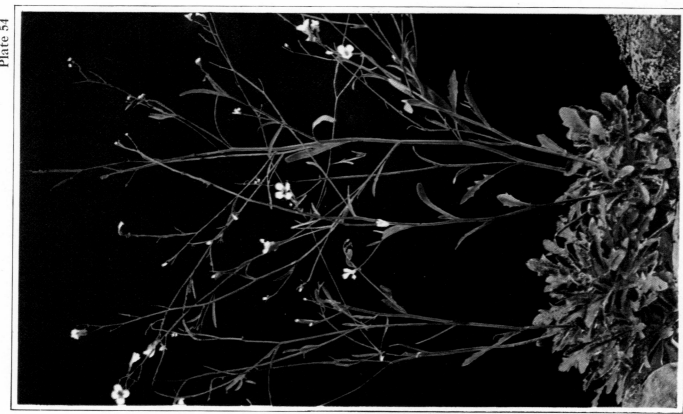

B. LYRE-LEAVED ROCK CRESS

A. CUCKOO-FLOWER; RAGGED ROBIN

Plate 55

AMERICAN NELUMBO OR LOTUS
Nelumbo lutea

Plate 56

LARGE YELLOW POND LILY; SPATTER-DOCK

Plate 57

SWEET-SCENTED WHITE WATER LILY
Castalia odorata

Plate 58

TUBEROUS WHITE WATER LILY
Castalia tuberosa

Plate 59

MARSH MARIGOLD; COWSLIP
Caltha palustris

Plate 60

A. GOLDTHREAD
Coptis trifolia

B. HISPID BUTTERCUP
Ranunculus hispidus

Plate 61

AMERICAN GLOBEFLOWER
Trollius laxus

Plate 62

(FLOWERS)   RED BANEBERRY   (FRUIT)

Plate 63

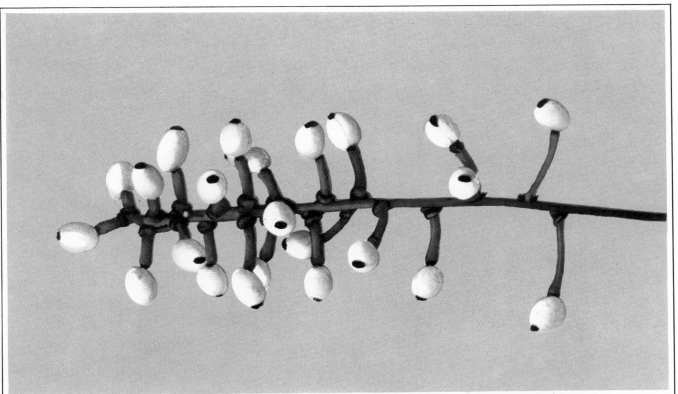

B. WHITE BANEBERRY; SNAKEROOT
Actaea alba

A. FIELD OR MEADOW CHICKWEED
Cerastium arvense

Plate 64

BLACK SNAKEROOT; BLACK COHOSH
Cimicifuga racemosa

Plate 65

WILD COLUMBINE; ROCK BELLS
Aquilegia canadensis

Plate 66

TALL ANEMONE; THIMBLEWEED
Anemone virginiana

Plate 67

CANADA OR ROUND-LEAVED ANEMONE
Anemone canadensis

Plate 68

A. WINDFLOWER; WOOD ANEMONE

B. RUE ANEMONE

Plate 69

B. SHARP-LOBED HEPATICA OR LIVERLEAF
Hepatica acutiloba

A. CAROLINA OR WIDE-LEAVED SPRING BEAUTY
Claytonia caroliniana

Plate 70

SWAMP OR MARSH BUTTERCUP
Ranunculus septentrionalis

Plate 71

EARLY MEADOW RUE
Thalictrum dioicum

Plate 72

FALL MEADOW RUE
Thalictrum polygamum

Plate 73

VIRGIN'S BOWER; WOODBINE; WILD CLEMATIS
Clematis virginiana

Plate 74

ERECT SILKY LEATHER FLOWER
Viorna ochroleuca

Plate 75

BLUE COHOSH
Caulophyllum thalictroides

Plate 76

MAY APPLE; WILD MANDRAKE

Plate 77

BLOODROOT; PUCCOON-ROOT
Sanguinaria canadensis

Plate 78

DUTCHMAN'S-BREECHES

Plate 79

B. MOUNTAIN FRINGE; ALLEGHANY VINE
Adlumia fungosa

A. STIFF WHITE WATER CROWFOOT
Batrachium circinatum

Plate 80

PINK OR PALE CORYDALIS
Capnoides sempervirens

Plate 81

B. TWO-LEAVED TOOTHWORT OR CRINKLEROOT
Dentaria diphylla

A. CUT-LEAVED TOOTHWORT OR PEPPERROOT
Dentaria laciniata

Plate 82

A. AMERICAN SEA ROCKET
Cakile edentula

B. YELLOW MOUNTAIN SAXIFRAGE
Leptasia aizoides

Plate 83

PITCHER PLANT; SIDESADDLE FLOWER
Sarracenia purpurea

Plate 84

SPATULATE-LEAVED SUNDEW
Drosera intermedia

Plate 85

GRASS-OF-PARNASSUS
Parnassia caroliniana

Plate 86

SWAMP SAXIFRAGE
Micranthes pennsylvanica

Plate 87

B. DITCH OR VIRGINIA STONECROP
Penthorum sedoides

A. EARLY SAXIFRAGE
Micranthes virginiensis

Plate 88

FOAMFLOWER; FALSE MITERWORT
Tiarella cordifolia

Plate 89

ALUMROOT
Heuchera americana

Plate 90

A. BULBOUS CRESS; CUCKOO-FLOWER
Cardamine bulbosa

B. TWO-LEAVED BISHOP'S CAP OR MITERWORT
Mitella diphylla

Plate 91

INDIAN PHYSIC; BOWMAN'S ROOT
Porteranthus trifoliatus

Plate 92

A. COMMON FIVE-FINGER OR CINQUEFOIL
Potentilla canadensis

B. SILVERWEED; WILD OR GOOSE TANSY
Argentina anserina

Plate 93

B. DEWBERRY; LOW RUNNING BLACKBERRY
Rubus procumbens

A. MEADOWSWEET; QUAKER LADY
Spiraea latifolia

Plate 94

A. HARDHACK; STEEPLEBUSH
Spiraea tomentosa

B. AMERICAN GREAT BURNET
Sanguisorba canadensis

Plate 95

ROUGH-FRUITED CINQUEFOIL
Potentilla recta

Plate 96

Plate 97

B. DALIBARDA; DEW DROP OR FALSE VIOLET
Dalibarda repens

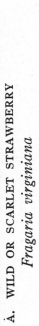

A. WILD OR SCARLET STRAWBERRY
Fragaria virginiana

Plate 98

A. YELLOW AVENS; CAMPROOT
Geum strictum

B. COMMON AGRIMONY
Agrimonia striata

Plate 99

BARREN OR DRY STRAWBERRY
Waldsteinia fragarioides

Plate 100

PURPLE OR WATER AVENS
Geum rivale

Plate 101

PURPLE-FLOWERING RASPBERRY; THIMBLEBERRY
Rubus odoratus

Plate **102**

LOW OR PASTURE ROSE
Rosa virginiana

Plate 103

BLACK CHOKEBERRY
Aronia melanocarpa

Plate 104

WILD OR AMERICAN SENNA

Plate 105

B. PARTRIDGE PEA; LARGE-FLOWERED SENSITIVE PEA
Chamaecrista fasciculata

A. SENSITIVE PEA; WILD SENSITIVE PLANT
Chamaecrista nictitans

Plate 106

WILD OR PERENNIAL LUPINE
Lupinus perennis

Plate 107

A. WILD INDIGO; HORSEFLY WEED
Baptisia tinctoria

B. WHITE OR TRUE WOOD SORREL; ALLELUIA
Oxalis acetosella

Plate 108

B. GOAT'S-RUE; WILD SWEET PEA

A. RABBIT-FOOT, OLD FIELD OR STONE CLOVER

Plate 109

CORONILLA; AXWORT; AXSEED
Coronilla varia

Plate 110

PROSTRATE TICK TREFOIL
Meibomia michauxii

Plate 111

LARGE-BRACTED TICK TREFOIL
Meibomia bracteosa

Plate 112

DILLEN'S TICK TREFOIL
Meibomia dillenii

Plate 113

A. HAIRY BUSH CLOVER
Lespedeza hirta

B. STUVE'S BUSH CLOVER
Lespedeza stuvei

Plate 114

WANDLIKE BUSH CLOVER
Lespedeza frutescens

Plate 115

BEACH PEA; SEASIDE PEA
Lathyrus maritimus

Plate 116

MYRTLE-LEAVED MARSH PEA
Lathyrus myrtifolius

Plate 117

GROUNDNUT; WILD BEAN
Glycine apios

Plate 118

B. TRAILING WILD BEAN

A. WILD OR HOG PEANUT

Plate 119

HERB ROBERT; RED ROBIN
Robertiella robertiana

Plate 120

WILD GERANIUM; WILD OR SPOTTED CRANE'S-BILL
Geranium maculatum

Plate 121

B. TALL YELLOW WOOD SORREL
Xanthoxalis cymosa

A. VIOLET WOOD SORREL
Ionoxalis violacea

Plate 122

B. PALE TOUCH-ME-NOT; JEWELWEED

A. SPOTTED OR WILD TOUCH-ME-NOT

Plate 123

B. CROSS-LEAVED OR MARSH MILKWORT
Polygala cruciata

A. ORANGE MILKWORT; WILD BACHELOR'S-BUTTON
Polygala lutea

Plate 124

B. RACEMED MILKWORT

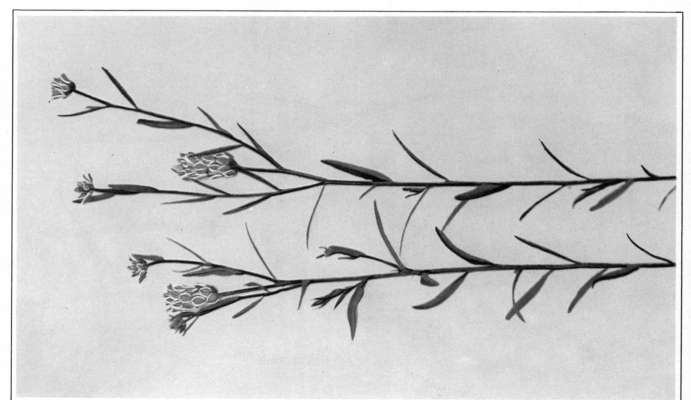

A. FIELD OR PURPLE MILKWORT

Plate 125

B. FRINGED MILKWORT; FLOWERING WINTERGREEN
Polygala paucifolia

A. SENECA SNAKEROOT; MOUNTAIN FLAX
Polygala senega

Plate 126

NEW JERSEY TEA; REDROOT
Ceanothus americanus

Plate 127

MARSH MALLOW; WYMOTE
Althaea officinalis

Plate 128

MUSK MALLOW; MUSK PLANT
Malva moschata

Plate 129

SWAMP ROSE MALLOW; MALLOW ROSE
Hibiscus moscheutos

Plate 130

A. GREAT OR GIANT SAINT JOHN'S-WORT
Hypericum ascyron

B. ELLIPTIC-LEAVED OR PALE
SAINT JOHN'S-WORT
Hypericum ellipticum

Plate 131

B. FROSTWEED; ROCKROSE
Crocanthemum canadense

A. COMMON SAINT JOHN'S-WORT
Hypericum perforatum

Plate 132

A. WOOLLY HUDSONIA; FALSE HEATHER
Hudsonia tomentosa

B. DWARF GINSENG OR GROUNDNUT
Panax trifolium

Plate 133

BIRD'S-FOOT VIOLET
Viola pedata var. *lineariloba*

Plate 134

B. SMOOTHISH YELLOW VIOLET

A. EARLY BLUE OR PALMATE-LEAVED VIOLET

Plate 135

B. LECONTE'S VIOLET
Viola affinis

A. WOOLLY BLUE VIOLET
Viola sororia

Plate 136

B. COAST OR BRITTON'S VIOLET

A. TRIANGLE-LEAVED VIOLET

Plate 137

B. ARROW-LEAVED VIOLET
Viola sagittata

A. OVATE-LEAVED VIOLET
Viola fimbriatula

Plate 138

A. MEADOW BEAUTY; DEER GRASS
Rhexia virginica

B. MARSH BLUE VIOLET
Viola cucullata

Plate 139

A. GREAT-SPURRED OR SELKIRK'S VIOLET
Viola selkirkii

B. LARGE-LEAVED WHITE VIOLET
Viola incognita

Plate 140

B.   LANCE-LEAVED OR WATER VIOLET

A.   PRIMROSE-LEAVED VIOLET

Plate 141

CANADA VIOLET
Viola canadensis

Plate 142

A. LONG-SPURRED VIOLET
Viola rostrata

B. AMERICAN DOG VIOLET
Viola conspersa

Plate 143

A. SWAMP LOOSESTRIFE; WILLOW-HERB
Decodon verticillatus

B. SPIKED OR PURPLE LOOSESTRIFE
Lythrum salicaria

Plate 144

A. GREAT HAIRY WILLOW-HERB
Epilobium hirsutum

B. FIREWEED; GREAT OR SPIKED WILLOW-HERB
Chamaenerion angustifolium

Plate 145

A. COMMON EVENING PRIMROSE
Oenothera biennis

B. SEEDBOX; RATTLEBOX
Ludwigia alternifolia

Plate 146

NORTHERN EVENING PRIMROSE
Oenothera muricata

Plate 147

A. COMMON SUNDROPS
Kneiffia fruticosa

B. SWEET PEPPER BUSH; WHITE ALDER
Clethra alnifolia

Plate 148

BIENNIAL GAURA
Gaura biennis

Plate 149

HEMLOCK WATER PARSNIP
Sium cicutaefolium

Plate 150

LOW OR DWARF CORNEL; BUNCHBERRY
Cornus canadensis

Plate 151

A. BOG WINTERGREEN
Pyrola uliginosa

B. SHINLEAF
Pyrola elliptica

Plate 152

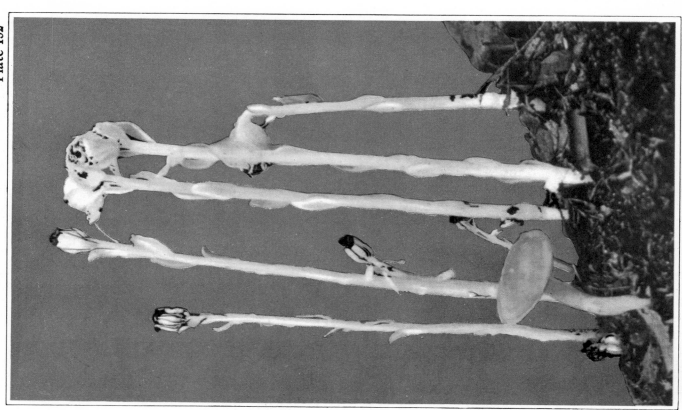

B. INDIAN PIPE; CORPSE PLANT

A. PIPSISSEWA; PRINCE'S PINE

Plate 153

A. PINESAP; FALSE BEECHDROPS
Hypopitys americana

B. TRAILING ARBUTUS; MAYFLOWER
Epigaea repens

Plate 154

PURPLE OR PINK AZALEA: PINKSTER FLOWER

Plate 155

B. STAGGERBUSH
Neopieris mariana

A. LABRADOR TEA
Ledum groenlandicum

Plate 156

A. MOUNTAIN LAUREL; CALICO BUSH
Kalmia latifolia

B. PALE OR SWAMP LAUREL
Kalmia polifolia

Plate 157

B. DWARF HUCKLEBERRY; GOPHERBERRY
Gaylussacia dumosa

A. LEATHERLEAF; DWARF CASSANDRA
Chamaedaphne calyculata

Plate 158

A. LARGE OR AMERICAN CRANBERRY
Oxycoccus macrocarpus

B. CREEPING OR SPICY WINTERGREEN; CHECKERBERRY
Gaultheria procumbens

Plate 159

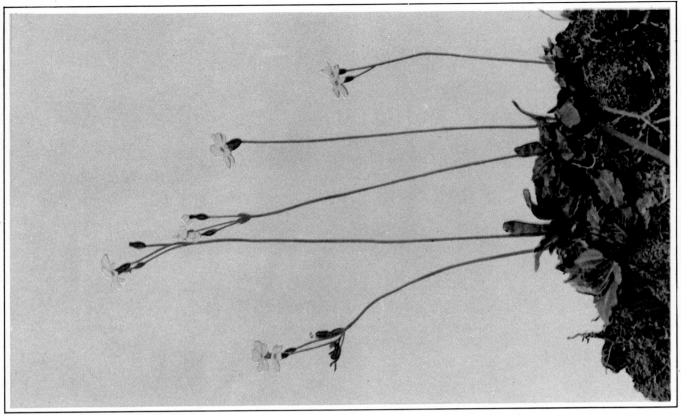
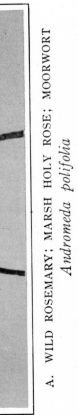

B. MISTASSINI OR DWARF CANADIAN PRIMROSE
Primula mistassinica

A. WILD ROSEMARY; MARSH HOLY ROSE; MOORWORT
Andromeda polifolia

Plate 160

A. SHEEP LAUREL; LAMBKILL; WICKY
Kalmia angustifolia

B. CROSSWORT; WHORLED LOOSESTRIFE
Lysimachia quadrifolia

Plate 161

A. BLUEWEED; VIPER'S BUGLOSS
Echium vulgare

B. BULB-BEARING LOOSESTRIFE;
SWAMP CANDLES
Lysimachia terrestris

Plate 162

FRINGED LOOSESTRIFE
Steironema ciliatum

Plate 163

TUFTED LOOSESTRIFE
Naumburgia thyrsiflora

Plate 164

B. UPRIGHT OR LOW BINDWEED

Convolvulus spithamaeus

A. MONEYWORT; CREEPING LOOSESTRIFE

Lysimachia nummularia

A. NARROW-LEAVED COWWHEAT
Melampyrum lineare

B. STAR FLOWER; CHICKWEED WINTERGREEN
Trientalis borealis

Plate 166

B. SEASIDE LAVENDER; MARSH ROSEMARY; CANKER-ROOT
Limonium carolinianum

A. SEA OR MARSH PINK
Sabbatia stellaris

Plate 167

FRINGED GENTIAN
Gentiana crinita

Plate 168

CLOSED BLUE OR BLIND GENTIAN
Dasystephana andrewsii

Plate 169

BUCKBEAN; MARSH TREFOIL
Menyanthes trifoliatus

Plate 170

B. GRONOVIUS'S DODDER; LOVE VINE

A. SPREADING DOGBANE

Plate 171

BUTTERFLY WEED; PLEURISY ROOT
Asclepias tuberosa

Plate 172

SWAMP MILKWEED
Asclepias incarnata

Plate 173

BLUNT-LEAVED MILKWEED
Asclepias amplexicaulis

Plate 174

FOUR-LEAVED MILKWEED
Asclepias quadrifolia

Plate 175

COMMON MILKWEED; SILKWEED
Asclepias syriaca

Plate 176

HEDGE OR GREAT BINDWEED
Convolvulus sepium

Plate 177

GARDEN PHLOX
Phlox paniculata

Plate 178

GROUND OR MOSS PINK
Phlox subulata

Plate 179

AMERICAN JACOB'S LADDER
Polemonium van-bruntiae

Plate 180

VIRGINIA WATERLEAF
Hydrophyllum virginianum

Plate 181

VIRGINIA COWSLIP; BLUEBELLS
Mertensia virginica

Plate 182

B. BLUE CURLS; BASTARD PENNYROYAL

A. FORGET-ME-NOT; MOUSE-EAR; SCORPION GRASS

Plate 183

B. BLUE OR FALSE VERVAIN
Verbena hastata

A. HOARY MOUNTAIN MINT; CALAMINT
Koellia incana

Plate 184

HAIRY GERMANDER OR WOOD SAGE
Teucrium occidentale

Plate 185

MAD-DOG OR BLUE SKULLCAP
Scutellaria lateriflora

Plate 186

A. HOODED OR MARSH SKULLCAP
Scutellaria galericulata

B. FIELD OR WILD BASIL; BASILWEED
Clinopodium vulgare

Plate 187

SELF-HEAL; HEAL-ALL
Prunella vulgaris

Plate 188

DRAGONHEAD; LION'S HEART
Dracocephalum virginianum

Plate 189

OSWEGO TEA; AMERICAN BEE BALM
Monarda didyma

Plate 190

A. WILD BERGAMOT

B. PURPLE BERGAMOT

Plate 191

A. AMERICAN WILD MINT
Mentha canadensis

B. SQUARE-STEMMED MONKEY FLOWER
Mimulus ringens

Plate 192

STONEROOT; RICHWEED; HORSE BALM
Collinsonia canadensis

Plate 193

CLAMMY GROUND CHERRY
Physalis heterophylla

Plate 194

A. CLIMBING OR BITTER NIGHTSHADE; BITTERSWEET
Solanum dulcamara

B. LONG-LEAVED HOUSTONIA
Houstonia longifolia

Plate 195

A. WHITE MULLEN
Verbascum lychnitis

B. MOTH MULLEN
Verbascum blattaria

Plate 196

BUTTER AND EGGS; RAMSTEAD
Linaria linaria

Plate 197

TURTLEHEAD; SNAKEHEAD; BALMONY
Chelone glabra

Plate 198

HAIRY BEARDTONGUE
Pentstemon hirsutus

Plate 199

B. AMERICAN BROOKLIME; SPEEDWELL
Veronica americana

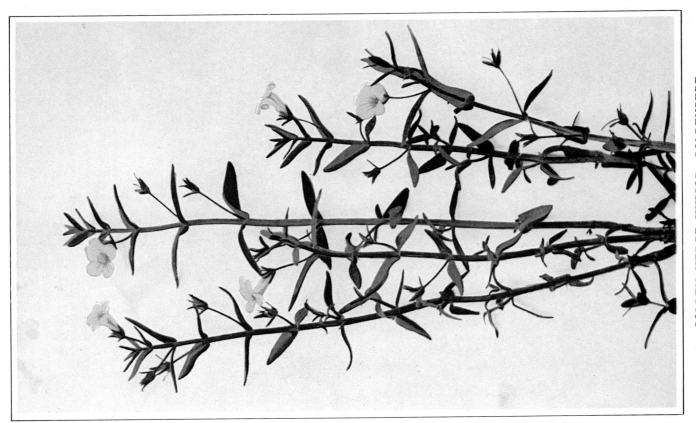

A. GOLDEN HEDGE HYSSOP; GOLDENPERT
Gratiola aurea

Plate 200

CULVER'S ROOT; BOWMAN'S ROOT; BEAUMONT'S ROOT
Leptandra virginica

Plate 201

FERN-LEAVED FALSE FOXGLOVE; FEVER-FLOWER
Aureolaria pedicularia

Plate 202

SMOOTH FALSE FOXGLOVE
Aureolaria glauca

Plate 203

LARGE PURPLE GERARDIA
Agalinis purpurea

Plate 204

SLENDER GERARDIA
Agalinis tenuifolia

Plate 205

WOOD OR HEAD BETONY; LOUSEWORT
Pedicularis canadensis

Plate 206

B. FLAT-LEAVED BLADDERWORT

A. SWAMP LOUSEWORT

Plate 207

WATER WILLOW
Dianthera americana

Plate 208

LOPSEED
Phryma leptostachya

Plate 209

B. BLUETS; INNOCENCE; EYEBRIGHT
Houstonia coerulea

A. NORTHERN BEDSTRAW
Galium boreale

Plate 210

BUTTONBUSH; BUSH GLOBEFLOWER
Cephalanthus occidentalis

Plate 211

B. PARTRIDGE BERRY; TWINBERRY; SQUAWBERRY
Mitchella repens

A. PEARLY EVERLASTING; MOONSHINE
Anaphalis margaritacea

Plate 212

B. BUSH HONEYSUCKLE

A. ROUGH BEDSTRAW

Plate 213

A. TWINFLOWER; DEER VINE
Linnaea americana

B. BEACH CLOTBUR
Xanthium echinatum

Plate 214

A. TRUMPET OR CORAL HONEYSUCKLE
Lonicera sempervirens

B. SWAMP FLY HONEYSUCKLE

Plate 215

A. WILD OR COMMON TEASEL; CARD TEASEL
Dipsacus sylvestris

B. CREEPING OR EUROPEAN BELLFLOWER
Campanula rapunculoides

Plate 216

ONE-SEEDED BUR CUCUMBER; STAR CUCUMBER
Sicyos angulatus

Plate 217

WILD BALSAM APPLE; WILD CUCUMBER

Micrampelis lobata

Plate 218

HAREBELL; BLUEBELLS OF SCOTLAND
Campanula rotundifolia

Plate 219

A. MARSH OR BEDSTRAW BELLFLOWER
Campanula aparinoides

B. VENUS'S LOOKING-GLASS
Specularia perfoliata

Plate 220

CARDINAL FLOWER; RED LOBELIA
Lobelia cardinalis

Plate 221

GREAT OR BLUE LOBELIA
Lobelia syphilitica

Plate 222

A. INDIAN OR WILD TOBACCO; EYEBRIGHT
Lobelia inflata

B. KALM'S OR BROOK LOBELIA
Lobelia kalmii

Plate 223

A. KING DEVIL
Hieracium florentinum

B. DEVIL'S-PAINTBRUSH; ORANGE HAWKWEED
Hieracium aurantiacum

Plate 224

ROUGH HAWKWEED
Hieracium scabrum

Plate 225

RATTLESNAKE-WEED; POOR-ROBIN'S-PLANTAIN
Hieracium venosum

Plate 226

GALL-OF-THE-EARTH; TALL RATTLESNAKE-ROOT
Nabalus trifoliolatus

Plate 227

IRONWEED
Vernonia noveboracensis

Plate 228

JOE-PYE WEED; PURPLE BONESET
Eupatorium purpureum

Plate 229

B. HYSSOP-LEAVED THOROUGHWORT
Eupatorium hyssopifolium

A. ROUGH OR VERVAIN THOROUGHWORT
Eupatorium verbenaefolium

Plate 230

COMMON THOROUGHWORT; BONESET
Eupatorium perfoliatum

Plate 231

WHITE SNAKEROOT
Eupatorium urticaefolium

Plate 232

B. SLENDER FRAGRANT GOLDENROD; QUOBSQUE WEED

A. CLIMBING HEMPWEED OR BONESET

Plate 233

B. MARYLAND GOLDEN ASTER
Chrysopsis mariana

A. WHITE-TOPPED ASTER
Sericocarpus asteroides

Plate 234

BUSHY, FRAGRANT OR FLAT-TOPPED GOLDENROD
Euthamia graminifolia

Plate 235

A. BLUE-STEMMED OR WREATH GOLDENROD
Solidago caesia

B. SEASIDE GOLDENROD
Solidago sempervirens

Plate 236

ZIGZAG OR BROAD-LEAVED GOLDENROD
Solidago flexicaulis

Plate 237

A. WHITE OR PALE GOLDENROD; SILVERROD
Solidago bicolor

B. DOWNY GOLDENROD
Solidago puberula

Plate 238

CANADA OR ROCK GOLDENROD
Solidago canadensis

Plate 239

A.   HOUGHTON'S GOLDENROD
Solidago houghtonii

B.   PHILADELPHIA FLEABANE; SKEVISH;
DAISY FLEABANE
Erigeron philadelphicus

Plate 240

LARGE-LEAVED ASTER
Aster macrophyllus

Plate 241

RED-STALKED OR PURPLE-STEMMED ASTER
Aster puniceus

Plate 242

A. LATE PURPLE ASTER
Aster patens

B. STIFF OR SAVORY-LEAVED ASTER
Ionactis linariifolius

Plate 243

SMOOTH ASTER
Aster laevis

Plate 244

SEASIDE OR LOW SHOWY ASTER
Aster spectabilis

Plate 245

NEW ENGLAND ASTER
Aster novae-angliae

Plate 246

B. STARVED OR CALICO ASTER

A. UPLAND WHITE ASTER

Plate 247

MOUNTAIN OR WHORLED ASTER
Aster acuminatus

Plate 248

TALL FLAT-TOP WHITE ASTER
Doellingeria umbellata

Plate 249

B. SPICY OR SALT-MARSH FLEABANE
Pluchea camphorata

A. NARROW-LEAVED OR SWAMP SUNFLOWER
Helianthus angustifolius

Plate 250

ELECAMPANE; HORSEHEAL
Inula helenium

Plate 251

CUP PLANT; INDIAN CUP
Silphium perfoliatum

Plate 252

OXEYE; FALSE SUNFLOWER
Heliopsis helianthoides

Plate 253

THIN-LEAVED CONEFLOWER
Rudbeckia triloba

Plate 254

BLACK-EYED SUSAN; YELLOW DAISY
Rudbeckia hirta

Plate 255

TALL OR GREEN-HEADED CONEFLOWER
Rudbeckia laciniata

Plate 256

TALL, GIANT OR WILD SUNFLOWER
Helianthus giganteus

Plate 257

ROUGH OR WOODLAND SUNFLOWER
Helianthus divaricatus

Plate 258

HAIRY WILD SUNFLOWER
Helianthus mollis

Plate 259

PALE-LEAVED WOOD SUNFLOWER
Helianthus strumosus

Plate 260

A. LANCE-LEAVED TICKSEED
Coreopsis lanceolata

B. YARROW; MILFOIL
Achillea millefolium

Plate 261

B. SMALL ROSE OR PINK TICKSEED
Coreopsis rosea

A. SNEEZEWEED; FALSE OR SWAMP SUNFLOWER
Helenium autumnale

Plate 262

SMALL OR NODDING BUR MARIGOLD
Bidens cernua

Plate 263

GOLDEN RAGWORT; SWAMP SQUAWWEED
Senecio aureus

Plate 264

SWAMP THISTLE
Cirsium muticum

Dogwood Family
C o r n a c e a e
Low or Dwarf Cornel; Bunchberry
Cornus canadensis Linnaeus
Plate 150

Flowering and leaf-bearing stems 3 to 9 inches high, from slender, underground, horizontal, perennial rootstocks which are somewhat woody. Leaves five to nine in number, whorled at the summit of the upright stem, sessile, ovate or obovate, smooth or minutely hairy, pointed at each end, entire, 1 to 4 inches long; the stem sometimes with one or two pairs of smaller, opposite leaves below the whorl. Flowers greenish or yellowish, very small, several in a dense, globose cluster on a stalk one-half to 2 inches long which terminates the stem; the flowers proper surrounded by four to six, usually four, white, petallike, ovate, involucral bracts, one-third to three-fourths of an inch long, so that the entire inflorescence appears at first glance to be a single flower. Fruit a cluster of globose, bright-red berries.

In open woods, usually where the soil is moist, sometimes in thickets and on recently cleared land, Newfoundland to Alaska south to New Jersey, West Virginia, Indiana, Colorado and California and in eastern Asia. Flowering in May or June or later in the far north.

This dwarf member of a group made up chiefly of large shrubs and trees has been placed in a separate genus by some recent authors, the chief objection to which is its name, Chamaepericlymenum. This generic name has priority over the more appropriate generic name, Cornella, given it by Doctor Rydberg.

The Flowering Dogwood (C y n o x y l o n f l o r i d u m (Linnaeus) Rafinesque) is a small tree or large shrub. The involucral bracts are white or pinkish, obovate and notched at the apex, 1 to 2½ inches long. Common from Maine and Ontario to Florida, Minnesota and Texas.

White Alder Family

Clethraceae

Sweet Pepper Bush; White Alder

Clethra alnifolia Linnaeus

Plate 147b

A much-branched shrub, 3 to 9 feet high with finely canescent twigs. Leaves obovate, blunt or pointed at the apex, narrowed or tapering at the base, sharply toothed, smooth or nearly so and green on both sides, 1 to 3 inches long, on very short petioles. Flowers white, about one-third of an inch broad, in elongated, slender racemes terminal on the branches, spicy-fragrant; calyx five-cleft, the segments oblong, blunt, nerved; petals five, very slightly united at the base, obovate; stamens ten; anthers sagittate, inverted in anthesis, the pollen sacs opening by apical pores; ovary three-celled, style longer than the stamens, with three stigmas. Fruit pods almost globose, about one-eighth of an inch long.

In marshy or swampy ground or low, sandy fields and wet woods near the coast from Maine to Florida and Mississippi. Flowering in July and August.

Wintergreen Family

Pyrolaceae

Bog Wintergreen

Pyrola uliginosa Torrey

Plate 151a

Leaves all basal, the blades orbicular or broadly oval, dull green, thick in texture, somewhat evergreen, blunt or rounded at the apex, 1 to 2 inches long, the margins very obscurely crenulate, petioles about as long or longer than the blades. Flowers pink or purplish pink, one-half to two-thirds of an inch broad; calyx lobes ovate-oblong, one-third as long as the blunt petals; stamens ten, anthers opening by a basal but apparently apical pore as the anther becomes reversed at flowering time, which is true of all species of Pyrola. Fruit capsules about one-fifth of an inch in diameter.

In bogs and swamps, Newfoundland to Alaska, south to Vermont, central New York, Michigan, Colorado and California. Considered by some botanists as identical with Pyrola incarnata Fischer, of northern Asia. Flowering in June and July. In New York rather abundant in open sphagnum bogs of Herkimer, Oneida, Oswego, Madison and Onondaga counties, also in Bergen swamp, Genesee county, and doubtless in other similar bogs throughout the western and northern part of the State.

Shinleaf

Pyrola elliptica Nuttall

Plate 151b

Leaves broadly oval or elliptical, not evergreen, rather thin and dark green, blunt, rounded or narrowed at the base, the margins wavy or plicate-crenulate with very low teeth; $1\frac{1}{2}$ to 4 inches long, usually longer than the petioles, all basal. Flowers whitish, nodding, one-half to two-thirds of an inch broad, fragrant, racemose on scapes or stalks, 5 to 10 inches high; calyx lobes five, ovate-triangular, sharp pointed; petals five, blunt, flat, about four times as long as the calyx lobes; stamens ten, declined, style also declined, its apex curved upward. Fruit capsule five-lobed, five-celled, the valves cobwebby on the margins when splitting open, about one-fourth of an inch in diameter.

In rich soil of rather dry woods and clearings, Nova Scotia to British Columbia, south to Maryland, Illinois, Iowa and in the Rocky mountains to New Mexico. Our commonest species of Pyrola. Flowering from the latter part of June to August.

Round-leaved American Wintergreen

Pyrola americana Sweet

Figure XX

Flowering scape 6 to 20 inches high with five to twenty flowers in a terminal raceme, the flowers in the axils of small bracts. Leaves basal, orbicular or oval, spreading, blunt, thick in texture, evergreen and shining above, the margins crenulate, narrowed, rounded or slightly heart-shaped

Figure XX
Round-leaved American Wintergreen
(P y r o l a a m e r i c a n a Sweet)

at the base, 1 to 4 inches long with petioles mainly shorter than the blades. Flowers white, or faintly tinged with pink, nodding and fragrant, one-half to two-thirds of an inch broad on pedicels one-fourth of an inch long or less. Calyx lobes oblong or lanceolate; petals about three times as long as the calyx lobes, thick and blunt; stamens and style declined, the style projecting conspicuously from the flower. Fruit a small capsule about one-fourth of an inch in diameter.

In dry woods, usually in sandy soil, Nova Scotia to South Dakota south to Georgia and Ohio. Flowering in June and July. The most showy of our native species of Wintergreen or Shinleaf, as they are sometimes called.

There are three additional species of Shinleaf or Wintergreen in our range. The Greenish-flowered Wintergreen (P y r o l a c h l o r a n-t h a Swartz), has small, orbicular, thick-textured leaf blades, one-half to 1½ inches long, and greenish white flowers about one-half of an inch broad. Frequent in dry woods.

The Liver-leaf Wintergreen (P y r o l a a s a r i f o l i a Michaux) has reniform leaf blades usually wider than long, and a raceme of nodding, purple or rose-colored flowers which are one-half to two-thirds of an inch broad. A boreal species, of cold, moist woods and swamps of the north, known in New York only from a few Adirondack localities.

The One-sided Wintergreen (P y r o l a s e c u n d a Linnaeus) has short, slender stems, not stiffly erect but ascending, 2 to 10 inches high, leaves oval, ovate or nearly orbicular in shape, pointed at the apex with crenulate-serrate margins; flowers usually many in a one-sided terminal raceme, white or greenish white and soon drooping, one-fourth to one-third of an inch broad.

The One-flowered Wintergreen (M o n e s e s u n i f l o r a (Linnaeus) A. Gray) is closely related to the Pyrolas and has a single flower, one-half to two-thirds of an inch broad on a stem 2 to 6 inches high. In general appearance and character of leaves it resembles most closely the small P y r o l a s e c u n d a.

Pipsissewa; Prince's Pine

Chimaphila umbellata (Linnaeus) Barton

Plate 152a

Stems trailing, creeping, branching and more or less horizontally subterranean and perennial, slightly woody in texture, sending up both leafy and flowering branches which are erect and 5 to 12 inches high. Leaves narrowly wedge-shaped, blunt or pointed at the apex, tapering at the base, sharply toothed, bright green and shining, 1 to 2½ inches long, one-fourth to 1 inch wide above the middle and remaining green over winter. Flowers one-half to two-thirds of an inch broad, several in an umbellate or subcorymbose cluster, white or pinkish, usually with a deep-pink ring; petals five, concave, nearly orbicular; stamens ten; style very stout, obconic; stigma large, orbicular, with five crenations or lobes. Capsules erect, globular, five-lobed and five-celled; the valves not woolly on the margins when separating, one-fourth to one-third of an inch thick.

In dry woods, often under or near pines, Nova Scotia to British Columbia, south to Georgia and the Rocky mountains. Flowering in the northern states from the latter part of June until August.

The Spotted Wintergreen (C h i m a p h i l a m a c u l a t a (Linnaeus) Pursh) has lanceolate leaves, broadest at or below the middle, mottled with white along the veins, and somewhat larger, white flowers.

Indian Pipe Family

M o n o t r o p a c e a e

Indian Pipe; or Corpse Plant

Monotropa uniflora Linnaeus

Plate 152b and Figure XXI

A white, scapose, succulent plant growing usually in clusters from a mass of matted, brittle roots, attached to partially decayed organic matter in the soil; stems 4 to 10 inches high, erect, each with a solitary nodding, terminal, inodorous, oblong-campanulate flower, one-half to 1 inch long; the fruit, which is a five-celled, many-seeded capsule becoming erect; sepals two to four, deciduous; petals four to five (rarely six), puberulent within, white or slightly pinkish, somewhat longer than the stamens, which are usually ten in number; ovary ovoid, pointed, narrowed into the short, thick style and funnelform stigma.

In moist, rich woods, Anticosti to Florida west to Washington and California. Flowering from June to August.

The Indian Pipe, or Corpse Plant, as it is frequently known, is one of the few flowering plants which possess a saprophytic habit, and is in consequence devoid of green leaves or green color in the stems. The flowers are said to be inodorous but I have usually noticed a peculiar faint odor to fresh flowers. The species of Pinesap (Hypopitys) and most of the members of the Broom Rape family also have the same habit, although many of them are pink, yellow or brown in color.

Photograph by George W. Kellogg

Figure XXI

Indian Pipe (M o n o t r o p a u n i f l o r a Linnaeus);
one-half natural size

Pinesap; False Beechdrops

Hypopitys americana (DeCandolle) Small

Plate 153a

Entire plant lemon-yellow or faintly pink in color, hairy, 3 to 10 inches tall from a dense mass of fleshy root-fibers. Stems scaly, the scales crowded on the lower part of the stems, one-eighth to one-half of an inch long, the upper ones sometimes toothed. Flowers nodding in a one-sided raceme which becomes erect. Terminal flowers usually five-parted, the lateral ones three or four-parted; petals three-fourths to 1 inch long, slightly pubescent and ciliate like the sepals; stigma not retrorsely bearded, the style sparingly pubescent. Fruit capsules oval, one-fourth to 1 inch long.

In open or sandy woods, Ontario and New York, south to North Carolina. Flowering from July until September.

The Hairy Pinesap (H y p o p i t y s l a n u g i n o s a (Michaux) Nuttall) is usually tawny or crimson and more conspicuously hairy than the species described above; the stigma retrorsely bearded, the sepals and petals long ciliated. By some botanists the two are regarded as forms of the same species.

Heath Family

E r i c a c e a e

Purple or Pink Azalea; Pinkster Flower

Azalea nudiflora Linnaeus

Plate 154

A much-branched shrub, 2 to 8 feet high, the twigs smooth or with some stiff hairs. Leaves thin, alternate, mostly clustered near the ends of the twigs, obovate or oblong, pointed at both ends, hairy on the principal veins and midrib beneath, usually smooth above; when young and just unfolding they are usually distinctly canescent, at least beneath. Flowers pink or nearly white, usually opening before the leaves are fully expanded or in shaded situations opening with the leaves, fragrant, $1\frac{1}{2}$ to 2 inches broad, somewhat two-lipped, the tube of the flower hairy on the outside, the five stamens projecting beyond the flower. Fruit a slender, oblong, erect, hairy capsule, two-thirds to three-fourths of an inch long.

In sandy or rocky woods and thickets, sometimes (especially in the north) in or around the borders of bogs and swamps, Massachusetts to Illinois, south to Florida and Texas. Flowering in May or early June. Often called Wild or Swamp Honeysuckle.

Mountain or Hoary Azalea

Azalea canescens Michaux

Figure XXII

A branching shrub, 3 to 10 feet high with oval, elliptic or obovate leaves, wider and shorter than those of the Pinkster, conspicuously soft-hairy beneath, rarely nearly smooth. Flowers rose color to white, very fragrant, on glandular pedicels, expanding with or earlier than the leaves; corolla $1\frac{1}{2}$ to 2 inches broad, the tube of the corolla densely glandular on the outside but scarcely viscid; stamens projecting somewhat from the flower.

In woods, New Hampshire and eastern and southern New York south to Florida and Louisiana. Flowering in May.

The White Azalea (A z a l e a v i s c o s a Linnaeus) is usually a lower shrub, 1 to 6 feet high, with small oblanceolate leaves which are smooth or with a few scattered hairs above and on the veins beneath, often whitish beneath; flowers white or rarely pink, very fragrant, appearing after the leaves unfold; the tube of the corolla very sticky and glandular. Frequent in swamps from Maine to Ohio, Arkansas and Florida. In New York rare or infrequent north of the Atlantic coastal region.

The Flame or Yellow Azalea (A z a l e a l u t e a Linnaeus) with very showy, orange-yellow or red flowers, is found in the lower Hudson valley, and from the Catskill region southward along the mountains.

Great Laurel; Rose Bay

Rhododendron maximum Linnaeus

Figure XXIII

A large shrub, in the south sometimes almost treelike. Leaves evergreen, thick, oblong, oblong-lanceolate or oblanceolate, dark green on both

Figure XXII
Mountain or Hoary Azalea
(A z a l e a c a n e s c e n s Michaux)

sides, sharply pointed at the apex, usually narrowed toward the base, 4 to 8 inches long, 1 to 2½ inches wide, drooping in winter. Flowers large, several or many from a scaly conelike bud forming a dense inflorescence or cluster. Pedicels sticky-pubescent; corolla 1½ to 2 inches broad, about 1 inch long, rather deeply five-cleft into oval obtuse lobes, rose color varying to white, with yellowish or orange spots within. Fruit a small capsule about two-thirds of an inch long.

In low woods and along streams, Nova Scotia, Quebec, Ontario and Ohio to Georgia and Alabama. In New York State rather local in distribution.

The Lapland Rose Bay (R h o d o d e n d r o n   l a p p o n i c u m Linnaeus) is a low, depressed or prostrate shrub less than 1 foot high, with small purple flowers about three-fourths of an inch broad. It is found only on the highest summits of the Adirondack mountains, and in alpine and subarctic regions of both hemispheres.

The Rhodora (R h o d o r a   c a n a d e n s i s Linnaeus) is closely allied to the Rhododendrons. It is a small shrub, 1 to 5 feet high. The flowers appear with or before the leaves, rose-purple in color; the corolla about an inch broad, the lower lip of the corolla divided into two linear-oblong, obtuse segments. In bogs and on wet slopes, Newfoundland to New Jersey, west to Quebec, central New York and Pennsylvania.

Labrador Tea

Ledum groenlandicum Oeder

Plate 155a

A small, much-branched shrub, a few inches to 4 feet high with densely tomentose twigs. Leaves oblong, blunt, sessile, thick and evergreen, somewhat fragrant when crushed, 1 to 2 inches long, one-fourth to two-thirds of an inch wide, strongly revolute on the margins, green above, densely brown-tomentose beneath. Flowers white, one-third to one-half of an inch broad, numerous in terminal clusters, each flower on a pedicel or stalk an inch long or less, which becomes strongly recurved in fruit; calyx small, five-toothed; petals five, separate, obovate; stamens five to seven; fruit capsule oblong, one-fourth of an inch long, five-valved, opening from the base upward.

Figure XXIII
Great Laurel or Rose Bay
(R h o d o d e n d r o n m a x i m u m Linnaeus)

In swamps, bogs and mountain summits, Greenland and Labrador to British Columbia, south to New England, Pennsylvania, Wisconsin and Washington. Flowering from June to August.

Sheep Laurel; Lambkill; Wicky

Kalmia angustifolia Linnaeus

Plate 160a

A small shrub, 6 to 24 inches high, sometimes taller, simple or with a few nearly erect branches. Leaves opposite or in threes, oblong or oblong-lanceolate, blunt or pointed at the apex, petioles short, blades dark green above, pale green beneath, persistent or evergreen into the second year, the new leaves light green, 1 to $2\frac{1}{2}$ inches long, one-fourth to three-fourths of an inch wide. Flowers one-fourth to one-half of an inch broad on slender pedicels, purplish or crimson, numerous in dense, lateral clusters; calyx five-parted, the segments ovate, pointed, glandular-canescent; corolla saucer-shaped, the limb strongly ten-keeled in bud, the margin five-lobed, with ten pouches close to the margin; stamens ten, shorter than the corolla, the anther sacs opening by large terminal pores, the anthers held in the pouches of the corolla limb as it expands and finally straightening out elastically when the corolla is fully expanded. Fruit capsule globular, indented at the summit, five-lobed, canescent, one-eighth to one-sixth of an inch in diameter, on recurved stalks, the style long and persistent on the capsule in fruit.

In sandy, moist soil, hillsides and swamps, Newfoundland to Hudson bay, south to Georgia and Michigan. Flowering in June and July.

Mountain Laurel; Calico Bush

Kalmia latifolia Linnaeus

Plate 156a

A much-branched shrub with stiff branches, 3 to 15 feet high, often forming dense thickets. In the south it sometimes attains the size of a small tree. Leaves smooth, oval or elliptic to ovate-lanceolate, pointed at both ends, on short petioles, green on both sides, usually paler beneath, thick and evergreen, 2 to 5 inches long, one-half to $1\frac{1}{2}$ inches wide. Flowers three-fourths to 1 inch broad, pink or white, numerous and showy in terminal clusters; pedicels of the flowers densely sticky-glandular and two-bracteolate at the base, slender, one-half to $1\frac{1}{2}$ inches long; both the calyx and the corolla sticky-glandular without, the corolla similar in structure to that of K a l m i a   a n g u s t i f o l i a, which is typical of all members of the genus Kalmia. Fruit capsule globular and indented at the top, five-lobed, one-sixth to one-fourth of an inch thick.

In rocky and sandy woods, thickets and recently cleared land, New Brunswick to Ontario and Indiana, south to Florida, Kentucky and Louisiana. Flowering in May and June. Known also as Spoonwood, Broad-leaved Ivy and Clamoun.

Pale or Swamp Laurel

Kalmia polifolia Wangenheim

Plate 156b

A small shrub, 6 inches to $2\frac{1}{2}$ feet high with erect or ascending branches and two-edged twigs. Leaves opposite, rarely in threes, nearly sessile, oblong or linear-oblong, blunt at the apex, green above, glaucous-white below, one-half to 2 inches long, one-sixth to one-half of an inch broad, with revolute margins. Flowers few or several, purple, one-half to three-fourths of an inch broad, in simple, terminal umbels on slender stalks one-half to $1\frac{1}{2}$ inches long which are erect in fruit. Segments of the calyx with rough margins. Corolla structure like that of K a l m i a   a n g u s t i f o l i a. Fruit capsules about one-fourth of an inch long or less.

In bogs from Newfoundland to Hudson bay and Alaska, south to New England, Pennsylvania, Michigan, Montana and California. Flowering in June and July.

Leatherleaf; Dwarf Cassandra

Chamaedaphne calyculata (Linnaeus) Moench

Plate 157a

A small, erect shrub with numerous branches, 1 to 4 feet high. Leaves alternate, leathery but rather thin, evergreen, very short petioled, blunt or pointed, oblanceolate or oblong in shape, covered on both sides and more densely so beneath with small, round, scurfy scales, especially when young, one-half to $1\frac{1}{2}$ inches long, the margins slightly toothed, the upper leaves reduced to bracts which subtend the flowers. Old leaves often bronzed or brownish in contrast to the bright green of the new leaves. Flowers white, fragrant, solitary in the axils of the upper small leaves, forming a terminal, leafy, one-sided raceme; corolla oblong-cylindric, about one-fourth of an inch long, narrowed at the throat, the margin with five recurved teeth. Stamens ten, not projecting from the flower. Fruit a globular capsule, about one-eighth of an inch in diameter.

In swamps, bogs and wet places, Newfoundland to Alaska, south to Georgia, Illinois, Michigan and British Columbia. Flowering in May and June.

Wild Rosemary; Marsh Holy Rose; Moorwort

Andromeda polifolia Linnaeus

Plate 159a

A small bog shrub, 1 to 3 feet high, simple or with a few branches. Leaves linear to oblong-lanceolate, pointed or blunt at the apex, narrowed at the base, the margins strongly revolute, dark green above, whitish beneath, 1 to $2\frac{1}{2}$ inches long, one-sixth to one-third of an inch wide, on very short petioles. Flowers white, drooping, few or several in terminal umbels, the pedicels or flower stalks one-third to one-half of an inch long. Corolla almost globular, one-sixth to one-fourth of an inch in diameter, much constricted at the throat, with five small, recurved teeth, the ten stamens not projecting from the flower. Fruit capsules about one-sixth of an inch in diameter.

In sphagnum bogs, Labrador to Alaska, south to New Jersey, Pennsylvania, Michigan and British Columbia. Also in northern Europe and Asia. Flowering in May and June.

Staggerbush

Neopieris mariana (Linnaeus) Britton

Plate 155b

A small, smooth shrub with erect or nearly erect, wandlike branches, 1 to 4 feet high. Leaves oval to oblong, smooth above, slightly hairy on the veins and also black-dotted beneath, pointed at the apex and base, the margins entire, $1\frac{1}{2}$ to 3 inches long, rather thin, somewhat persistent over winter, but scarcely evergreen. Flowers white or pink, showy, about one-half of an inch long, cylindric, nodding, few or several in lateral umbels or clusters on the almost leafless branches of the preceding season; segments of the calyx large and long pointed, almost leaflike. Fruit an ovoid-pyramidal capsule, one-eighth or one-sixth of an inch long.

In sandy fields, thickets and clearings, near the coast from Rhode Island to Florida and west to Tennessee and Arkansas. Flowering in May and June.

Trailing Arbutus; Mayflower

Epigaea repens Linnaeus

Plate 153b

A prostrate, perennial, slightly woody plant, more or less hairy, especially on the new stems and leaves, extensively spreading on the ground and often forming patches of considerable size. Leaves oval or suborbicular, thick, coriaceous, evergreen, blunt or pointed at the apex, rounded or heart-shaped at the base, 1 to 4 inches long, one-half to 2 inches wide, smooth above when mature; petioles short and hairy. Flowers few or several in dense clusters at the ends of the branches, often more or less concealed by the leaves, very fragrant, pink or white, one-half to two-thirds of an inch long. Corolla with a tube expanding at the summit into a five-lobed margin or limb, nearly as broad as the length of the flower and very hairy within. Fruit a fleshy, hairy, slightly five-lobed, almost globular capsule about one-fourth to one-third of an inch in diameter, splitting at maturity along the partitions into five valves which spread backward into a five-parted rosette, exposing the fleshy interior.

In woods, preferring sandy or rocky soil, often under or near evergreens, Newfoundland to Saskatchewan, south to Florida and Wisconsin. Flowering in April and May.

Among our wild flowers, the Trailing Arbutus, often called Mayflower, is perhaps the greatest favorite and because of its prostrate habit and short stems, impossible to pick without uprooting some of the plant. It is also very sensitive to fire and sudden changes in the character of its surroundings, such as lumbering and grazing, so that in many localities where it was once common it is now rare or entirely exterminated.

Creeping or Spicy Wintergreen; Checkerberry

Gaultheria procumbens Linnaeus

Plate 158b

A low, aromatic, semiwoody plant with creeping or subterranean, perennial stems, branches erect or nearly so, 2 to 6 inches high, bearing several oval, oblong or obovate, blunt or pointed, thick, evergreen leaves, dark green and shining above, pale beneath, 1 to 2 inches long, margins slightly revolute and serrate with low bristle-tipped teeth. Flowers white or slightly pink, usually solitary in the axils of the leaves, on recurved stalks. Corolla urn-shaped, with five recurved teeth. Stamens ten, included within the flower, the anther sacs opening by a terminal pore. Fruit a nearly globular berry usually somewhat indented at the summit and slightly five-lobed, bright red when mature, one-third to one-half of an inch in diameter, mealy and very spicy in flavor, ripe in late autumn and persisting on the branches well into the next season.

In woods and open places, especially under or near evergreen trees, and most abundant in sandy regions, Newfoundland to Manitoba, New Jersey, Georgia, West Virginia, Indiana and Michigan.

The generic name was given to this plant by Peter Kalm in honor of Doctor Gaultier who lived at Quebec in the middle of the eighteenth century.

Huckleberry Family

Vacciniaceae

Dwarf Huckleberry; Gopherberry

Gaylussacia dumosa (Andrews) Torrey & Gray

Plate 157b

A low, branching shrub, 1 to 2 feet high from a horizontal or spreading base and woody rootstock, the branches erect or nearly so, usually leafless below, the young parts glandular and pubescent. Leaves oblanceolate or oblong-obovate, blunt, entire, firm, green on both sides, shining when mature, sparingly hairy or smooth, resinous or glandular, 1 to 1½ inches long, sessile or nearly so. Flowers white, pink or nearly red, in rather long and loose racemes with numerous oval, leaflike bracts; corolla bell-shaped, slightly less than one-fourth of an inch long, the margin five-lobed; filaments pubescent. Fruit a black berry, without bloom, one-fourth to one-third of an inch in diameter and rather tasteless.

In sandy or rocky soil, often in swampy depressions, Newfoundland to Florida and Louisiana, near the coast. Flowering in May and June.

Large or American Cranberry

Oxycoccus macrocarpus (Aiton) Pursh

Plate 158a

A trailing bog plant with perennial, somewhat woody, slender, creeping stems, rooting at the nodes, the branches 5 to 10 inches long, and ascending, forming dense mats or thickly interwoven with moss and other vegetation of the bog. Leaves alternate, very short petioled, thick, ever-green, oval, oblong or slightly obovate, blunt at both ends, entire, one-fourth to two-thirds of an inch long, one-third of an inch wide or less, pale or glaucous beneath and slightly revolute on the margins. Flowers pink, one-third to one-half of an inch broad, nodding on erect stalks, usually somewhat racemosely clustered. Stamens eight or ten, the filaments distinct, the anthers united into a long-pointed cone, prolonged upward when the flower is opened, and conspicuous as the petals are recurved; anthers opening by a pore at the apex. Fruit a globose or oblong, juicy, red berry, many-seeded and acidulous, one-third to three-fourths of an inch long.

In bogs or boggy meadows, Newfoundland to Ontario, south to Virginia and Arkansas. Flowering in June and July. Fruit ripe in September and October. Extensively cultivated in New England and New Jersey for its fruit.

The Small Cranberry (Oxycoccus oxycoccus (Linnaeus) MacMillan) has smaller, thicker, ovate leaves and pink flowers about one-third of an inch broad; the fruit is about one-third of an inch in diameter or less and often spotted when young. It is found in cold bogs, especially northward.

The Creeping Snowberry (Chiogenes hispidula (Linnaeus) Torrey & Gray) resembles somewhat the Small Cranberry and grows in similar situations. It is somewhat hairy, and the small oval or ovate leaves one-sixth to one-third of an inch long are smooth above but sprinkled beneath with numerous, appressed, stiff, brownish hairs; flowers few, nodding, about one-sixth of an inch long, white; fruit a small, snow-white berry.

Primrose Family

Primulaceae

Mistassini or Dwarf Canadian Primrose

Primula mistassinica Michaux

Plate 159b

A small, perennial, scapose herb, 1 to 6 inches high. Leaves all basal, spatulate to rhombic-ovate or obovate in shape, green on both sides, somewhat toothed, blunt at the apex, tapering at the base, sessile or with short petioles, one-half to $1\frac{1}{2}$ inches long, one-eighth to one-half of an inch wide. Flowers two to eight, forming a loose cluster at the summit of the scape. Corolla pink or pale purple, with or without a yellow eye, funnelform, the tube longer than the five-lobed calyx, the lobes of the corolla obcordate, one-eighth to one-fifth of an inch long; stamens five, fastened to the inside of the corolla tube. Fruit a small, erect, narrowly oblong capsule, one-fifth to one-third of an inch long.

On wet banks and rocks, Maine to Newfoundland, Michigan and Saskatchewan. In New York known only in a few localities in the northern and western parts of the State, cliffs along Fish creek, north of Taberg, Oneida county; Cayuga lake; Fall creek, Ithaca; Portage and Niagara Falls.

Crosswort; Whorled Loosestrife

Lysimachia quadrifolia Linnaeus

Plate 160b

Stems usually simple, slender, erect, 1 to 2½ feet high, more or less pubescent. Leaves whorled, usually in fours or fives, sometimes the lower ones opposite, sessile or nearly so, lanceolate to ovate, pointed at the apex, 1 to 4 inches long, one-fourth to 1 inch wide, usually black-dotted, the upper ones usually reduced to a small size. Flowers yellow, one-fourth to one-half of an inch broad, axillary, usually one in the axis of each of the four or five leaves at each node, on slender stalks, one-half to 1½ inches long. Corolla rotate, streaked with dark lines or spotted; sepals narrow and long pointed. Fruit a small capsule about as long as the calyx.

In moist soil, thickets and marshes, New Brunswick to Minnesota, south to Georgia, Tennessee and Wisconsin. Flowering from June to August.

Bulb-bearing Loosestrife; Swamp Candles

Lysimachia terrestris (Linnaeus) Britton, Sterns & Poggenberg

Plate 161b

Stem simple or sparingly branched, erect, smooth, 8 to 20 inches high. Leaves usually opposite, lanceolate or oblong-lanceolate, sharp pointed at both ends, nearly sessile and usually dotted with black, 1 to 3 inches long, one-sixth to two-thirds of an inch wide; often bearing, after flowering time, long bulblets (suppressed branches) in the axils, especially in the autumn. It was this condition that was mistaken by Linnaeus for a Mistletoe, under which group he originally classified it. Flowers one-fourth to one-third of an inch broad, chiefly in the axils of the upper and smaller leaves and forming a terminal leafy raceme; stalks of the flowers slender, one-half to three-fourths of an inch long; sepals long-ovate, pointed; corolla rotate, parted nearly to the base, usually into five segments, yellow with purple streaks or dots. Fruit a capsule about one-eighth of an inch in diameter.

In marshes, swamps and moist thickets, Newfoundland to Manitoba, south to Georgia and Arkansas. Flowering from July to September.

Moneywort; Creeping Loosestrife

Lysimachia nummularia Linnaeus

Plate 164a

Stems creeping and usually rooting at the nodes, 1 to 2 feet long or longer, smooth. Leaves opposite, broadly oval or orbicular, one-half to 1½ inches long, with short petioles. Flowers two-thirds to 1 inch broad, solitary in the axils of the leaves, bright yellow; sepals pointed, half as long as the five blunt lobes of the dark-dotted corolla.

Native of Europe and naturalized in moist grassy places throughout the eastern states. Flowering from June to August.

Fringed Loosestrife

Steironema ciliatum (Linnaeus) Rafinesque

Plate 162

Stems simple or sparingly branched, erect, smooth, 1 to 3½ feet high. Leaves opposite, thin, ovate to ovate-lanceolate, sharp pointed at the apex, blunt to slightly heart-shaped at the base, 2 to 6 inches long, one-half to 3 inches wide, the margins and short petioles hairy. Flowers one-half to 1 inch broad, on slender stalks in the upper axils; lobes of the calyx lanceolate and sharp pointed, shorter than the five yellow segments of the corolla, which are finely toothed toward their tips; stamens five. Fruit a five-valved capsule, slightly longer than the calyx.

In moist thickets and open woods, Nova Scotia to British Columbia, south to Georgia, Kansas and Arizona. Flowering from June to August.

Tufted Loosestrife
Naumburgia thrysiflora (Linnaeus) Duby

Plate 163

Stems mainly simple, often several together from a slender, perennial rootstock, 1 to 2½ feet high, smooth or slightly pubescent. Leaves opposite, lanceolate or oblong-lanceolate, pointed at the apex, narrowed at the base, sessile, 2 to 5 inches long, one-third to 1 inch wide, the lower leaves reduced to ovate scales. Flowers yellow, spotted with black, one-sixth to one-fourth of an inch broad, in dense, spikelike, oblong or ovoid racemes on stout axillary stalks which are one-half to 1½ inches long; sepals five to seven-divided and spotted, the segments narrow; corolla deeply five to seven-parted with rather narrow segments. Fruit a globose capsule which, when mature, is about as long as the sepals or slightly longer.

In swamps, low woods and wet meadows, Nova Scotia to Alaska, south to Pennsylvania, Missouri, Montana and California. Flowering from the latter part of May to July. The same species is also found in Europe and Asia.

Star Flower; Chickweed Wintergreen
Trientalis borealis Rafinesque
(*T. americana* Pursh)

Plate 165b

Stems (rootstocks) buried, creeping and horizontal, several inches long, sending up simple branches, 3 to 9 inches high, each of which bears a whorl of five to ten leaves at the summit, and a few scalelike leaves on the lower part of the stem. Leaves thin, lanceolate or oblong-lanceolate, sharp pointed at both ends, sessile or nearly so, 1½ to 5 inches long, one-third to 1¼ inches wide, the margins minutely crenulate. Flowers one-third to one-half of an inch broad, white, one to three or four, on very slender peduncles at the summit of the leaf-bearing stems; sepals very narrow and spreading, usually seven in number; corolla with five to nine (usually seven) oblong or somewhat obovate, pointed segments. Fruit a small, globular capsule shorter than the sepals.

In moist woodlands and thickets, Labrador to Manitoba, south to Virginia, Illinois and Michigan. Flowering in May and June.

On Mount McIntyre, and on other high mountains of the Adirondacks, occurs a form with leaves elliptical-ovate to ovate-lanceolate in shape, rather thick in texture and only 1 to 2 inches long. In Bergen swamp, Genesee county, New York, occurs a form with linear-lanceolate leaves, 1 to 3 inches long.

Plumbago Family

Plumbaginaceae

Seaside Lavender; Marsh Rosemary; Canker-root

Limonium carolinianum (Walter) Britton

Plate 166b

A rather fleshy, smooth plant of salt meadows near the coast, with a thick tapering or branched, astringent root. Flower-bearing scapes slender, much branched above, 6 to 18 inches high. Leaves all at the base of the plant, oblanceolate in shape, blunt at the apex, narrowed below into margined petioles, the margins of the leaf blades entire or slightly undulate, 2 to 10 inches long, one-half to $1\frac{1}{2}$ inches wide. Flowers pale purple, erect, in many one-sided clusters forming a large, paniculate, terminal inflorescence, each flower about one-sixth of an inch high; calyx five-toothed, the calyx tube with ten faint ribs below and closely subtended by the small bracts; petals five, spatulate in shape.

On salt meadows, Labrador to Florida and Texas. Also in Bermuda. Flowering from July to October.

Gentian Family

Gentianaceae

Sea or Marsh Pink

Sabbatia stellaris Pursh

Plate 166a

A small, herbaceous plant with stems slightly four-angled below, 5 to 20 inches high and with numerous alternate branches toward the summit.   Leaves oblong-lanceolate to linear, opposite, sessile, blunt at the apex, the lower leaves usually smaller and obovate, the upper ones narrower and smaller.   Flowers numerous, three-fourths to $1\frac{1}{2}$ inches broad, each flower at the apex of a branch or slender stalk.   Calyx without distinct ribs, its lobes, usually five in number, narrowly linear, usually somewhat shorter than the five oblong or obovate corolla segments.   Corolla pink with a yellowish, starry eye, bordered with red, rarely the entire corolla white; style two-cleft to below the middle.   Fruit a small capsule about one-fourth of an inch high.

In and around salt meadows near the coast, from Massachusetts to Florida.   Flowering from the latter part of July until September.

The Slender Marsh Pink (Sabbatia campanulata (Linnaeus) Torrey) with calyx lobes as long or longer than the corolla, and with narrower leaves, is also found in salt meadows along the coast.

The Large Marsh Pink (Sabbatia dodecandra (Linnaeus) Britton, Sterns & Poggenberg), (figure XXIV) has eight to twelve corolla segments, and is occasionally found in the salt marshes along the coast, but more rarely than the other two species.

The Common Rose Pink or Bitterbloom (Sabbatia angularis (Linnaeus) Pursh), with square stems, opposite branches, and ovate, clasping leaves, is usually found in thickets and damp, grassy places in southern, central and western New York and southward.

Fringed Gentian

Gentiana crinita Linnaeus

Plate 167

Stems somewhat angled, leafy and often with numerous opposite branches above, 1 to 3 feet high from a fibrous root which is usually biennial. Leaves obovate and blunt below, the upper leaves 1 to 2 inches long, sessile and rounded at the base, pointed at the apex.   Flowers several or numerous, each at the end of a branch or stalk, each flower about 2 inches high. Calyx lobes lanceolate, pointed, unequal, their midribs decurrent on the angles of the calyx tube.   Corolla four-parted, bright blue, rarely white, narrowly bell-shaped, the lobes obovate, rounded and conspicuously fringed at the ends, spreading when mature but apparently closing at night.

Figure XXIV
Large Marsh Pink
(S a b b a t i a d o d e c a n d r a (Linnaeus) Britton, Sterns and Poggenberg)

Stamens four, attached to the inner base of the corolla and not projecting out of the flower.

In low meadows and moist, open woods, Quebec to Minnesota, south to Georgia and Iowa. Flowering in September and October.

The Smaller Fringed Gentian (Gentiana procera Holm) has linear leaves and the corolla segments fringed mainly on the sides with shorter hairs. Rare along the Great Lakes and west to Iowa.

The Stiff Gentian (Gentiana quinquefolia Linnaeus), (Figure XXV) has smaller flowers in dense clusters at the ends of the branches; the blue corolla tube is one-half to three-fourths of an inch long with five equal, triangular lobes which are not fringed. Rather common in dry or moist shady woods.

Closed Blue or Blind Gentian

Dasystephana andrewsii (Grisebach) Small

Plate 168

Stems stout, smooth, 1 to 2 feet high, and usually unbranched, from a perennial root. Leaves opposite, ovate to lanceolate, three to seven-nerved, pointed at the apex, narrowed or rounded at the sessile base, rough-margined. Flowers 1 to 1½ inches high, sessile in dense, terminal clusters and usually with one or two in the axils of the upper leaves. Each flower with two bracts beneath the calyx. Calyx lobes five, ovate-lanceolate, ciliate, somewhat spreading. Corolla blue, rarely white, club-shaped, nearly or quite closed at the summit, its lobes indistinct, the intervening appendages very broad and light colored. Stamens five, their anthers united into a tube.

In moist soil and damp thickets, Quebec to Manitoba, south to Georgia and Nebraska. Flowering from late in August to October.

The Soapwort Gentian (Dasystephana saponaria (Linnaeus) Small) closely resembles the Closed Gentian, but the leaves are usually pointed at each end and the corolla lobes distinct, and longer than or equaling the intervening plaits. The Yellowish Gentian (Dasystephana flavida (A. Gray) Britton) has a greenish or yellowish white corolla, distinctly open at the summit, and ovate-lanceolate leaves.

The Narrow-leaved or Bog Gentian (Dasystephana linearis (Froelich) Britton) possesses an open, blue corolla and linear-lanceolate

Figure XXV
Stiff Gentian; Agueweed
(Gentiana quinquefolia Linnaeus)

leaves.   These, together with the rare Gray's Gentian (D a s y s t e p h a n a g r a y i (Kusnezow) Britton), are all natives of New York, but not so common as the Closed Gentian, although the Narrow-leaved or Bog Gentian is frequent in the Adirondacks.

Buckbean Family

M e n y a n t h a c e a e

Buckbean; Marsh Trefoil

Menyanthes trifoliata Linnaeus

Plate 169

Rootstock creeping, scaly, thick, often a foot or more long.   Leaves erect or ascending from the growing end of the rootstock, 2 to 10 inches long, divided into three leaflets, the petioles sheathing the stem at their bases.   Leaflets usually obovate, blunt at the apex, narrowed at the base, 1 to 3 inches long.   Flowers white, few or several, forming a cluster or raceme on a long, leafless stalk which rises from the rootstock.   Each flower about one-half of an inch long; calyx five-lobed; corolla short funnel-form, five-lobed, densely bearded with white hairs within, the lobes spreading; stamens five, fastened to the inside of the corolla tube and shorter than the tube.   Fruit an ovoid, blunt capsule about one-third of an inch long.

In bogs, marshes and wet places, Greenland to Alaska, south to Long Island, Pennsylvania, Nebraska and California.   Flowering from May to July.

Dogbane Family

A p o c y n a c e a e

Spreading Dogbane

Apocynum androsaemifolium Linnaeus

Plate 170a

A rather slender, branching herb with perennial, horizontal rootstock and stems 1 to 4 feet high, with milky juice.   Leaves entire, opposite, ovate or oval, pointed at the apex, narrowed or rounded at the base, smooth above, pale and more or less hairy beneath, $1\frac{1}{2}$ to 4 inches long, three-fourths to $2\frac{1}{2}$ inches wide; petioles short and usually less than one-third of an inch long. Flowers fragrant, pink or pink and white, numerous in loose, terminal clusters (cymes); each flower about one-fourth of an inch broad; calyx with five short, pointed lobes; corolla narrowly bell-shaped with five reflexed lobes; stamens five, attached to the base of the corolla within and alternate with its lobes. Fruit a slender pod (follicle) about 4 inches long and one-eighth of an inch thick.

In fields and thickets, New Brunswick to British Columbia, south to Georgia and Arizona. Flowering in June and July.

About five closely related species, all with smaller flowers, are recognized by botanists as native in the eastern states.

Milkweed Family

Asclepiadaceae

The Milkweeds are familiar and well-known plants, but in order to distinguish some of the closely related species, a special study of the flower structure is necessary. They are perennial herbs with milky juice and flowers in umbellate clusters. The calyx is small and inferior (below the ovary), five-lobed; its tube short or none. The corolla varies in shape from bell-shaped to urn-shaped, funnelform or saucer-shaped, five-lobed; the lobes or segments commonly reflexed when the flower is fully open. The flowers of the Milkweeds are further characterized by possessing a third floral envelope, consisting of a five-lobed or five-parted crown (corona) between the corolla and the stamens and attached to one or the other. Stamens five, fastened to the corolla, usually near its base, sometimes the filaments of the stamens being attached to one another. The ovary consists of two carpels, with two short styles connected at the summit by a shield-shaped stigma. The fruit consists of two large, fleshy pods (follicles) developing from each flower, but usually only one or a very few flowers of an umbel develop fruit. Seeds flattened and appendaged by a long coma of white or whitish hairs.

Key to the Common Milkweeds

Corona hoods unappendaged, entire at the apex; umbels of flowers sessile; flowers green (Green Milkweed)...................................Acerates viridiflora

Corona hoods each with an incurved horn within (Asclepias)

    Corolla and corona orange; leaves mostly alternate......Asclepias tuberosa

    Corolla bright red or purple; leaves opposite

        Flowers one-third of an inch broad or broader; corona hoods one-fourth of an inch high; leaves oblong, ovate or ovate-oblong; hoods oblong and pointed....

                Asclepias purpurascens

        Flowers one-third of an inch broad or less; corona hoods one-twelfth to one-eighth of an inch high

            Plant nearly or quite glabrous; leaves lanceolate or oblong-lanceolate.......

                Asclepias incarnata

            Plant pubescent; leaves oblong.................Asclepias pulchra

    Corolla greenish, purplish, yellowish or white; leaves opposite

        Leaves ovate, oblong, ovate-lanceolate, obovate or orbicular

            Plants, at least the lower surfaces of the leaves, canescent or tomentose; corona hoods short and blunt.................Asclepias syriaca

            Plants smooth throughout or minutely pubescent above; umbels on long stalks

                Leaves wavy-margined and sessile or nearly so

                    Leaves cordate-clasping.......Asclepias amplexicaulis

                    Leaves rounded at the base and short petioled...................

                        Asclepias intermedia

                Leaves petioled and flat

                    Corolla greenish, umbels loose, pedicels drooping.................

                        Asclepias exaltata

                    Corolla white; umbels dense.........Asclepias variegata

                    Corolla pink or white, some of the leaves verticillate in fours......

                      Asclepias quadrifolia

Leaves narrowly linear, mostly verticillate in threes to sixes: hoods entire.......

                Asclepias verticillata

Butterfly Weed; Pleurisy Root

Asclepias tuberosa Linnaeus

Plate 171

Stems very hairy, rather stout, usually branched above, erect or ascending, 1 to 2 feet high from a stout, perennial root, with slightly milky sap. Leaves alternate, oblong to lanceolate, pointed or blunt at the apex, narrowed, rounded or heart-shaped at the base, sessile or very short petioled, 2 to 6 inches long, one-fourth to 1 inch wide. Flowers bright orange or yellow, numerous in terminal, cymose umbels; lobes or segments of the corolla about one-fourth of an inch long, reflexed in flower; the segments of the five-parted crown (corona) about one-third of an inch long; hoods erect, oblong, bright orange or yellow and two to three times as long as the stamens and longer than the filiform horns. Fruit a finely pubescent pod (follicle), 4 to 5 inches long.

In dry fields and roadsides, Maine to Ontario and Minnesota, south to Florida and northern Mexico. Flowering from July to September.

Swamp Milkweed

Asclepias incarnata Linnaeus

Plate 172

Stems slender, often 2 to 5 feet tall and leafy throughout, more or less branched, smooth or minutely pubescent in two lines along the upper part of the stem. Leaves opposite, oblong-lanceolate, pointed at the apex, narrowed or sometimes slightly heart-shaped at the base, 3 to 7 inches long, one-half to $1\frac{1}{2}$ inches wide; petioles very short. Flowers numerous in many-flowered terminal, stalked umbels; pedicels of the flowers pubescent, one-half to 1 inch long; corolla red or rose-purple, its lobes oblong; column more than one-half as long as the obtuse pink or purplish hoods; horns slender, incurved, longer than the hoods. Fruit an erect pod (follicle), 2 to 4 inches long.

In marshy or swampy places, New Brunswick to Saskatchewan, south to Tennessee and Colorado. Flowering from July to September.

The Hairy Swamp Milkweed (A s c l e p i a s   p u l c h r a   Ehrhart) is similar to this species, but is softly tomentose-pubescent on the stems, the leaves smooth above and pubescent beneath, the flowers commonly lighter red or pink.

Blunt-leaved Milkweed

Asclepias amplexicaulis J. E. Smith

Plate 173

Stems stout, erect or nearly so, smooth, pale green and glaucous, rarely somewhat pubescent, 2 to 3 feet high. Leaves opposite, oblong-ovate or oblong, blunt and minutely pointed at the apex, cordate-clasping at the base, 3 to 5 inches long, 1 to 2 inches wide, the margins wavy-crisped. Flowers numerous in a terminal, solitary, long-stalked umbel; pedicels of the flowers downy, about 1 inch long. Flowers greenish purple; corolla segments oblong, about one-third of an inch long; column thick, hoods pinkish, shorter than the subulate incurved horn. Fruiting follicles 4 to 6 inches long, erect on recurved pedicels.

In dry, mostly sandy soil, New Hampshire to Minnesota, south to Florida and Texas. Flowering in June and July. Young plants of this and other species of milkweed are said to make excellent greens.

The Intermediate Milkweed (A s c l e p i a s   i n t e r m e d i a   Vail) has been found only at Lawrence, Long Island, and is probably a hybrid between A. s y r i a c a and A. a m p l e x i c a u l i s.

Four-leaved Milkweed

Asclepias quadrifolia Jacquin

Plate 174

Stems rather slender, rarely branched, 1 to 2 feet high. Leaves thin, slightly pubescent on the veins beneath, ovate to lanceolate, 2 to 6 inches long, one-half to 2 inches wide, long pointed at the apex, the middle leaves in whorls of four, the upper and lower leaves smaller and usually opposite. Flowers numerous in one to four terminal umbels on slender stalks; corolla pink or nearly white, its lobes lanceolate-oblong; column short, hoods white, obtuse at the apex, twice as long as the anthers and short incurved horns. Fruiting follicles 3 to 5 inches long, erect on ascending pedicels.

In woods and thickets, Maine to Minnesota, south to Alabama and Arkansas.

The Polk or Tall Milkweed (Asclepias exaltata (Linnaeus) Muhlenberg) is 3 to 6 feet tall, with thin, oval, ovate or oblong leaves, long pointed at each end. Flowers greenish purple, drooping and arranged in few or several umbels toward the top of the plant. Frequent in woods and thickets.

The White Milkweed (Asclepias variegata Linnaeus) occurs only from southern New York southward. The leaves are opposite, ovate, obovate or oblong, thick in texture and sometimes the middle ones verticillate in fours. Flowers white or the segments purplish near the base.

The Whorled Milkweed (Asclepias verticillata Linnaeus) is very slender and leafy, the leaves linear and verticillate in threes to sixes. Flowers greenish white. It is found in dry or sandy fields in southern New England westward to Saskatchewan.

Common Milkweed; Silkweed

Asclepias syriaca Linnaeus

Plate 175

Stems stout, rarely branched, 2 to 5 feet high, finely pubescent above. Leaves oblong to ovate, finely but densely hairy beneath, smooth above when mature, pointed or blunt at the apex, rounded or slightly heart-shaped at the base, 4 to 8 inches long, 2 to 4 inches wide; petioles short, one-fourth to three-fourths of an inch long. Flowers numerous in one to several umbels on long stalks from the upper axils of the leaves; corolla purplish to greenish purple or greenish white, the segments oblong-lanceolate, one-fourth to one-third of an inch long; column short and thick, the hoods ovate-lanceolate with a tooth on each side, longer than the anthers and the incurved horn. Fruiting follicles 3 to 5 inches long, erect on recurved stalks, tomentose and covered with short, soft processes.

Roadsides, fields and waste places, New Brunswick to Saskatchewan, south to North Carolina and Kansas. Flowering from July to September.

The form illustrated here is the purple-flowered form which is not so common as the greenish purple-flowered form.

The Purple Milkweed (A s c l e p i a s p u r p u r a s c e n s Linnaeus), rather rare northward, has smooth or puberulent stems, ovate, elliptic or oblong leaves, smooth above and finely pubescent beneath; flowers deep purple; corona hoods oblong or ovate and nearly twice as long as the anthers, the horns broad at the base, slender and incurved at the apex. The follicles are downy and without the soft processes of the Common Milkweed.

Morning-glory Family

Convolvulaceae

Upright or Low Bindweed

Convolvulus spithamaeus Linnaeus

Plate 164b

Stems erect or ascending, sometimes the tip of the stem feebly twining, 5 to 15 inches high, hairy or in late summer becoming nearly smooth. Leaves alternate, oval, short petioled or the upper leaves sessile, usually blunt or but slightly pointed at the apex, somewhat heart-shaped or rounded at the base, 1 to 2 inches long, one-half to 1½ inches wide. Flowers white, open funnelform, about 2 inches long, solitary on long stalks from the axils of the middle or lower leaves; the calyx inclosed by two oval bracts.

In dry, sandy or rocky fields, banks and open woods, Nova Scotia to Manitoba, south to Florida and Kentucky. Flowering in June and July. Rarely seen in sections with rich loamy or clayey soils.

Hedge or Great Bindweed

Convolvulus sepium Linnaeus

Plate 176

Stems high, twining or trailing, often several feet long, smooth or sometimes slightly hairy. Leaves triangular in outline, slender petioled, hastate at the base, pointed at the apex, 2 to 5 inches long, the basal lobes divergent, usually pointed or toothed. Flowers pink with white stripes or entirely white, funnelform, 2 to 3 inches long, with a spreading, slightly five-lobed margin, solitary on slender axillary stalks; the calyx inclosed by two large, ovate, pointed bracts; stamens five, attached to the base of the corolla tube within. Fruit a globular, thin-walled capsule, about one-third of an inch in diameter, containing four black, angled seeds.

Roadsides, fields and thickets, usually in moist soil, Newfoundland to British Columbia, south to Georgia and New Mexico. Often a troublesome weed. Flowering from June to August. The pink and white flowered form is thought by some to be the native form of this species, which is in part introduced and naturalized from Europe.

The Small Bindweed (Convolvulus arvensis Linnaeus) is smaller in every way, trailing on the ground, the leaves 1 to 2 inches long, sagittate or hastate at the base; flowers pink or nearly white, about $1\frac{1}{2}$ inches long. Native of Europe and common as a weed in fields and waste places.

The Trailing or Hedge Bindweed (Convolvulus repens Linnaeus) resembles the Great Bindweed, but is more softly hairy or tomentose. Leaves ovate or oblong, cordate or sagittate at the base. Flowers pink or white, about 2 inches long. It is common in moist thickets and marshes along the coast.

Dodder Family

Cuscutaceae

Gronovius's Dodder; Love Vine

Cuscuta gronovii Willdenow

Plate 170b

A slender, herbaceous annual with yellowish or orange-colored stems, climbing over and around various shrubs and herbs. Flowers numerous, short-stalked in dense clusters. Calyx five-lobed without bracts, the lobes ovate, blunt, shorter than the corolla tube. Corolla white, bell-shaped, about one-eighth of an inch long, with five ovate, rounded and blunt spreading lobes, the lobes nearly as long as the tubular part of the corolla. Within the corolla there are five fringed scales alternate with the lobes of the corolla and shorter than the corolla tube. Stamens five, alternate with the corolla lobes and inserted upon the upper part of the tube of the corolla. Fruit a globular capsule, one-eighth of an inch in diameter, enveloped or capped by the withering corolla.

Parasitic on various shrubs and herbs in low meadows, thickets and open swamps, Nova Scotia to Manitoba and Montana, south to Florida and Texas. Flowering in July and August.

In most localities this is the commonest species of Dodder, although in some places there are to be found other species, especially C u s c u t a c o m p a c t a Jussieu; the Flax Dodder (C u s c u t a e p i l i n u m Weihe), always upon flax; and the Clover Dodder (C u s c u t a e p i t h y- m u m Murray) usually upon clover.

Phlox Family

P o l e m o n i a c e a e

Garden Phlox

Phlox paniculata Linnaeus

Plate 177

Stems stout or slender, erect, simple or somewhat branched above, smooth or slightly pubescent, $1\frac{1}{2}$ to 5 feet tall, usually several stems from a perennial root. Leaves opposite, entire, thin, oblong to oblong-lanceolate, long pointed at the apex, usually narrowed at the base, 2 to 6 inches long, one-half to $1\frac{1}{2}$ inches wide. Flowers in dense, terminal, paniculate clusters, forming an inflorescence 3 to 12 inches long; calyx with five small, slender teeth; corolla pink, purple or white, about an inch long, consisting of a slender tube and an expanded limb with five obovate lobes, the limb one-half to two-thirds of an inch broad. Fruit a small, oval, blunt capsule.

In woods and thickets, native from Pennsylvania to Illinois, south to Florida, Louisiana and Kansas. Common in cultivation. Freely escaping from gardens, and established in the northeastern states. In cultivation consisting of many varieties, differing in leaf form, size and color of flowers and in pubescence. Flowering from July to September.

Ground or Moss Pink

Phlox subulata Linnaeus

Plate 178

Stems densely tufted and extensively branched, forming mats, often of considerable extent, pubescent or nearly smooth. Leaves linear-lanceolate, one-third to 1 inch long, stiff and clustered at the nodes of the stems, their margins ciliate. Flowers on slender stalks, clustered in simple few-flowered cymes; calyx teeth about as long as the calyx tube; corolla pink, purplish with a darker eye, or sometimes white, about one-half to two-thirds of an inch broad, the five lobes of the corolla entire or often slightly indented at the apex.

In dry, sandy or rocky soil of fields, banks and open woods, southern New York to Michigan, south to Florida and Kentucky. Flowering in May and June. Occasionally cultivated farther north.

The Wild Sweet William (P h l o x m a c u l a t a Linnaeus) is found wild from southern New York southward, and frequently escaped from cultivation farther northward. Its stems are usually spotted with purple; leaves lanceolate or the upper ones ovate-lanceolate; flowers pink or purple, rarely white, in compact clusters forming a many-flowered terminal inflorescence, 4 to 10 inches long. A race with white flowers and unspotted stems is known as P h l o x m a c u l a t a var. c a n d i d a Michaux (P. s u a v e o l e n s Aiton).

The Downy or Prairie Phlox (P h l o x p i l o s a Linnaeus) occurs rather locally in New York. It is softly hairy with linear or lanceolate, long-pointed leaves and pink, purple or white flowers forming a terminal cluster.

The Wild Blue Phlox (P h l o x d i v a r i c a t a Linnaeus) (Figure XXVI) is frequent in some localities. It is finely viscid-pubescent, the stems rooting at the nodes near the base, but the tops erect; leaves oblong or ovate, those on the flowering stems lanceolate or ovate-lanceolate; flowers fragrant, bluish, the corolla lobes deeply notched at the ends.

American Jacob's Ladder

Polemonium van-bruntiae Britton

Plate 179

Stems herbaceous, erect, smooth below, a little pubescent above, 1 to 3 feet tall, from a stout, horizontal, perennial rootstock clothed with numerous fibrous roots. Basal leaves 6 to 12 inches long, odd-pinnate, with eleven to seventeen sessile, ovate-lanceolate, pointed leaflets, one-half to $1\frac{1}{2}$ inches long; stem leaves and upper leaves with only three to seven leaflets. Flowers bluish purple or blue, three-fourths to 1 inch broad in

Figure XXVI
Wild Blue Phlox
(Phlox divaricata Linnaeus)

terminal or panicled cymose clusters; corolla tubular-campanulate with five rounded lobes, the five stamens projecting out of the flower.

In swamps, marshy meadows and along streams, Vermont and New York to Maryland. Flowering from the latter part of May until July. A local plant, as beautiful as it is rare. It has been found locally abundant at several places in the southern and western portions of the Catskills, in the Schoharie valley, southern Herkimer county and at Peterboro, Madison county, New York. Also in Vermont and Connecticut southward to Maryland.

The Greek Valerian or Bluebell (P o l e m o n i u m   r e p t a n s Linnaeus) occurs in woods from western New York, westward. It is entirely smooth, the stems weak and reclining, only the tips erect; the blue flowers one-half to two-thirds of an inch broad and the stamens not projecting from the flower.

Waterleaf Family

H y d r o p h y l l a c e a e

Virginia Waterleaf

Hydrophyllum virginianum Linnaeus

Plate 180

Stems slender, smooth or but slightly pubescent, usually unbranched, ascending or erect but not stiff, 1 to 3 feet long, from a perennial, scaly rootstock. Lower and basal leaves, 6 to 10 inches long, pinnately divided into five to seven oblong-ovate or ovate-lanceolate, pointed, toothed or incised segments, 1 to 2 inches long; upper leaves similar but smaller, shorter petioled and with fewer segments. Flowers white or violet (at high altitudes nearly purple) in simple or forked, slender-stalked cymes, the pedicels of the flowers hairy. Calyx deeply parted into five linear, hairy, spreading segments. Corolla about one-third of an inch long, bell-shaped, with five oblong, blunt lobes. Stamens five, projecting from the flower. Fruit a capsule about one-sixth of an inch in diameter.

In rich woods and thickets, Quebec to South Dakota, south to South Carolina and Kansas. Flowering in June and July or in the north as late as August.

The Appendaged Waterleaf (H y d r o p h y l l u m a p p e n d i c-u l a t u m Michaux) is rough-hairy all over; the flowers violet to purple and one-half to two-thirds of an inch long with short, reflexed appendages between the calyx lobes. The Broad-leaved Waterleaf (H y d r o-p h y l l u m c a n a d e n s e Linnaeus) has leaf blades nearly orbicular, palmately five to nine-lobed and the entire plant smooth or nearly so.

Borage Family

B o r a g i n a c e a e

Virginia Cowslip; Bluebells

Mertensia virginica (Linnaeus) De Candolle

Plate 181

Stems erect or nearly erect, simple or somewhat branched, 1 to 2 feet tall from a perennial root; smooth and rather stout. Leaves oblong, the upper ones sessile, blunt at the apex, 2 to 5 inches long, the lower leaves tapering into margined petioles, obovate in shape. Flowers blue-purple, or blue turning purple with age, showy, about 1 inch long, in short racemes forming a terminal corymbose inflorescence; calyx lobes five, oblong-lanceolate, blunt; corolla trumpet-shaped with a slender tube and a five-lobed, plaited limb, pubescent at the base within but not crested in the throat; stamens five, attached to the inside of the corolla tube.

In low meadows and along streams, central New York and southern Ontario to New Jersey, South Carolina, Minnesota and Kansas. Flowering in April and May.

Forget-me-not; Mouse-ear; Scorpion Grass

Myosotis scorpioides Linnaeus

Plate 182a

A small, slender plant with perennial rootstocks or stolons freely rooting at the nodes; stems pubescent, decumbent below, the ends ascending or erect, 6 to 18 inches long. Leaves oblong to oblong-lanceolate, blunt, narrowed at the base, 1 to 3 inches long, only the lower ones petioled. Flowers in several or many-flowered loose racemes. curving over at the tip. Calyx lobes five, equal, triangular-ovate, pointed, shorter than the calyx tube. Corolla one-fourth to one-third of an inch broad with five rounded lobes, light blue with a yellow eye. Stamens five, not projecting out of the flower; ovary four-divided, in fruit becoming four small, angled nutlets.

In brooks, marshes and wet meadows, Newfoundland to New York, Ontario, Pennsylvania and Tennessee. Said to be a native of Europe, but well established and common in many places, often far from habitations. Flowering from May to July.

Blueweed; Viper's Bugloss

Echium vulgare Linnaeus

Plate 161a

A very bristly-hairy, biennial, herbaceous weed, with a long, black taproot, the erect, spotted stem 1 to 2½ feet high and finally much branched. Leaves entire, hairy, oblong to linear-lanceolate, 2 to 6 inches long, sessile, with the exception of the basal leaves which are narrowed into long petioles. Flowers showy, bright blue (pinkish in bud, reddish-purple when old), numerous, clustered on short, one-sided, curved spikes which are densely hairy, rolled up at first and straightening out as the flowers expand. Calyx deeply five-parted, corolla about an inch long, funnelform, unequally five-lobed with five reddish stamens inserted on the tube of the corolla, unequal in length and exserted beyond the corolla. Fruit consists of four roughened or wrinkled, one-seeded nutlets, dark brown, fixed by a flat base, sharply angled on the inner face, rounded on the outer, possessing a fancied resemblance to a serpent's head, whence the plant derives one of its common names.

Native of Europe, thoroughly naturalized throughout the eastern and middle states in waste places, roadsides and fields, preferring limestone and gravelly or poor soil. It seems to have been introduced into this country as early as 1683, and is now a troublesome weed in pasture lands and old fields.

The Hound's-tongue or Gipsy Flower (C y n o g l o s s u m o f f i c i - n a l e Linnaeus) is another plant of European origin, common as a weed in fields and waste places. Stems erect and leafy, 1 to 3 feet high, pubescent and with a rather strong unpleasant odor. Flowers numerous in simple or branched racemes; corolla reddish purple, about one-third of an inch broad. Fruit pyramidal in shape consisting of four hispid nutlets. It is also called Dog's-tongue, Sheep-lice and Dog Bur.

Vervain Family

Verbenaceae

Blue or False Vervain

Verbena hastata Linnaeus

Plate 183b

Stems erect, stiff, four-sided and usually branched, roughish pubescent, 2 to 7 feet tall from a perennial root. Leaves oblong-lanceolate to lanceolate, pointed at the apex, sharply toothed, 3 to 6 inches long, the lower leaves sometimes hastately three-lobed at the base, the others blunt or abruptly tapering to the petiole. Flowers blue, numerous in slender-panicled spikes, 2 to 6 inches long. Calyx tubular, somewhat unequally five-toothed; corolla about one-eighth of an inch broad, the limb five-lobed and very slightly two-lipped, dark blue, varying sometimes to pink or rarely white.

In moist places, fields, meadows and roadsides, Nova Scotia to British Columbia, south to Florida and Arizona. Flowering from June to September.

Mint Family

Labiatae

Hairy Germander or Wood Sage

Teucrium occidentale A. Gray

Plate 184

Stems erect, four-angled, hairy, slender or rather stout, usually branched with ascending branches, 1 to 3 feet high. Leaves ovate-lanceolate, thin, pointed at the apex, sharply toothed, rounded at the base, 1 to 4 inches long, one-half to 1½ inches wide with slender petioles shorter than the blades. Flowers purplish pink in dense, terminal, spikelike panicles. Calyx ten-nerved, unequally five-toothed, bracts, calyx and axis of the spike hairy and often glandular. Corolla one-third to one-half of an inch long, with a short tube, the limb irregularly five-lobed, the two short upper lobes oblong, the lower lobes broader and declined. Stamens four, projecting from between the two upper lobes of the corolla.

In moist soil in woods and thickets. Maine to Ontario and British Columbia, south to eastern Pennsylvania, Ohio and New Mexico. Flowering from July to September.

The American Germander or Wood Sage (T e u c r i u m c a n a d e n s e Linnaeus) is very similar, but the calyx, bracts etc. are canescent without being hairy or glandular. The Narrow-leaved Germander (T e u c r i u m l i t t o r a l e Bicknell), common on or near the coast, has narrower, sharply toothed leaves, often densely canescent.

Blue Curls; Bastard Pennyroyal

Trichostema dichotomum Linnaeus

Plate 182b

A small, annual, minutely viscid-pubescent plant, with rather stiff, much-branched stems, 6 to 20 inches high, the branches spreading or ascending. Leaves oblong or oblong-lanceolate, rather blunt at the apex, narrowed at the base into short petioles, 1 to 3 inches long, the upper leaves smaller. Flowers one-half to three-fourths of an inch long, borne one to three together on two-bracteolate stalks in a paniculate inflorescence. Calyx oblique, very unequally five-lobed, the three upper lobes much longer and more united than the two lower ones. Corolla blue, pinkish or rarely nearly white, the tube shorter than the five-cleft limb, the lobes or segments of the corolla more or less declined. Stamens four, blue or violet, curved and projecting far out of the flower.

In dry or sandy fields, Maine to New York, Ontario and Missouri, south to Florida and Texas. Flowering from July to October.

Mad-dog or Blue Skullcap

Scutellaria lateriflora Linnaeus

Plate 185

Stems slender, erect or ascending, leafy and usually branched, 5 to 25 inches high, from a perennial root, propagating by slender stolons. Leaves ovate-oblong or ovate-lanceolate, thin, pointed at the apex, rounded or slightly heart-shaped at the base, coarsely toothed, 1 to 3 inches long, on slender petioles, the upper leaves smaller. Flowers blue, several in axillary and also terminal one-sided racemes, one-fourth to nearly one-half of an inch long, sometimes nearly white; the lips of the corolla about equal, the upper lip arched. Calyx two-lipped, the lips entire, the upper one with a crest or protuberance upon its back.

In wet meadows and marshes, Newfoundland to British Columbia, south to Florida, New Mexico and Oregon. Flowering from July to September.

Hooded or Marsh Skullcap

Scutellaria galericulata Linnaeus

Plate 186a

Stem erect and usually branched, 1 to 3 feet high, finely pubescent, from a perennial root, propagating by threadlike stolons but not tuber-bearing. Leaves oblong-lanceolate to oblong-ovate, thin, short petioled, the upper ones sessile, pointed at the apex, rounded or heart-shaped at the base, the margins dentate with low teeth or the upper leaves smaller and entire. Flowers solitary in the axils of the upper leaves, usually turned in the same direction and appearing paired, blue; the corolla about an inch long with a slender tube and slightly enlarged throat.

In swamps, wet meadows and along streams, Newfoundland to Alaska, south to New Jersey, western North Carolina, Ohio, Nebraska and Washington. Also in Europe and Asia. Flowering from June to September.

There are several additional species of Scutellaria in our range of more limited distribution than the two preceding. The Showy Skullcap

(Scutellaria serrata Andrews) with oval or elliptic, coarsely toothed leaves and blue flowers about an inch long in terminal clusters, is the most conspicuous species of the genus in this State. It is found from southern New York southward.

The Larger or Hyssop Skullcap (Scutellaria integrifolia Linnaeus) of about the same range, has thin, linear to oblong, entire, blunt leaves and blue flowers, usually whitish beneath, in terminal racemes, the corolla 1 to 1¼ inches long.

Self-heal; Heal-all

Prunella vulgaris Linnaeus

Plate 187

Stems slender, procumbent or ascending, rooting at the nodes below, the tips at least erect and simple or branched, 3 to 20 inches high, pubescent or nearly smooth and four-angled. Leaves ovate, oblong or oblong-lanceolate, blunt or somewhat pointed at the apex, usually narrowed at the base, entire or with a few teeth, 1 to 4 inches long, the lower leaves usually shorter. Flowers in dense terminal spikes which are one-half to 1 inch long, becoming 2 to 4 inches long in fruit. Calyx oblong, green or sometimes purplish, recticulate-veined, deeply two-lipped, closed in fruit, upper lip nearly truncate with three low teeth, lower lip two-cleft with lanceolate teeth. Corolla violet, purple or lilac, sometimes white, one-third to one-half of an inch long, the top of the flower strongly two-lipped, the upper lip entire and arched, the lower lip three-lobed and spreading or drooping; the four stamens ascending under the upper lip of the corolla.

In fields, woods and waste places, everywhere common. Probably native but also naturalized from Europe. Flowering from May to October.

Dragonhead; Lion's Heart

Dracocephalum virginianum Linnaeus

Plate 188

Stems erect or the base somewhat decumbent, slender or stout, simple or usually branched above, 1 to 4 feet tall. Leaves firm, oblong-lanceolate or lanceolate, sessile or the lowest ones petioled, sharp pointed at the apex, narrowed at the base, the margins sharply toothed, 2 to 5 inches long and usually ascending. Flowers numerous in dense spikes, terminating the stem and branches, the spikes becoming 4 to 8 inches long in fruit. Calyx bell-shaped with five ovate, pointed teeth about half as long as the tube of the calyx, in fruit becoming oblong, one-third to nearly one-half of an inch long. Corolla pale purple, rose or rarely white, about 1 inch long, temporarily remaining in whatever position it is placed, which accounts for one of the common names of the plant (Obedient Plant). Tube of the corolla gradually enlarged upward, its limb strongly two-lipped; upper lip concave, rounded, entire; lower lip spreading, three-lobed, the middle lobe notched at the apex; the four stamens ascending under the upper lip of the corolla, their filaments pubescent.

In moist meadows, roadsides and fields, Quebec to Minnesota, south to Florida and Texas. Flowering from July to September.

Oswego Tea; American Bee Balm
Monarda didyma Linnaeus

Plate 189

Stems slender or rather stout, pubescent or nearly smooth, 2 to 4 feet high from a perennial root, simple or sparingly branched above. Leaves thin, ovate or ovate-lanceolate, usually pubescent, at least beneath, sharp pointed at the apex, rounded or narrowed at the base, sharply toothed on the margins, 2 to 6 inches long, 1 to 3 inches wide, the petioles one-half to 1 inch long or the upper ones shorter. Flowers in terminal, solitary clusters at the ends of the branches or stems, subtended by several red or partially red bracts. Calyx tubular, narrow, fifteen-nerved with five small, awnlike teeth, smooth without, hairy within. Corolla scarlet, 1½ to 2 inches long, the limb two-lipped, the upper lip erect, the lower lip spreading and three-lobed, the middle lobe the largest. Stamens four, but only two of them anther-bearing and projecting out of the flower, the other two stamens rudimentary.

In moist soil, especially along streams, Quebec to Michigan, south to Georgia and Tennessee. Flowering in July and August.

Wild Bergamot

Monarda fistulosa Linnaeus

Plate 190a

Stems slender, usually branched, especially above, 2 to 3 feet high, hairy or nearly smooth, from a perennial root.   Leaves opposite, lanceolate, narrowed or heart-shaped at the base.   Flower clusters solitary and terminal or rarely also in the uppermost axils; bracts whitish or purplish. Calyx teeth awl-shaped, about as long as the diameter of the tubular calyx. Corolla yellowish pink, lilac or purplish, 1 to $1\frac{1}{2}$ inches long, hairy on the upper lip, otherwise resembling in floral structure the flowers of the Oswego Tea.

On dry hills and in thickets, Maine to Minnesota, south to Florida and Kansas.   Flowering from June to September.

The Pale Wild Bergamot (M o n a r d a   m o l l i s   Linnaeus) possesses a short, fine pubescence and has paler green leaves, otherwise closely resembling M. f i s t u l o s a.

Purple Bergamot

Monarda media Willldenow

Plate 190b

Resembling the common Wild Bergamot, but usually very sparingly hairy or nearly smooth and bright green; bracts of the inflorescence deep purple and very conspicuous; the flowers purple or purple-red and showy.

In moist thickets, Maine to Ontario, south to Pennsylvania and Virginia.   Flowering from June to August.

The Horsemint (M o n a r d a   p u n c t a t a   Linnaeus) is densely pubescent or downy with lanceolate, linear-lanceolate or narrowly oblong leaves; flower clusters terminal and also axillary in the upper leaves; bracts white or purplish and showy; corolla yellowish, spotted with purple, about an inch long.   Common in dry fields, southern New York southward and westward.

Field or Wild Basil; Basilweed

Clinopodium vulgare Linnaeus

Plate 186b

Stems slender, erect from an ascending base which is perennial by short, creeping stolons, hairy, usually branched or sometimes simple, 10 to 24 inches high. Leaves ovate to ovate-lanceolate, short petioled, entire, undulate or crenate toothed on the margins, 1 to $2\frac{1}{2}$ inches long. Flowers in dense, axillary and terminal capitate clusters about 1 inch in diameter, with setaceous, hairy bracts. Calyx hairy, the two lower teeth somewhat longer than the three upper ones. Corolla purple, pink or white, with a straight tube a little longer than the calyx teeth, two-lipped; upper lip erect; lower lip spreading and three-lobed. Stamens four, two of them projecting out of the flower.

In fields, open woods, thickets and roadsides, Newfoundland to Manitoba, south to North Carolina and Tennessee and in the Rocky mountains. Also in Europe and Asia. Flowering from June to September.

Hoary Mountain Mint; Calamint

Koellia incana (Linnaeus) Kuntze

Plate 182a

Stems rather stout, $1\frac{1}{2}$ to $3\frac{1}{2}$ feet high, finely pubescent or smooth below. Leaves thin, opposite, ovate to ovate-lanceolate, pointed at the apex, sharply toothed, $1\frac{1}{2}$ to 3 inches long, the upper leaves smaller, white-canescent beneath, the upper leaves usually white-canescent on both sides. Flowers in loose terminal and axillary clusters, 1 to $1\frac{1}{2}$ inches broad, canescent. Calyx slightly two-lipped, with very slender somewhat unequal teeth; corolla white with purple dots, about one-half of an inch long, two-lipped, the tube of the corolla equaling or longer than the calyx.

Dry thickets, open woods and hillsides, Maine to Ontario, south to Florida, Alabama and Missouri. Flowering from August to October.

Several other species of this genus occur in the eastern and central states, most of them are less conspicuous than the one here described and illustrated.

American Wild Mint

Mentha canadensis Linnaeus

Plate 191a

Stems slender, erect, simple or sometimes branched, more or less hairy or nearly smooth, 6 to 25 inches high, from a perennial root which propagates by suckers. Leaves opposite, oblong to oblong-lanceolate, acute at the apex, or the lower ones blunt, sharply toothed, narrowed at the base into short, slender petioles, smooth or sparingly pubescent, 1 to 3 inches long, one-half to 1 inch wide, and when crushed giving off the odor of Pennyroyal. Whorls of flowers all axillary, often shorter than the petioles. Calyx oblong-campanulate, hairy all over, five-nerved, with five acute, short teeth. Corolla white or slightly pink, about one-eighth of an inch broad, four-lobed, the posterior lobes broader than the others.

Marshes, swamps and moist soil, New Brunswick to British Columbia, south to Virginia and New Mexico. Flowering in summer and often in flower as late as October.

Stoneroot; Richweed; Horse Balm

Collinsonia canadensis Linnaeus

Plate 192

Stems rather stout, erect, more or less branched, 1 to 4 feet high, from a large, thick, hard and woody perennial root, smooth or with some glandular pubescence above. Leaves ovate or ovate-oblong, blunt or sometimes heart-shaped at the base, the upper leaves nearly sessile, the lower ones with slender petioles; blades 4 to 8 inches long, all sharply and coarsely toothed. Flowers lemon-scented, numerous, in several racemes, forming a terminal inflorescence sometimes a foot long. Calyx bell-shaped, ten-nerved, two-lipped; upper lip three-toothed, lower lip with two much longer teeth. Corolla light yellow, about one-half of an inch long, obliquely bell-shaped, five-lobed, four of the lobes nearly equal, the fifth pendent, fringed and larger than the others, appearing like a lower lip; fertile stamens two, long exserted from the flower.

In moist, rich, usually rocky woodlands, Quebec to Wisconsin, south to Florida, Alabama and Arkansas.

Potato Family
Solanaceae
Clammy Ground Cherry

Physalis heterophylla Nees von Esenbeck

Plate 193

Stems erect, becoming decumbent and spreading, 1 to 3 feet high, from a perennial, slender, creeping rootstock, viscid, glandular and hairy with long-spreading, jointed, flat hairs. Leaves alternate, ovate, at least the lower ones usually somewhat heart-shaped, the apex pointed, texture rather thick, the margins sinuate toothed or nearly entire. Calyx hairy, the margin with five-pointed lobes. Corolla three-fourths to seven-eighths of an inch broad, greenish yellow with a purplish or purplish brown center, open bell-shaped, five-lobed; anthers usually yellow. Fruit a small, yellow berry inclosed by the enlarged calyx.

In rich soil, along roads and banks, usually where the soil has been disturbed. Flowering in July and August.

There are several additional species of Physalis in the eastern states, most of which are perennial by rootstocks. The Smooth Ground Cherry (P h y s a l i s s u b g l a b r a t a Mackenzie & Bush), is easy to identify because it is smooth or nearly smooth with ovate or ovate-lanceolate leaves.

The Virginia Ground Cherry (P h y s a l i s v i r g i n i a n a Miller) is not easy to distinguish from the Clammy Ground Cherry, but is usually hairy and little or not at all viscid, the berry reddish, and the fruiting calyx smoother and deeply sunken at the base.

The Jamestown or Jimson Weed (D a t u r a s t r a m o n i u m Linnaeus) (Figure XXVII) is a stout, smooth annual plant, 1 to 5 feet high; large, thin, ovate leaves with irregularly lobed margins; flowers white or violet, 3 to 4 inches long, funnelform, with a five-lobed margin; fruit an ovoid, densely prickly capsule about 2 inches high. Frequent in waste places and fields as a weed, naturalized from tropical regions.

Figure XXVII
Stramonium.   Jamestown or Jimson Weed.   Thorn Apple
(D a t u r a   s t r a m o n i u m Linnaeus)

Climbing or Bitter Nightshade; Bittersweet

Solanum dulcamara Linnaeus

Plate 194a

A climbing vine, herbaceous above, usually somewhat woody and perennial below, smooth or pubescent, branching, 2 to 8 feet long. Leaves petioled, ovate or hastate, three-lobed or sometimes entire or only two-lobed, with the terminal lobe much the largest, the margins otherwise entire, 2 to 4 inches long, 1 to $2\frac{1}{2}$ inches wide with a pointed apex. Flowers arranged in compound lateral cymes on slender, drooping stalks. Calyx five-cleft; corolla blue, violet or white, about one-half of an inch broad, rotate, five-lobed, the lobes triangular-lanceolate, slender pointed and curved backward. Stamens five; attached to the throat of the corolla, their filaments short; the anthers long and narrow, united to form a cone. Berry oval or globose, turning from yellow to orange and finally becoming bright red.

In waste places or moist woods and thickets, Nova Scotia to Minnesota and Washington, south to New Jersey, Pennsylvania and Kansas. Native of Europe, but thoroughly naturalized in our eastern states.

The genus Solanum contains a number of cultivated species, weeds and adventive plants. The Black, Deadly or Garden Nightshade (S o l a n u m n i g r u m Linnaeus), with white flowers and black berries, is a common weed almost everywhere. The Sand Brier (S o l a n u m c a r o l i n e n s e Linnaeus) has prickly stems and leaves and smooth, orange-yellow berries. The Sand Bur (S o l a n u m r o s t r a t u m Dunal) has yellow flowers about an inch broad, prickly stems and leaves and the berry inclosed by the prickly, enlarged calyx. The Potato (S o l a n u m t u b e r o s u m Linnaeus) is also a member of this group, while the Tomato is classed in the related genus Lycopersicon.

Figwort Family

S c r o p h u l a r i a c e a e

White Mullen

Verbascum lychnitis Linnaeus

Plate 195a

Stems stout, angled, branched above, 2 to 5 feet high, densely covered, as well as the lower surface of the leaves, with a white pubescence. Leaves oblong, ovate or oblong-lanceolate, the margins crenately toothed, 2 to 8 inches long, the upper leaves sessile and pointed at the apex, the lower leaves blunt or pointed and narrowed at the base into margined petioles. Flowers in large, terminal panicles and racemes on the branches, white or cream-colored, about one-half of an inch broad. Corolla flat, five-lobed, the lobes a little unequal. Stamens five, unequal, the filaments of the three shorter ones with white hairs.

Sandy fields and waste places, Ontario to New Jersey and Pennsylvania. Native of Europe. Flowering from June to September. From a little distance the entire plant appears to be almost white, and when growing abundantly in a field presents a marked appearance. The plant is very common in sandy fields on the south side of Fish creek near where it empties into Oneida lake, New York. It must have been introduced there many years ago, because J. A. Paine, jr (Plants of Oneida County and Vicinity, 1865, page 107) remarks concerning its abundance there.

Moth Mullen

Verbascum blattaria Linnaeus

Plate 195b

Stems erect, stiff, smooth or slightly glandular-pubescent, usually simple but occasionally branched, 2 to 6 feet high. Leaves oblong, ovate or lanceolate, toothed or cut on the margins, sharp pointed at the apex, the upper ones clasping the stem, one-half to $2\frac{1}{2}$ inches long, the basal leaves sessile or petioled, much larger and often several inches long, but usually dying or withering by the time the flowers open. Flowers yellow or white, two-thirds to 1 inch broad, in a loose, terminal raceme, which is 1 to 2 feet long; corolla usually marked with brown on the back; filaments of the stamens pilose with violet-colored hairs.

In fields and waste places. Common. Naturalized from Europe, as is the Common or Velvet Mullen (Verbascum thapsus Linnaeus) which has yellow flowers in very dense terminal spikes and is densely woolly or velvety all over.

Butter and Eggs; Ramstead

Linaria linaria (Linnaeus) Karsten

Plate 196

A slender-stemmed, herbaceous plant, 1 to 3 feet high from a deep, perennial root, stems erect, with sessile, narrowly linear leaves which are pale green or glaucous, one-half to 1½ inches long, or the lower leaves longer. The stems often several or many together and simple or with a few branches. Flowers in erect, dense, terminal spikes or racemes. Calyx five-parted, the segments overlapping. Corolla about an inch long, spurred at the base, the spur nearly as long as the body of the corolla, the apex of the corolla two-lipped, the upper lip two-lobed and erect, light yellow, lower lip three-lobed and spreading, light yellow with a rounded projection or fold (palate), deep orange in color, which nearly closes the throat of the flower. Stamens four, in pairs and not projecting out of the flower.

In fields and waste places, everywhere common, often a troublesome weed. Naturalized from Europe. Flowering from June to October.

Turtlehead; Snakehead; Balmony

Chelone glabra Linnaeus

Plate 197

Stems slender, smooth, erect and stiff, 1 to 3 feet high from a perennial root, simple or with erect or ascending branches. Leaves opposite, short petioled, linear-lanceolate to ovate-lanceolate, with sharply toothed margins, the principal veins rather prominent. Flowers 1 to 1½ inches long, white or slightly pinkish, crowded in a dense terminal spike and often a few in the upper axils. Calyx five-parted, segments ovate-oblong, with smooth bracts at the base. Corolla irregular, tubular, inflated and two-lipped; upper lip arched, concave, entire or slightly notched and covering the lower lip while the flower is immature; under lip three-lobed, spreading in maturity and woolly within. Stamens five, only four of which bear anthers, the sterile one smaller. Fruit an ovoid capsule about one-half of an inch high.

In swamps, wet meadows, along streams and in low, wet woods, Newfoundland to Florida, west to Alabama, Kansas and Manitoba. Flowering from July to September.

Hairy Beardtongue

Pentstemon hirsutus (Linnaeus) Willdenow

Plate 198

A slender-stemmed, erect herb, 1 to 3 feet high from a perennial root. Stems downy, puberulent or hairy, usually several from a root. Leaves puberulent or smooth; the pedicels, calyx and corolla pubescent. Leaf blades denticulate, the lower ones oblong or ovate, somewhat obtuse at the apex; petioled, 2 to $4\frac{1}{2}$ inches long, one-half to 2 inches wide; upper leaves smaller, lanceolate, long pointed, sessile or clasping the stem. Flowers borne on short pedicels in a loose thyrse, purplish or violet in color. Calyx five-parted, the lobes overlapping; corolla consisting of an elongated tube about 1 inch long, dilated at the point of separation of the upper and lower lips; upper lip two-lobed; lower lip three-lobed; throat of the tube nearly closed by a hairy palate. Stamens five, four of which are anther-bearing, the fifth sterile and densely bearded for about one-half its length.

Dry woods, thickets and fields, Maine to Ontario and Minnesota, south to Florida, Alabama and Missouri. Flowering in May, June and July.

The Smooth Beardtongue (P e n t s t e m o n p e n t s t e m o n (Linnaeus) Britton (figure XXVIII), P. l a e v i g a t u s Solander) is smooth except the

Figure XXVIII
Smooth Beardtongue
(P e n t s t e m o n p e n t s t e m o n
(Linnaeus) Britton)

somewhat glandular inflorescence; the tube of the corolla gradually enlarged above, its throat wide open and scarcely or not at all bearded. Common in woods, thickets and fields; native from Pennsylvania southward.

The Foxglove Beardtongue (P e n t s t e m o n d i g i t a l i s (Sweet) Nuttall), also probably an escape in this part of its range, is similar to the Smooth Beard-tongue, but the leaves are somewhat broader and more clasping at the base; the corolla is white and 1 to 1½ inches long, abruptly expanded upward and the throat wide open.

Square-stemmed Monkey Flower

Mimulus ringens Linnaeus

Plate 191b

Stems smooth, four-angled, erect, 1 to 3 feet high from a perennial root. Leaves opposite, oblong to lanceolate in shape, with serrate margins, acute at the apex, sessile or auricled-clasping at the base, 2 to 4 inches long, one-half to 1 inch wide. Flowers violet-purple, borne solitary in the axils of the upper leaves on long, slender stalks. In fruit these stalks become 1 to 2 inches long and two to four times as long as the calyx. The calyx is prismatic, five-angled, with five slender, pointed teeth. Corolla about 1 inch long, consisting of a cylindrical tube which is longer than the calyx, and an upper and a lower lip; upper lip two-lobed and reflexed, lower lip three-lobed and spreading, the throat of the flower closed by a prominent yellow palate. The plant derives its name from the fancied resemblance of the flower to a grinning face.

In swamps, marshes, wet meadows and along streams from Nova Scotia to Manitoba, south to Virginia, Tennessee, Nebraska and Texas. Flowering from June to September.

Golden Hedge Hyssop; Goldenpert

Gratiola aurea Muhlenberg

Plate 199a

Stems decumbent, creeping, ascending at the ends, simple or usually branched, 4 to 12 inches long, from a perennial root. Leaves lanceolate to linear-oblong, one-half to 1 inch long, sessile and somewhat clasping at the base. Calyx five-parted with narrow lobes. Corolla irregular, its tube cylindric, the end of the flower more or less two-lipped, bright yellow, about one-half of an inch long; upper lip entire, lower lip three-lobed. Stamens four, only two of which bear anthers. Fruit a short, almost globular, capsule.

In sandy, wet places and borders of ponds and marshes in sandy soil, Quebec to Ontario, south to New Jersey and Virginia. Flowering from June to September. Frequent on the sandy, coastal plain, but rather rare and local in the interior.

American Brooklime; Speedwell

Veronica americana Schweinitz

Plate 199b

A rather small, smooth herb, with creeping stems and perennial root-stock freely rooting at the nodes, the ends erect, 6 inches to 3 feet long. Leaves opposite and petioled, oblong, ovate or oblong-lanceolate, toothed, 1 to 3 inches long, one-fourth to 1 inch wide. Flowers blue or whitish, striped with purple or blue lines, about one-fifth of an inch broad in loose, axillary, elongated racemes, each flower subtended by a small, green bract. Calyx four-lobed; corolla rotate and also four-lobed, the lower lobe commonly the narrowest. Stamens two, wide-spreading, attached to the base of the upper lobe of the corolla on either side. Fruit a globose capsule, about one-eighth of an inch high, slightly compressed.

Frequent in brooks, ditches and swamps, Anticosti to Alaska, south to Pennsylvania, Nebraska, New Mexico and California. Flowering from spring until late summer.

There are a number of other Veronicas or Speedwells, many of them small, introduced weeds with inconspicuous flowers. The Marsh or Skullcap Speedwell (Veronica scutellata Linnaeus) has light-blue flowers about the size of those of V. americana, and linear or linear-lanceolate, sessile leaves. The Common Speedwell or Gipsyweed (Veronica officinalis Linnaeus) is hairy all over with oblong, oval or obovate leaves and blue flowers in spikelike racemes from the axils of the upper leaves.

Culver's Root; Bowman's Root; Beaumont's Root

Leptandra virginica (Linnaeus) Nuttall

Plate 200

A tall, stout, erect herb with smooth stems, branched only at the inflorescence, 2 to 7 feet high. Leaves whorled, three to nine leaves at a node or some of the upper ones opposite, lanceolate or oblong-lanceolate, long pointed at the apex, narrowed and short petioled at the base, the margins finely sharp toothed, smooth on both sides, or slightly hairy beneath, 3 to 6 inches long. Flowers small and numerous in dense spikes, 2 to 9 inches long, terminating the stem and branches of the inflorescence. Calyx four-parted with pointed, ovate-lanceolate segments. Corolla tubular, white or bluish, about one-sixth of an inch long, with four nearly equal lobes which are about one-fourth as long as the tube of the corolla. Stamens two, and like the style projecting beyond the flower. Fruit an ovoid-oblong capsule, two to three times as long as the calyx.

In moist woods, thickets and meadows, often along old roads, Ontario to Manitoba, south to Massachusetts, Alabama and Texas. Flowering from late in June until early September.

Fern-leaved False Foxglove; Fever-flower

Aureolaria pedicularia (Linnaeus) Rafinesque

(*Gerardia pedicularia* Linnaeus)

Plate 201

Stems rather slender and much branched, leafy, erect or spreading-ascending, 1 to 4 feet high, glandular-pubescent, viscid and somewhat hairy. Leaves sessile or the lower ones petioled, pinnately divided, ovate or ovate-lanceolate in outline, 1 to 3 inches long, the lobes cut-toothed. Flowers on short stalks from the upper axils of the reduced leaves of the stems and branches. Calyx bell-shaped, with five oblong, toothed lobes, becoming one-third of an inch long in fruit. Corolla slightly irregular, funnelform, 1 to 1½ inches long, hairy without, about 1 inch broad, with five spreading, rounded lobes, dull yellow or slightly brownish yellow in color. Stamens four, not projecting from the flower. Fruit an oblong, hairy capsule about one-half of an inch long.

In dry woods and thickets, Maine to Ontario and Minnesota, south to Florida and Missouri. Flowering in late summer, from the latter part of July to September.

Smooth False Foxglove

Aureolaria glauca (Eddy) Rafinesque

(*Gerardia quercifolia* Pursh; *Gerardia virginica* Britton, Sterns & Poggenberg; Gray's manual, ed. 7, 730, 1908. *Gerardia glauca* Eddy, Med. Repos. N. Y. Rex 2, v. 126. 1808)

Plate 202

Stems rather stout, stiff, smooth and often purplish with a whitish or glaucous bloom, usually branched, 2 to 5 feet high from a perennial root. Leaves usually petioled, ovate or ovate-lanceolate in outline, the lower one to two-pinnatifid, 4 to 6 inches long, the upper ones pinnatifid or deeply incised, the lobes lanceolate or oblong, pointed, entire or toothed, often nearly at right angles to the midvein. Fruiting stalks longer than the calyx; calyx lobes five, ovate or ovate-lanceolate, pointed, entire, about equaling the tube in length. Corolla yellow, 1½ to 2 inches long, smooth outside, slightly irregular, funnelform, not widely spreading at the mouth, pubescent within, the margin five-lobed. Stamens four, in two pairs. Fruit an oblong, smooth, pointed capsule about twice as long as the calyx.

In dry or moist woods and thickets, Maine to Minnesota, south to Florida and Illinois. Flowering from July to September.

The Downy False Foxglove, A u r e o l a r i a v i r g i n i c a (Linnaeus) Pennell, [A u r e o l a r i a v i l l o s a (Muhlenberg) Rafinesque; D a s y-s t o m a p u b e s c e n s Benthem; D . f l a v a Wood; R h i n a n t h u s v i r g i n i c u s and G e r a r d i a f l a v a Linnaeus] is grayish downy all over with fewer, stiff, erect stems; leaves entire or shallowly toothed or the lower ones somewhat pinnatifid; corolla smooth outside, much expanded at the end; the fruiting capsule pubescent. Common in dry woods and thickets, especially southward.

Large Purple Gerardia

Agalinis purpurea (Linnaeus) Pennell

(*Gerardia purpurea* Linnaeus)

Plate 203

Stems slender or rather stout, branched, annual, smooth or somewhat roughish, 8 to 25 inches high with ascending or spreading branches. Leaves opposite, narrowly linear, 1 to 2 inches long. Flowers purple or rarely white, racemose on the branches, their stalks very short. Calyx bell-shaped with five pointed, triangular-ovate teeth about half the length of the tube. Corolla with a bell-shaped tube and a spreading, five-lobed and slightly two-lipped limb, hairy without and more or less so within. Stamens four, attached to the corolla tube within and not projecting out of the flower. Fruit a globose capsule somewhat longer than the calyx.

In moist fields and meadows, Maine to Florida, most abundant in the coastal region, but also found westward to Wisconsin and Missouri.

Slender Gerardia

Agalinis tenuifolia (Vahl) Rafinesque

(*Gerardia tenuifolia* Vahl.)

Plate 204

An annual, smooth herb with very slender stems, 6 to 24 inches high, and narrow, flat leaves one-half to $1\frac{1}{4}$ inches long which become blackened in drying. Stem branched, especially above, the branches spreading or ascending. Flowers light purple and spotted, one-half to three-fourths of an inch long, on slender stalks longer than the corollas, from the axils of the upper reduced leaves of the stem and branches; corolla funnelform, vertically flattened and slightly two-lipped, the margin with five rounded lobes, smooth within. Fruit a small globular capsule, one-sixth to one-seventh of an inch in diameter, and longer than the calyx.

In dry woods, thickets and fields, Quebec to Georgia, west to western Ontario, Kansas and Texas. Flowering from August to October.

The Seaside or Salt-marsh Gerardia (Agalinis maritima Rafinesque) is rarely over a foot high, smooth and fleshy, with linear leaves and small, purple flowers, one-half to two-thirds of an inch long. Common in salt marshes along the coast. Another species (Agalinis acuta Pennell), of sandy fields and depressions of the coastal plain, has stems 1 to 2 feet tall and branched like A. purpurea, but the flowers are somewhat smaller, light purple or rose-purple, and each of the five lobes of the corolla indented.

Swamp Lousewort

Pedicularis lanceolata Michaux

Plate 206a

Stems rather stout, simple or usually somewhat branched above with ascending branches, smooth, 1 to 3 feet high. Leaves sessile, opposite or some of them alternate, narrowly lanceolate, 2 to 5 inches long, the lower ones deeply lobed, the lobes oblong, blunt, short and crenately toothed, with a thickened margin. Flowers pale yellow, three-fourths to 1 inch long, in short clusters or spikes at the ends of the stems and branches, the flowers subtended by the upper reduced leaves. Calyx two-lobed, the lobes with toothed leaflike margins. Corolla with a slender tube and deeply two-lipped, the upper lip (galea) laterally compressed, arched and terminated by a short, blunt beak, the lower lip three-lobed, erect-ascending, the middle lobe smallest. Stamens four, attached to the inside of the corolla tube and ascending within the upper lip but not projecting out of the flower. Fruit a small, ovate capsule as long as or but slightly longer than the calyx.

In low, wet meadows, swamps and marshes, Ontario to Manitoba and South Dakota, south to Connecticut, North Carolina, Ohio and Nebraska. Flowering from August to September.

Wood or Head Betony; Lousewort

Pedicularis canadensis Linnaeus

Plate 205

Stems usually several together from a perennial root, erect or ascending, 6 to 18 inches high, hairy. Leaves rather thick, oblong-lanceolate, 3 to 5 inches long, at least the lower on slender petioles and divided almost to the midrib into numerous incised or sharply toothed segments, giving the leaf a fernlike appearance. Flowers borne in short, dense, spikes lengthening to 5 or 6 inches in fruit. Calyx oblique, tubular, cleft on the lower side. Corolla yellow, varying to yellowish brown or purplish brown in certain individuals, two-thirds to three-fourths of an inch long, tubular, two-lipped, the upper lip (galea) arched, incurved, minutely two-toothed below the apex, laterally compressed into a hood with the four stamens ascending within it; lower lip erect with three spreading lobes. Fruit an oblique capsule, flattened, lanceolate-oblong or sword-shaped, about two-thirds of an inch long and one-sixth of an inch wide, fully three times the length of the calyx.

In dry woods and thickets, Nova Scotia to Manitoba, south to Florida, Kansas and Colorado. Flowering from April to June.

Narrow-leaved Cowwheat

Melampyrum lineare Lamarck

Plate 165a

A low, slender herb, 6 to 18 inches high; stem slender, puberulent, with opposite, wide-spreading branches. Leaves lanceolate or linear-lanceolate to ovate, opposite on the stem, short petioled, 1 to 1½ inches long, one-eighth to one-half of an inch wide, the lower ones entire, the upper floral leaves mostly toothed with several bristle-pointed teeth at the base.

Flowers small, one-third to one-half of an inch long, white, greenish white or pale yellow with a rather bright yellow apex to the flower, borne on short stalks in the upper axils of the leaves, or in terminal, leafy-bracted clusters. Calyx bell-shaped with four long, slender teeth. Corolla tubular, enlarging above, two-lipped, the upper lip not lobed, the lower lip three-toothed and spreading. Stamens four in two pairs of unequal length, ascending under the upper lip. Fruit a flat, oblique capsule, about one-third of an inch long with a rather long beak, two to four-seeded.

Common in dry woods and thickets, Nova Scotia to British Columbia, south to Georgia, Tennessee, Iowa and Idaho. Flowering from July to September.

Bladderwort Family

Lentibulariaceae

The Bladderworts, of which there are no less than fifteen species, form a very interesting group of plants. Few of them, however, have conspicuous

Figure XXIX
Horned Bladderwort
(Stomoisia cornuta (Michaux) Rafinesque)

flowers. Nearly all of them are aquatic, but two or three are found growing in moist or wet sand.

One of the most conspicuous and beautiful of the Bladderworts is the Horned Bladderwort (S t o m o i s i a c o r n u t a (Michaux) Rafinesque), figure XXIX, frequent in bogs and on sandy shores. Unlike most other species of the group, it possesses only a few inconspicuous and delicate leaves at the base of the scape; the latter, however, is conspicuously brownish, 2 to 13 inches high, bearing one to five bright yellow, fragrant flowers; the lower lip of the flower is nearly two-thirds of an inch long, with a conspicuous hoodlike palate, the spur often one-half of an inch long and pendulous beneath the flower.

In addition to the two species illustrated here, S t o m o i s i a c o r- n u t a and U t r i c u l a r i a i n t e r m e d i a, the other species may be identified by means of the following key.

Calyx inclosing the fruit; bracts at the base of the pedicels accompanied by a pair of
    bractlets; plants terrestrial, rooting in sand beneath shallow water or on wet shores
    Corolla much exceeding the calyx (genus Stomoisia Rafinesque)
        Lower lip of corolla one-half to two-thirds of an inch long; spur one-fourth to
        one-half of an inch long........................S t o m o i s i a c o r n u t a
        Lower lip of corolla one-third of an inch long; spur about one-third of an inch
        long or less....................................S t o m o i s i a j u n c e a
    Corolla shorter than or about equaling the calyx.......S t o m o i s i a v i r g a t u l a
Calyx not inclosing the fruit; bracts at the base of the pedicels without bractlets
    Lateral lobes of the lower lip of corolla saccate, branches verticillate and verticillately
    or oppositely decompound; corolla red-purple (genus Vesiculina Rafinesque)......
                              V e s i c u l i n a p u r p u r e a
    Lateral lobes of lower lip of corolla not saccate; branches alternate or none
        Bract solitary, tubular, surrounding the scape; scales none; flowers purple (genus
        Lecticula Barnhart)........................L e c t i c u l a r e s u p i n a t a
        Bracts and scales peltate; plants terrestrial in wet sand (genus Setiscapella
        Barnhart)
            Corolla yellow, lower lip conspicuous, one-eighth to one-third of an inch
            long; spur conic......................S e t i s c a p e l l a s u b u l a t a
            Corolla white or purplish, both lips minute; flowers about one-sixteenth of
            an inch broad or less.............S e t i s c a p e l l a c l e i s t o g a m a

Bracts, and scales if present, flat, usually attached, plants aquatic; flowers yellow
(genus Utricularia Linnaeus)

Scape 2 inches long or less with a whorl of more or less united conspicuous
floats; corolla one-half to two-thirds of an inch long..................
Utricularia radiata

Scapes without floats

Stems free-floating, except for a single point of attachment

Scape two to five-flowered, without scales, cleistogamous flowers
also present.................Utricularia geminiscapa

Scape six to twenty-flowered, with one to five scales; cleistogamous
flowers none...............Utricularia macrorhiza

Stems creeping on the bottom in shallow water; some or all of the leaves
rootlike

Spur a mere sac; palate obsolete; pedicels recurved in fruit........
Utricularia minor

Spur and palate conspicuous; pedicels ascending in fruit

Segements of some leaves linear, flat, bristly-serrulate; upper
lip of corolla about one-half the length of the lower lip......
Utricularia intermedia

Segments of leaves all capillary; lips of corolla nearly equal in
length

Spur stout, conic, shorter than the lower lip............
Utricularia gibba

Spur slender, equaling or exceeding the lower lip

Spur tapering from base to apex; leaves all alike; bladder-
bearing; scapes 2 to 5 inches high...................
Utricularia pumila

Spur conic at the base, linear above; leaves not all bladder-
bearing; scape 4 to 16 inches high..................
Utricularia fibrosa

Flat-leaved Bladderwort

Utricularia intermedia Hayne

Plate 206b

Stems aquatic, rooted in shallow water, the horizontally submerged
branches radiating from the base of the scape.   Leaves alternate, one-fourth
to two-thirds of an inch long, three-forked at the base, the divisions again

two or three times divided into linear, flat, bristly-serrulate segments without bladders. Other branches or portions of branches usually bear shorter, rootlike leaves with capillary segments and a few large bladders. The flower-bearing scape naked or with one to several minute scales, 2 to 8 inches high and bearing one to four flowers on slender pedicels one-fourth to three-fourths of an inch long. Calyx two-lobed. Corolla yellow, strongly two-lipped, the upper lip broadly triangular, about one-third of an inch broad, the lower lip slightly three-lobed and about one-half of an inch broad with a prominent palate on its face. Spur pointed, about as long as the lower lip. In midsummer, when the plant is in flower, the leafy stems produce at their tips numerous conspicuous, obovate, velvety winter buds which afford the chief means of propagation.

Frequent in shallow water of slow streams, ponds and bogs, Newfoundland to British Columbia south to New Jersey, Indiana and California. Flowering in July and August or as late as early September.

The Greater Bladderwort or Hooded Water Milfoil (U t r i c u l a r i a m a c r o r h i z a LeConte) is perhaps the most abundant species of the group throughout most parts of its range. It has free-floating stems horizontally spreading beneath the surface. Leaves finely divided, but not flat, bearing numerous small, conspicuous bladders. Scape stout, 3 to 20 inches high, with four to eighteen flowers, pedicels one-fourth to two-thirds of an inch long, becoming longer and recurved in fruit. Corolla yellow, three-fourths of an inch long, strongly two-lipped, the lower lip a little longer and much broader than the upper and with a spreading, undulate, slightly three-lobed border and a prominent palate; spur shorter than the lower lip, subulate and upwardly curved.

Broom Rape Family

Orobanchaceae

Pale or Naked Broom Rape; Cancer-root

Thalesia uniflora (Linnaeus) Britton

Figure XXX

Stems nearly subterranean, forming a dense mat, often several inches in extent, parasitic upon the roots of various plants, bearing several ovate-oblong scales and one to four slender, erect, glandular-puberulent, naked,

Figure XXX
Pale or Naked Broom Rape
(T h a l e s i a u n i f l o r a (Linnaeus) Britton)

one-flowered stalks, 3 to 8 inches high. Calyx bell-shaped, pubescent and glandular, about one-third of an inch long, less than half the length of the corolla, with five lanceolate, long-pointed lobes. Corolla white or violet, puberulent without, two-thirds to 1 inch long, oblique, the curved tube about three times the length of the slightly two-lipped limb, which has five short, oval or obovate, blunt lobes. Fruit a small, ovoid capsule. Stamens four, not projecting out of the flower.

In woods and thickets, parasitic upon roots of various herbs, Newfoundland to Ontario and south to South Carolina and Texas. Flowering from May to July.

This and the two following species are the common members in the eastern states of the Broom Rape family (Orobanchaceae), which consists of a number of parasitic flowering herbs with brown, yellowish, purplish or nearly white stems, and leaves reduced to alternate appressed scales. Because of their parasitic habit they do not require green leaves for the purpose of manufacturing food and hence are devoid of any green coloring matter or real leaves.

Squawroot; Cancer-root

Conopholis americana (Carl von Linné) Wallroth

Figure XXXI

Plants smooth, 3 to 10 inches high, from a thickened base, densely scaly, light brown, usually clustered, covered all over with stiff, overlapping scales. Upper scales lanceolate or ovate, pointed, one-half to 1 inch long, lowest scales much smaller. Flowers yellowish, each with two small bracts beneath the calyx, together forming a thick, dense spike, one-half to 1 inch thick; each flower about one-half of an inch long. Calyx oblique, deeply split on the lower side, three to four-toothed on the upper side. Corolla pale yellow, strongly two-lipped, the tube slightly curved, the upper lip concave, nearly erect and notched, the lower lip spreading, three-lobed and shorter than the upper lip. Stamens projecting from the flower. Fruit an ovoid-globose capsule nearly one-half of an inch long.

In rich woods at the base of trees and parasitic upon their roots, Maine to Ontario and Michigan, south to Florida, Alabama and Tennessee. Flowering from May to August.

Figure XXXI
Squawroot or Cancer-root
(C o n o p h o l i s a m e r i c a n a (Carl von Linné) Wallroth)

Beechdrops

Leptamnium virginianum (Linnaeus) Rafinesque

Figure XXXII

Stems erect, rather stiff and branching, slender, smooth, yellowish brown or purplish yellow, 6 to 20 inches high from a thick, scaly base, the roots fibrous and brittle; scales few and small. Flowers sessile, of two kinds, distantly spicate on the branches; the lower flowers cleistogamous and abundantly fertile, the upper complete but mostly sterile. Calyx short, nearly equally five-toothed. Corolla of the upper flowers cylindric, slightly flattened laterally, one-third to nearly one-half of an inch long and about one-tenth of an inch thick, the slender tube much longer than the four-lobed limb, upper lobe concave, larger than the three lower lobes. Stamens about as long as the corolla. Lower flowers small, about one-eighth of an inch long, not unfolding, borne at the summit of the ovoid ovary and resembling the hood of a moss capsule. Fruit a small capsule about one-fourth of an inch high.

In woods, parasitic upon the roots of the beech, Nova Scotia to Ontario and Michigan, south to Florida, Louisiana and Missouri. Flowering from August to October.

Acanthus Family

Acanthaceae

Water Willow

Dianthera americana Linnaeus

Plate 207

Stems erect, grooved and angled, 1 to 4 feet high, slender and usually simple or slightly branched above, smooth. Leaves narrowly lanceolate, 3 to 8 inches long, one-fourth to 1 inch wide, entire, sessile or short petioled. Flowers violet or nearly white, in dense, short spikes or heads at the ends of the slender axillary peduncles which are shorter than or equal to the leaves in length; bractlets under the flowers linear-subulate and shorter than the flowers. Calyx deeply four to five-parted. Corolla two-lipped,

Figure XXXII
Beechdrops
(Leptamnium virginianum (Linnaeus) Rafinesque)

about one-half of an inch long, the tube shorter than the lip, the upper lip erect, concave, entire; lower lip spreading and three-cleft, the base of the lower lip rough and palatelike. Fruit a capsule about one-half of an inch long, slightly compressed below.

In wet places and shallow water along lakes, rivers and ponds, Quebec to Michigan, south to Georgia and Texas. Flowering from May to August. Usually growing in dense colonies and from a distance easily mistaken for a coarse sort of grass. Very abundant along the Seneca river and along the shores of Oneida lake, New York.

Lopseed Family

P h r y m a c e a e

Lopseed

Phryma leptostachya Linnaeus

Plate 208

A rather slender, perennial herb with erect, puberulent, somewhat four-angled stem, branched above, 1 to 3 feet high, the branches slender and opposite. Leaves opposite, thin, ovate, pointed at the apex, coarsely toothed, the lower ones long petioled, the upper ones short petioled or sessile, 2 to 5 inches long. Flowers small, about one-fourth of an inch long, in narrow spikes terminating the stem and branches, usually the flowers opposite each other. Calyx cylindrical, two-lipped, the upper lip cleft into three long bristle or hairlike teeth, the lower lip divided into two short, slender teeth. Corolla tube cylindrical, two-lipped, pinkish purple, the upper lip erect, concave and notched, the lower lip larger and divided into three spreading, convex and blunt lobes. Stamens four, included within the tube of the corolla. Flowers erect at first, soon becoming at right angles to the stem when in full bloom and later as the fruit matures becoming abruptly deflexed against the axis of the stem, whence the name " lopseed."

In woods and thickets, New Brunswick to Manitoba, south to Florida and Kansas; also in Bermuda and eastern Asia. Flowering from June to August.

Madder Family

Rubiaceae

Bluets; Innocence; Eyebright

Houstonia coerulea Linnaeus

Plate 209b

Stems erect or nearly so, smooth, perennial by slender rootstocks and forming dense tufts. Lower and basal leaves spatulate or oblanceolate, about one-half of an inch long or less, sometimes slightly hairy, narrowed into petioles. Flowers solitary on very slender terminal and axillary stalks. Corolla one-fourth to one-third of an inch long, and as broad or broader when expanded, the tube pale yellow and slightly enlarged above, the limb of the corolla nearly flat when expanded with four oblong or elliptic, slightly pointed lobes, light blue or violet in color, the throat of the corolla yellow, surrounded by a narrow white band. Calyx deeply four-parted with oblong, blunt lobes, the lobes separated from one another by about their width. Fruit a small capsule about one-sixth of an inch broad and broader than long, compressed and divided or deeply notched at the summit, shorter than the calyx.

In open grassy places, on wet rocks or in open, rocky woods, Nova Scotia to Quebec, New York and Michigan, south to Georgia, Alabama, Tennessee and Missouri. It is inclined to be somewhat local in distribution, but when found is apt to be present in great abundance. Flowering from April to July, usually at its best in New York during the latter part of May, and usually producing a few flowers through the summer.

Long-leaved Houstonia

Houstonia longifolia Gaertner

Plate 194b

A small, low, tufted perennial, smooth or somewhat pubescent, 5 to 10 inches high. Basal leaves spatulate or oblanceolate, blunt and short petioled, but not ciliate. Stem leaves opposite, linear-oblong, usually pointed at the apex and one-nerved, one-half to 1 inch long. Flowers pale purple, pinkish or nearly white, in corymbed, cymose clusters. Calyx with five very slender lobes. Corolla about one-fourth of an inch long, with five pointed lobes which, when expanded, are somewhat more than one-eighth of an inch across, each lobe about one-third the length of the corolla tube. Fruit a small, globular capsule.

In dry, open or rocky places, Maine to Saskatchewan, south to Georgia and Missouri. Flowering from June to September.

The Fringed Houstonia (H o u s t o n i a c i l i o l a t a Torrey) is similar but the margins of the leaves are conspicuously ciliate.

Buttonbush; Bush Globeflower

Cephalanthus occidentalis Linnaeus

Plate 210

A shrub, 3 to 10 feet high, rarely treelike and taller; branches smooth or somewhat pubescent. Leaves opposite or in whorls, petioled, entire, oval or ovate, pointed at the apex, rounded or narrowed at the base, 3 to 6 inches long, 1 to 2½ inches wide. Flowers small, white, sessile, borne in dense terminal or axillary and stalked globose heads, about 1 inch in diameter. Corolla one-third to one-half of an inch long, tubular-funnel-form, with four erect or spreading lobes. Stamens four, attached to the throat of the corolla with very short filaments. Style very slender and about twice the length of the corolla.

In swamps, low ground and shallow water along lakes, streams and ponds, New Brunswick to western Ontario and Wisconsin, south to Florida, Texas, Arizona and California. Flowering from June to September.

Partridge Berry; Twinberry; Squawberry

Mitchella repens Linnaeus

Plate 211b

A small, creeping, evergreen herb, with slender, trailing stems, freely rooting at the nodes, 6 to 15 inches long, with numerous branches. Leaves dark green, opposite, short petioled, ovate-orbicular, blunt at the apex, usually somewhat heart-shaped at the base, one-fourth to seven-eighths of an inch long. Flowers white, waxy, fragrant, borne in pairs united at the base. Corolla funnelform, about one-half of an inch long with four recurved or spreading lobes, densely bearded on the inner side. Stamens as many as the lobes of the corolla and attached to its throat, the anthers protruding from the flower. The slender style with its four threadlike stigmas long exserted, in which case the stamens are not exserted, or vice versa, the stamens may be exserted, in which case the style is shorter than the corolla. Fruit composed of two united drupes usually containing eight roundish nutlets; when ripe the fruit is red, broader than high, one-sixth to one-third of an inch in diameter, persistent through the winter and edible.

In woods, Nova Scotia to western Ontario, Minnesota and Arkansas, south to Florida and Texas. Flowering in spring, from April to June and sometimes flowering a second time in the autumn. Sometimes the leaves are whitish-veined.

Rough Bedstraw

Galium asprellum Michaux

Plate 212a

A weak, perennial herb, much branched and usually reclining on bushes or surrounding vegetation, sometimes erect; stems retrorsely hispid on the angles, 2 to 6 feet long. Leaves in whorls of sixes or fives, or those of the branches rarely in fours, narrowly oval or slightly oblanceolate, sharply pointed at the apex, narrowed at the base, and sometimes appearing petioled, one-third to three-fourths of an inch long, one-twelfth to one-sixth of an inch wide, the margins and midrib rough. Flowers white, arranged in many-flowered cymes, which are terminal and axillary. Stalks or peduncles bearing the flowers short and two to three times forked. Corolla four-lobed. Fruit smooth and about one-twelfth of an inch broad.

In moist soil, Newfoundland to western Ontario and Wisconsin, south to North Carolina, Illinois and Nebraska. Flowering from June to August.

Northern Bedstraw

Galium boreale Linnaeus

Plate 209a

Stems erect, smooth, rather stiff, sharply angled, simple or branched, 1 to 2½ feet high, usually a few or several stems from a perennial root. Leaves in fours, lanceolate or linear, entire, conspicuously three-nerved, blunt or pointed at the apex, sometimes the margins ciliate, 1 to 2½ inches long, one-twelfth to one-fourth of an inch wide. Flowers white, panicled in small, compact cymes, forming a terminal inflorescence often 3 to 6 inches long. Corolla four-lobed. Fruit hispid when young, sometimes becoming almost smooth when mature, about one-twelfth of an inch broad.

In rocky soil or along streams and lake shores, Quebec to Alaska, south to New Jersey, Pennsylvania, Michigan, Missouri, New Mexico and California. Also found in Europe and northern Asia. Flowering from May to August.

There are about twenty-five species of Bedstraw (Galium) found in the eastern states, most of them with small, inconspicuous flowers, some of them introduced species. The Yellow Bedstraw (G a l i u m v e r u m Linnaeus) with yellow flowers, is native of Europe, but frequent as a naturalized plant in many localities.

Honeysuckle Family

C a p r i f o l i a c e a e

Twinflower; Deer Vine

Linnaea americana Forbes

Plate 213a

A creeping and trailing, slender, vinelike plant, with scarcely woody, perennial stems, 6 to 24 inches long, slightly pubescent. Leaf blades evergreen, opposite, rounded or obovate, obscurely crenate on the margins, one-fourth to three-fourths of an inch wide and rather thick in texture on petioles one-twelfth to one-sixth of an inch long. Flowers fragrant, pink, borne in pairs at the summit of elongated terminal stalks. Calyx five-lobed. Corolla funnelform, nodding, one-third to one-half of an inch long and five-lobed at the end. Stamens four, attached at the base of the corolla tube within. Ovary three-celled, two of the cavities filled with abortive ovules, the other with one perfect, pendulous ovule. Fruit a nearly globose, three-celled capsule, two of the cells empty, the other with a single, oblong seed.

In cold woods throughout the north, common in the Adirondack and Catskill mountains, otherwise rather local, ranging south to Maryland, west to the mountains of Colorado, California, British America, and eastward to Newfoundland. Flowering from June to August.

Trumpet or Coral Honeysuckle

Lonicera sempervirens Linnaeus

Plate 2148

A slender, high-climbing vine with glabrous or somewhat hairy stems and foliage. Leaves oval, the uppermost usually united around the stem, the lower ones smaller, narrower and somewhat pointed at the apex, all conspicuously glaucous and often pubescent beneath, dark green above. Flowers numerous in two or three verticillate clusters, close together at the ends of the stems. Corolla scarlet or yellow, $1\frac{1}{2}$ to 2 inches long, slightly expanded upward, the stamens and style scarcely or but slightly protruding from the flower. Fruit a cluster of scarlet berries which are ripe in late autumn.

In thickets and open woods along streams and low ground, common in the south from Florida to Texas and northward to Nebraska, less abundant in its northeastern range which extends to New York and Maine. In New York State known only from a few localities in the southeastern part of the State, but frequently seen in cultivation farther northward, except in the extreme northern part of the State where it is not hardy. It is usually found in flower from May or June until autumn because of the growth of new lateral shoots bearing flowers.

Swamp Fly Honeysuckle

Lonicera oblongifolia (Goldie) Hooker

Plate 214b

An erect, branching shrub, 2 to 8 feet high, the branches and twigs with opposite, elliptical or elliptical-oblong leaves, rather thick and firm when mature, glaucous and reticulate-veined, smooth when mature, downy-pubescent, but not ciliate when young. Flowers in pairs on axillary stalks which are as long or longer than the flowers. Corolla strongly two-lipped, yellowish or purplish within, three-fourths of an inch long, tube of the corolla enlarged on one side at the base. Stamens five, attached to the tube of the corolla within. Fruit consisting of two fleshy, bright-red berries at the summit of each peduncle, remaining distinct or more or less grown together.

In bogs and swamps, New Brunswick to Manitoba, south to Pennsylvania, Michigan and Minnesota. Flowering in May and June.

The Early Fly Honeysuckle (L o n i c e r a c a n a d e n s i s Marshall), of moist and rich rocky woodlands, has thin, green, ciliate leaves and yellow or greenish yellow flowers, appearing with the leaves in April or early May. It is also a small shrub, 2 to 5 feet high.

The Blue or Mountain Fly Honeysuckle (L o n i c e r a c a e r u l e a Linnaeus) (figure XXXIII) occurs in swamps and low grounds, chiefly in the Adirondacks. It is a small shrub with oval or obovate, blunt leaves and small, yellow flowers. The fruit is a bluish black, two-eyed berry.

The Hairy Honeysuckle (L o n i c e r a h i r s u t a Eaton) is a twining and climbing vine several feet long with the foliage and new stems hairy, the upper leaves united around the stem, flowers 1 to 1½ inches long, orange-yellow turning reddish.

The Smooth-leaved or Glaucous Honeysuckle (L o n i c e r a d i o i c a Linnaeus) (figure XXXIV) of rocky woodlands and sometimes in swamps, is smooth throughout, twining or climbing, the upper leaves united around the stem, all of them whitish or glaucous beneath, flowers small, yellowish green tinged with purple, fruit bright-red.

Figure XXXIII
Blue or Mountain Fly Honeysuckle
(L o n i c e r a c a e r u l e a Linnaeus)

Bush Honeysuckle

Diervilla diervilla (Linnaeus) MacMillan

Plate 212b

A low shrub with opposite leaves and branches, 1 to 4 feet high, smooth or nearly so. Leaves ovate or oval, long pointed at the apex, usually rounded at the base, 2 to 5 inches long, irregularly crenulate and often slightly ciliate on the margins; petioles very short. Flowers in clusters of one to six on slender stalks which are terminal or in the axils of the upper leaves. Each flower about three-fourths of an inch long, narrowly funnel-form, the tube with a slight sac at the base, the limb nearly regular, five-lobed, yellowish and more or less pubescent within and without, usually three of the lobes somewhat united. Calyx with five very slender lobes. Stamens five. Fruit a linear-oblong, smooth capsule, with a slender beak, tipped with the persistent calyx lobes.

In dry, sandy or rocky woods, fields and roadsides, Newfoundland to Manitoba, south to North Carolina, Michigan and Wisconsin.

Teasel Family

Dipsacaceae

Common or Card Teasel

Dipsacus sylvestris Hudson

Plate 215a

A bristly, prickly, coarse biennial, tall and stout, 3 to 6 feet high. The stem, branches, peduncles, midribs of the leaves and the involucre all bear many short prickles. Leaves sessile, lanceolate or oblong, often 1 foot long. Flowers lilac-colored in dense, cylindrical heads which are 3 to 5 inches long, made up of long, spiny bracts in the axils of which are borne the flowers, which usually are exceeded in length by the spiny bracts. The lower flowers open first and appear as a violet or bluish ring of bloom around the spiny head, the ring of flowers gradually spreading upward.

In waste places, old fields and roadsides, Maine to Ontario and

Figure XXXIV
Smooth-leaved or Glaucous Honeysuckle
(Lonicera dioica Linnaeus)

Michigan, south to North Carolina. Native of Europe, and established as a weed in many localities.

Gourd Family

Cucurbitaceae

One-seeded Bur Cucumber; Star Cucumber

Sicyos angulatus Linnaeus

Plate 216

An annual, succulent, herbaceous vine, climbing by means of branched tendrils; stem angled, clammy-hairy, often climbing or trailing a distance of 15 to 25 feet. Leaves broad, nearly orbicular, of thin texture, but roughened on both surfaces, heart-shaped at the base and five-angled or five-lobed, the lobes sharp pointed, but the sinuses between the lobes usually not very deep. Petioles stout, 1 to 4 inches long. Flowers small, greenish white, of two kinds, staminate and pistillate. The staminate flowers arranged in loose racemes on very long stalks, with a five-toothed cup-shaped calyx tube, a five-parted rotate corolla and three stamens with their filaments united to form a short column, their anthers coherent. The pistillate or fertile flowers are arranged several together in capitate clusters, on short stalks, also with a five-parted calyx and corolla. Fruit a one-seeded, indehiscent burlike pod, dry when mature, armed with slender, rough spines, sessile in clusters of three to ten, each " cucumber " about one-half of an inch long.

In moist soil, chiefly along streams and rivers or in thickets and low woods, Quebec to Ontario and South Dakota, south to Florida, Texas and Kansas. Flowering from June to September.

Wild Balsam Apple; Wild Cucumber

Micrampelis lobata (Michaux) Greene

Plate 217 and Figure XXXV

An herbaceous, annual vine, climbing and twining, several feet long, sometimes confused with the One-seeded Bur Cucumber. Stems angular and grooved, nearly glabrous and not clammy-hairy, but sometimes hairy at

Figure XXXV
Wild Balsam Apple;   Wild Cucumber
(Micrampelis lobata (Michaux) Greene)

the nodes. Leaves thin, roughish on both sides, heart-shaped at the base, with five (varying from three to seven) triangular-lanceolate, sharp-pointed lobes with deep sinuses between them. Flowers greenish white, the staminate flowers in narrow, compound racemes; the pistillate flowers solitary or sometimes two together; lobes of the corolla five to six, narrow and sharp pointed. Fruit a small, fleshy pod (pepo), dry when mature, armed with slender spines; inner part fibrous-netted, usually two-celled with two flat seeds in each cavity; ovoid in shape, $1\frac{1}{2}$ to 2 inches long, green, and opening at the apex when mature.

In rich, moist or wet soil in thickets or woods along streams or rivers, New Brunswick to Ontario, Manitoba, Montana, south to Virginia, Kentucky, Texas and Kansas. Flowering from July to September. Frequent in cultivation and perhaps largely introduced or escaped in the northeast.

Bellflower Family
Campanulaceae
Harebell; Bluebells of Scotland
Campanula rotundifolia Linnaeus

Plate 218

A slender, graceful, wiry-stemmed herb, perennial by slender rootstocks, usually smooth, sometimes pubescent. Stems erect or decumbent, often several from the same root, 6 inches to 3 feet high. Basal leaves nearly orbicular, usually heart-shaped at the base, one-fourth to 1 inch wide, toothed or entire, on long, slender, weak petioles, usually withering or dying before the flowers open, but new ones developing in late summer. Stem leaves slender, linear or linear-lanceolate, 1 to 3 inches long. Flowers usually racemose, rarely solitary, at the apex of the stem, drooping on slender, hairlike stalks. Calyx with five threadlike spreading lobes. Corolla bright blue or violet-blue, bell-shaped, one-half to nearly 1 inch broad, the margin with five pointed lobes. Fruit an ovoid capsule, ribbed and opening by short clefts near the base.

In fissures and cracks of rocks near waterfalls and in rocky woods, sometimes in meadows and sandy fields. Exhibiting in its varying habitats marked differences in growth and appearance. Labrador to Alaska, south to New Jersey, Pennsylvania, Illinois, Nebraska and in the Rocky mountains to Arizona, in the Sierra Nevada to California and also in Europe and Asia. Flowering from June to September.

Creeping or European Bellflower

Campanula rapunculoides Linnaeus

Plate 215b

A perennial herb with slender rootstocks and smooth or pubescent stems, usually not branched, leafy, erect and rather stout, 1 to 3 feet high, the base of the stem decumbent and freely rooting at the nodes. Lower leaves 3 to 6 inches long, 1 to 2 inches wide, ovate with heart-shaped base, pointed or acuminate, the margin crenately toothed, often the blade slightly pubescent; upper leaves similar but smaller and sessile. Flowers borne in long, one-sided racemes, the individual flowers about 1 or $1\frac{1}{2}$ inches long, drooping on short stalks, subtended by small, leafy bracts. Corolla bell-shaped, blue or violet, five-lobed. Calyx lobes five in number, linear and spreading. Fruit a nodding, globose capsule, about one-third of an inch in diameter, opening by pores at the base.

In fields and along roadsides, and as an escape from gardens, often along fences and village streets. Naturalized from Europe. New Brunswick to Ontario, southern New York, Pennsylvania and Ohio. Flowering from July to September.

The Nettle-leaved Bellflower or Throatwort (C a m p a n u l a t r a c h e l i u m Linnaeus) is similar in appearance, but the calyx and outer surface of the unexpanded corolla is bristly-ciliate with long, pale hairs. Called also Canterbury Bells.

The Tall Bellflower (C a m p a n u l a a m e r i c a n a Linnaeus) is a native species, not common in eastern or southern New York. Its flowers are pale blue, the corolla wheel-shaped, deeply cleft into five-pointed lobes.

Marsh or Bedstraw Bellflower

Campanula aparinoides Pursh

Plate 219a

A perennial herb with very slender, weak stems, reclining or diffusely spreading, rough with short, retrorse bristles, leafy and paniculately branched, 6 inches to 3 feet long. Leaves lanceolate or linear-lanceolate, sessile, rough on the margins and midrib, pointed at both ends, one-half to $1\frac{1}{2}$ inches long and not more than one-fourth of an inch wide. Flowers white or very faintly tinged with blue, on threadlike stalks chiefly terminating the widely divergent leafy branches; buds nodding. Calyx lobes triangular, half the length of the deeply five-cleft, bell-shaped corolla which is about one-third of an inch long; style not projecting beyond the corolla. Fruit a small, nearly globose, erect capsule, opening at maturity near the base.

In grassy swamps and marshes, from Maine to Georgia, west to Colorado and Kentucky. Flowering from June to August. In habit it resembles some of the Bedstraws (Galium).

The Blue Marsh Bellflower (C a m p a n u l a u l i g i n o s a Rydberg) is similar; flowers blue with darker veins, cleft into lanceolate lobes.

Venus's Looking-glass

Specularia perfoliata (Linnaeus) A. DeCandolle

Plate 219b

Stems weak, decumbent and branched at the base, the ends slender, erect, very leafy, 6 inches to 2 feet tall, angled and hairy on the angles. Leaves rounded, one-fourth to 1 inch broad, clasping the stem by a broad, heart-shaped base, pointed or blunt, about as long as broad. Flowers violet-blue or rarely white, borne solitary or two or three together, sessile in the axils of the leaves; corolla wheel-shaped, those in the axils of the upper leaves with five triangular-lanceolate, long-pointed, rigid calyx lobes and a five-lobed, deeply cleft corolla, one-half to three-fourths of an inch broad, those in the axils of the lower leaves with a shorter, three or four-lobed calyx, longer than the rudimentary corolla. Fruit an oblong capsule, one-sixth to one-fourth of an inch long, opening at maturity at about the middle.

In dry woods and dry soil, especially sandy fields and waste places, Maine and Ontario to British Columbia south to Florida, Louisiana, Mexico, Arizona and Oregon. Also in the mountains of Jamaica and Santo Domingo. Flowering in New York from May to September.

Lobelia Family
Lobeliaceae
Cardinal Flower; Red Lobelia
Lobelia cardinalis Linnaeus

Plate 220

A tall, stiffly erect herb, $1\frac{1}{2}$ to 4 feet high with smooth stems from a perennial root, rarely branched, leafy, bearing an elongated, rather one-sided raceme or spike of several or many bright-red flowers, subtended by leaflike bracts. Leaves thin, somewhat toothed, oblong-lanceolate, 2 to 6 inches long, one-fourth to $1\frac{1}{2}$ inches wide, pointed at both ends, and alternate on the stem, the upper leaves becoming successively smaller. Flowers with a five-cleft calyx; corolla five-lobed, about 1 inch long, two-lipped, the lower lip conspicuously cleft into three prominent, spreading lobes, upper lip erect with two small lobes. Stamens five, free from the corolla and united by their anthers to form a tube around the style, two of the anthers possessing hairy tufts at the summit; stigma two-lobed. Fruit a two-celled, many-seeded pod, opening at the top.

Low or wet ground in meadows, swamps and marshes, or in wet grassy places along streams or ditches. New Brunswick to Ontario, south to Florida and Texas, west to Kansas and Colorado. Flowering from July to September.

Great or Blue Lobelia
Lobelia syphilitica Linnaeus

Plate 221

A tall, stiffly erect herb, perennial by short offsets at the base; stem 1 to 3 feet high, stout, leafy, simple, slightly hairy, bearing a long, many-flowered raceme of bright-blue flowers, each flower subtended by a leafy bract.   Leaves smooth or sparingly pubescent, 2 to 6 inches long, one-half to 2 inches wide, long pointed at the apex, narrowed at the base, the lower leaves petioled, the upper sessile, irregularly toothed and alternate.   Calyx hairy, with five long, narrow, pointed lobes with large appendages between the lobes.   Corolla about 1 inch long, blue fading to pale blue, marked with white on the lobes of the lower lip; upper lip of the corolla two-lobed and erect, the lobes nearly as large as the three lobes of the lower lip.   The flowers are rarely entirely white.

In moist or wet soil, along streams, in wet thickets and marshes, Maine to Ontario and South Dakota, south to Georgia, Louisiana, Kansas and Colorado.   Flowering from July to October.

Indian or Wild Tobacco; Eyebright

Lobelia inflata Linnaeus

Plate 222a

An acrid, poisonous herb, 1 to 3 feet high; stem hairy and leafy, paniculately branched, from an annual root.   Leaves ovate or oblong, bluntly toothed, alternate, the upper sessile and pointed, the lower petioled and blunt, 1 to $2\frac{1}{2}$ inches long, rather thin and pubescent.   Flowers small, pale blue or violet, arranged rather loosely in spikelike, leafy racemes, each flower subtended by a leaflike bract, the lower bracts longer than the flowers.   Calyx tube greatly inflated in fruit forming a rounded, ribbed capsule containing many seeds.   In structure the corolla is similar to the other species of Lobelia, but much less conspicuous.

In dry fields and thickets, often in poor soil, Labrador to Saskatchewan, south to Georgia, Arkansas and Kansas.   Flowering from July to October. The different names given in different localities to this plant (Gagroot, Emetic Weed, Asthma Weed, etc.) give some idea of the herbal character of the species.   It was formerly much used as an emetic and the Indians are supposed to have smoked and chewed the bitter leaves, hence the name " Indian tobacco."

Kalm's or Brook Lobelia

Lobelia kalmii Linnaeus

Plate 222b

A small, low, slender herb, perennial by short offsets; stems 6 to 20 inches long, smooth, very slender, erect or reclining, leafy and paniculately branched. Lower and basal leaves spatulate, narrowed into short petioles; upper leaves sessile and shorter. Flowers light blue, about one-third to one-half of an inch long, arranged in a loose raceme at the ends of the stems and branches on threadlike stalks as long as the flowers but not exceeding the linear-lanceolate bracts which subtend them. Calyx tube top-shaped or obovoid, half as long as the lanceolate lobes. Corolla two-lipped, the upper lip two-cleft and narrow, the lower lip cleft into three spreading lobes which are much broader than those of the upper lip. Fruit a small globose capsule, not inflated.

On wet banks, boggy meadows and swamps, or on wet ledges of rocks about waterfalls, from Nova Scotia to New Jersey, west to Ontario, Manitoba, Ohio, Michigan and Iowa. Flowering from July to September.

The Water Lobelia (Lobelia dortmanna Linnaeus) is an aquatic perennial with numerous white, fibrous roots. Leaves linear, 1 to 2 inches long, fleshy, tufted at the base of the hollow stem and submerged. Flowers pale blue in a loose raceme at summit of the stem. Borders of ponds, from New Jersey and Pennsylvania to Newfoundland, Wisconsin and British Columbia.

The Spiked Lobelia (Lobelia spicata Lamarck) has pale blue flowers in an elongated spikelike raceme sometimes 1 to 2 feet long, each flower one-fourth to one-third of an inch long. Leaves broadly oblong at base of stem, becoming spatulate higher up and finally narrowing down to linear bracts subtending the flowers. In moist or dry sandy soil, Prince Edward Island to Saskatchewan, south to North Carolina, Alabama, Louisiana and Arkansas.

Nuttall's Lobelia (Lobelia nuttallii Roemer & Schultes) is very slender. The pedicels are longer than the bracts but shorter than the small pale-blue flowers. Common in sandy swamps along the coast.

Chicory Family

Chicoriaceae

A family closely allied to the Sunflower family (Compositae). Stems usually with milky, acrid or bitter juice. Flowers in heads, surrounded by involucral bracts; flowers all alike and perfect. Calyx tube completely adnate to the ovary, its limb (pappus) of scales, simple or plumose bristles, or both wanting. Corolla gamopetalous, with a short or long tube, and a strap-shaped (ligulate), usually five-toothed limb (ray).

In addition to those species illustrated here, the Chicory family contains many other species, including the common Chicory, Dandelion, Oyster Plant or Salsify, Sow Thistle, Lettuce, Wild Prickly Lettuce and several additional species of Hawkweeds and Rattlesnake weeds.

Devil's-paintbrush; Orange Hawkweed

Hieracium aurantiacum Linnaeus

Plate 223b

A perennial, low-growing, very hairy weed, spreading by means of vigorous and rapidly growing leafy stolons. Leaves basal, spatulate or oblong, blunt at the apex, narrowed at the base, usually entire, 2 to 5 inches long, one-fourth to 1 inch wide, very hairy. Flowers borne on a slender, hairy, leafless stem (rarely with one or two small leaves), 6 to 20 inches high, the heads of flowers bright orange-red in color, one-half to 1 inch broad, few or several in a rather dense inflorescence or cluster at the summit of the stem, the upper part of the stem and the inflorescence thickly dotted with black, glandular-tipped hairs. Flowers of the head all alike, with five-toothed, strap-shaped corollas. Involucres one-third to one-half of an inch high, composed of linear-lanceolate green bracts, densely covered with black hairs, the bracts arranged in two or three series.

In fields, woods and along roadsides, widely distributed as an obnoxious weed in the eastern states, but native of the Old World. Flowering from June to September.

King Devil

Hieracium florentinum Allioni

Plate 223a

Stems slender, smooth or somewhat hispid, 1 to 3 feet high from a perennial root. Leaves all basal, oblong or spatulate, entire, either pointed or blunt at the apex and narrowed at the base into margined petioles, somewhat hirsute with stiff hairs, or smooth, 2 to 4 inches long, one-fourth to three-fourths of an inch wide. Sometimes one to three smaller leaves are borne on the stem near its base. Inflorescence of several bright-yellow heads of flowers, each head one-third to one-half of an inch broad, arranged in a corymb on short, somewhat glandular-hairy peduncles. The involucre about one-fourth of an inch high, composed of linear, pointed bracts, pilose and somewhat glandular-hairy, overlapping in about two series.

In fields, meadows and thickets and along roadsides, New York and Ontario to Quebec and Maine. Native of Europe. In some places an obnoxious weed. Unlike the Orange Hawkweed, it does not spread by leafy stolons, and hence is usually not so abundant.

Rough Hawkweed

Hieracium scabrum Michaux

Plate 224

Stems stout and leafy up to the inflorescence, without a basal tuft of leaves at flowering time, 1 to 4 feet high, very hairy with rather reddish hairs and glandular-hairy above. Leaves hairy, oblong or broadly spatulate, 2 to 4 inches long, 1 to 2 inches wide, blunt at the apex, the lower leaves narrowed into margined petioles, the upper narrowed to a sessile base, their margins sparingly denticulate. Inflorescence of numerous yellow heads, one-half to three-fourths of an inch broad, on reddish colored, stout, densely glandular-hairy peduncles. Involucres one-third to one-half of an inch high, glandular-hairy, the principal bracts linear and pointed, in one series with a few very small outer ones.

In dry woods and clearings, Nova Scotia to Minnesota, Georgia and Iowa. Flowering from July to September.

Rattlesnake-weed; Poor-Robin's-plantain

Hieracium venosum Linnaeus

Plate 225

A perennial herb, sending up a smooth, usually solitary and leafless stem, paniculately branched above, 1 to 3 feet high, with a tuft of basal leaves spreading on the ground. Leaves smooth or sometimes hairy, characteristically marked with purple veins, suggestive of the markings on a snakeskin, oblong-spatulate, blunt at the apex, narrowed at the base into petioles, though sometimes sessile, 1 to 5 inches long, one-half to 1½ inches wide, paler on the under surface, the margins glandular-denticulate. Inflorescence consisting of several yellow heads, about two-thirds of an inch broad, each containing fifteen to forty ray flowers, and borne on rather long, slender, spreading peduncles, smooth or slightly glandular-hairy. Involucre cylindric, about one-fourth of an inch high, with one series of long, narrow, nearly smooth bracts and a few short outer ones.

In dry woods and thickets, usually in poor or sandy soil. Maine and Ontario to Manitoba, south to Georgia, Kentucky and Nebraska. Flowering from late in May to October. Individuals are sometimes found without the purple-colored veins in the leaves.

Gall-of-the-earth; Tall Rattlesnake-root

Nabalus trifoliolatus Cassini

Plate 226

Stems smooth, stout and sometimes purplish, with milky juice, leafy and 3 to 9 feet high, from a perennial root. Leaves thin, the lower ones very long petioled, the upper short petioled or sessile, all usually divided into three segments, which are sometimes stalked, irregularly toothed, or the upper leaves sometimes entire. Inflorescence consisting of many drooping heads, in loose clusters of few or several together. Heads with seven to twelve whitish or pale yellowish ray flowers (no disk flowers), surrounded by a pale green, narrow, smooth, cylindric involucre about one-half of an inch long, becoming purplish when old, consisting of six to eight principal bracts, equaling the pappus in length, and a few small bracts at the base of the involucre. Pappus light brown in color.

In woods and thickets, Newfoundland to Pennsylvania, Indiana, Delaware and Tennessee. Flowering from August to October. Not a showy plant but rather odd in appearance and representative of a group which contains about ten related species in the eastern states.

Sunflower Family

Compositae

The Sunflower family comprises the largest group of flowering plants, including in the flora of the whole world about one-tenth of the known species, or some 12,000 in number. They are chiefly herbs in our region, but in warmer parts of the world, shrubs and tree forms also occur. In New York, about one-fifth of all plants which have rather conspicuous flowers, and might in consequence be designated as wild flowers, belong to this family. In this Memoir, over 50 species, or nearly one-eighth of the total number of plants illustrated, belong to the Sunflower family, and the number would be larger if it were not deemed unnecessary to illustrate all of the many kinds of Goldenrods and Wild Asters.

The chief characteristics of the family, which will aid considerably in an understanding of the descriptions of the following species, is the crowding together of the true flowers into heads. These floral heads, commonly referred to as the "flower," namely, the Sunflower, the Daisy etc. are in reality made up of many small, individual flowers, in contrast to the single flower of the rose or violet. The head is surrounded by an involucre, composed of one to several series of bracts or scales, performing as a whole the function of a calyx for the entire flower head. The individual bracts are often leaflike in character.

Two kinds of flowers are to be noted in the " heads " of certain Compositae. They are the regular five-toothed or five-lobed corolla, as seen in the different species of Eupatorium, and the irregular, strap-shaped or ligulate corolla, in the ray flowers of the Wild Asters. Sometimes both kinds are found in the same head, as in the common Daisy, and then the strap-shaped flowers around the margin are referred to as ray flowers, and the densely packed tubular flowers in the center of the head are called disk flowers. Very often the disk flowers are of one color and the ray flowers of a different color. In some cases we find heads composed entirely of disk flowers (Thistles).

The stamens are five in number, attached to the inside of the corolla tube and usually cohere by their anthers in a ring around the style, which is commonly two-cleft at the summit, that is, a two-parted stigma. The ray flowers are usually without stamens, when disk flowers are present, and sometimes some flowers (either disk or ray, as the case may be) are entirely neutral (without stamens or pistils). The ovary is one-celled, containing one ovule which ripens into a small, dry, one-celled, one-seeded, indehiscent fruit, known as an achene. This achene is admirably adapted for seed dissemination by means of the persistent pappus, which matures along with the fruit. In the case of Bidens, the pappus consists of two barbed processes projecting from the achene, which catch in the shaggy coats of animals and on the clothing of passing persons and is thus distributed wide distances. In other cases the pappus consists of hairlike tufts, as in the Thistle, which enable the seed to be carried great distances by the wind.

The Compositae represent the most highly developed family of flowering plants, in respect to floral structure. By massing the flowers in heads, there is a great economy of space and tissue gained for the plant, and also greater certainty of pollination for the individual flowers, as a visit from one insect may result in the pollination of from several to many flowers. The showiness gained by massing the small flowers together serves as an added attraction to insects.

The Compositae contain many cultivated plants, including ornamental species. The Asters, Chrysanthemums, Pyrethrams, Gaillardias, Heleniums, Helianthus (Sunflowers), Rudbeckias (Coneflowers), Dahlias and many others are some of the common and highly ornamental species.

Beach Clotbur

Xanthium echinatum Murray

Plate 213b

An annual, coarse, rough herb of seashores and river beaches, with rough, purplish or blotched stems, 1 to 2 feet high. Leaves alternate, tough, coarse, very rough with scattered, short, papillose hairs and obscurely toothed and more or less lobed. Inflorescence rather small, consisting of heads of greenish discoid flowers, the staminate ones clustered in heads at the ends of the branches, the pistillate or fertile flowers axillary in the upper leaves. Flowers of the staminate heads with tubular corollas; the pistillate heads consisting of an ovoid or oblong closed involucre covered with hooked spines, with no corolla or pappus. Fruit a prickly bur, usually several clustered in the axils of the leaves, ovoid to oval, one-half to two-thirds of an inch long and one-third to one-half of an inch thick, covered with hooked prickles, and densely hairy with reddish hairs, the summit of the bur bearing two stout, hispid, incurving clawlike beaks, the interior of the bur two-celled, each cavity containing one obovoid or oblong achene.

On sea beaches, lake and river shores, and occasionally in waste ground, Nova Scotia to North Carolina, west to Minnesota and North Dakota. In New York found mainly in sandy soil and on beaches of Long Island and Staten Island, the Great Lakes and a few inland localities. Flowers appear in July and August and the bur is ripe in September or October.

The Common Cocklebur or Clotbur (X a n t h i u m c a n a d e n s e Miller) is a common weed almost everywhere. It resembles the one illustrated here, but is usually larger in every way, the beaks of the bur being almost straight and more or less divergent.

The Clotburs (Xanthium) are usually placed in the Ragweed family (Ambrosiaceae) but here retained for convenience in the Sunflower family.

Ironweed

Vernonia noveboracensis (Linnaeus) Willdenow

Plate 227

Stems erect, stiff, coarse, simple or somewhat branched, 3 to 9 feet high from a perennial root, roughish-pubescent or nearly smooth. Leaves alternate, narrowly oblong to lanceolate, pointed or elongated at the apex, narrowed at the base into slender petioles, or the upper leaves nearly sessile, margins serrulate, 3 to 10 inches long, one-half to 1 inch wide. Inflorescence consisting of several or many heads of deep-purple flowers, arranged in a loose, cymose panicle at the summit of the leafy stem. Each head one-third to one-half of an inch broad and containing twenty to forty flowers. Involucre of brownish purple or greenish bracts, overlapping in several series, with long, spreading and slender tips, usually two or three times their own length. Flowers all tubular with a regular, five-toothed corolla. Pappus purplish in color.

In moist soil and low grounds, Massachusetts to Pennsylvania and Missouri, south to North Carolina, West Virginia and Mississippi. Flowering in late summer and early fall. In New York, not common north of the lower Hudson valley region and the coastal plain.

Joe-pye Weed; Purple Boneset

Eupatorium purpureum Linnaeus

Plate 228

Stems tall, smooth, often purplish and glaucous, frequently straight, simple or branched only at the summit, 3 to 10 feet high from a perennial root. Leaves ovate, oval or ovate-lanceolate, petioled, toothed, 4 to 13 inches long, one-half to 3 inches wide, veiny and sometimes slightly pubescent on the under side of the leaf, arranged in whorls of threes to sixes, commonly in fours. The inflorescence consists of large, terminal, loose, compound clusters of numerous flower heads, pinkish lavender to purple in color; each head composed of tubular flowers only. Involucres of individual heads cylindric, with pinkish purple, oblong, blunt bracts, overlapping in four or five series.

In moist soil, woods and low thickets, especially common in wet places along streams, New Brunswick to Manitoba, south to Florida and Texas. Flowering in August and September.

The Spotted Joe-pye Weed (Eupatorium maculatum Linnaeus) is similar to E. purpureum, but the stem is spotted with purple and usually rough or pubescent; the flowers usually pinkish purple in color.

Hyssop-leaved Thoroughwort

Eupatorium hyssopifolium Linnaeus

Plate 229b

Stems roughish-puberulent, rather bushy, 1 to 2 feet high, from a perennial root, bearing opposite, linear leaves and densely corymbosely branched above. Numerous smaller leaves fascicled in the axils of the stem or on short, axillary branches; leaf blades entire, blunt at the apex, narrowed at the base, one-half to 2 inches long, one-twelfth to one-sixth of an inch wide, firm and usually with more or less revolute margins. Heads white, arranged in a flat-topped panicle, each head about one-third of an inch high with about five tubular flowers, surrounded by a campanulate involucre, composed of linear-oblong, puberulent bracts imbricated in about three series, the outer ones shorter.

In dry fields, Massachusetts to Florida and Texas. Flowering in August and September.

Rough or Vervain Thoroughwort

Eupatorium verbenaefolium Michaux

Plate 229a

Stems erect, more or less branched at the summit, rough-pubescent, slender, 2 to 7 feet high from a perennial root. Leaves opposite, rough-pubescent, closely sessile or rarely short petioled, blunt at the apex, rounded at the base, crenate toothed 1 to 4 inches long, one-half to 1 inch wide, the upper pairs smaller and distant. Heads white, about one-fourth of an inch high, each with about five tubular flowers, the heads arranged in a cymose panicle; involucre bell-shaped, composed of about three series of overlapping linear-lanceolate, pointed and densely pubescent bracts, the outer ones shorter.

In moist, usually sandy soil, mainly near the coast from Massachusetts to Florida, West Virginia and Louisiana. Flowering from July to September.

Common Thoroughwort; Boneset

Eupatorium perfoliatum Linnaeus

Plate 230

Stems stout, rigid, hairy, branched above, 2 to 5 feet high from a perennial root. Leaves tough, veiny and wrinkled on both surfaces, opposite and united by their bases (connate-perfoliate), the upper pairs usually not united, lanceolate, long pointed at the apex, 4 to 8 inches long, 1 to $1\frac{1}{2}$ inches wide, pubescent on the under surface, the margins finely crenate-toothed. Inflorescence consisting of many heads in a rather congested, nearly flat-topped cyme; each head one-sixth to one-fourth of an inch high and ten to sixteen-flowered, dull leaden-white in color. Involucre campanulate, pubescent, with lanceolate bracts arranged in two or three series.

Common in wet meadows and low grounds, especially along streams in marshes and swamps, Nova Scotia and New Brunswick to Manitoba, south to Florida, Texas and Nebraska. Flowering in late summer, from July to September. In former times and even yet in some rural sections, boneset tea, made from the dried leaves of this plant, is prized for certain medicinal properties.

White Snakeroot

Eupatorium urticaefolium Reichard

Plate 231

Stems erect, smooth, usually much branched, 1 to 4 feet high from a perennial root. Leaves opposite, ovate, thin, coarsely and sharply toothed, 3 to 6 inches long, 1 to 3 inches wide, on slender petioles, one-half to $2\frac{1}{2}$ inches long; leaf blades rounded, truncate or cordate at the base, usually long pointed at the apex, showing some resemblance to the leaves of the Nettle (Urtica). Inflorescence a rather loose cymose-paniculate cluster of small heads, each with ten to thirty white, tubular flowers; involucres campanulate, one-sixth of an inch high, the bracts linear and arranged in two nearly equal series.

In rich woods or in thickets and clearings, New Brunswick to Florida, west to Ontario, Nebraska and Louisiana. The plant is said to be poisonous to cattle.

Climbing Hempweed or Boneset

Mikania scandens (Linnaeus) Willdenow

Plate 232a

Stems smooth and twining or climbing over surrounding vegetation, 5 to 15 feet long, from a perennial root. Leaves opposite, ovate or hastate, deeply cordate at the base with rounded basal lobes, long pointed at the apex, somewhat triangular in shape, 2 to 4 inches long, 1 to 2 inches wide, borne on slender petioles. Heads in compound clusters, borne at the ends of the branches, each head four-flowered, surrounded by oblong involucres of four narrow bracts. Corollas white or pink.

In swamps and moist soil in woods and thickets along streams or in low, wet places, Maine to western Ontario, south to Florida and Texas. Flowering from July to September.

Maryland Golden Aster

Chrysopsis mariana (Linnaeus) Elliott

Plate 233b

Stems stout, loosely hairy, usually more than one from a stout, perennial root, nearly erect or ascending, 1 to 2½ feet high and corymbosely branched at the summit. Upper leaves oblong to lanceolate, pointed or blunt, sessile, 1 to 2 inches long; the lower leaves oblanceolate or spatulate and narrowed into petioles, usually blunt, 2 to 4 inches long, one-half to 1 inch wide. Heads of flowers usually numerous, bright yellow, three-fourths to 1 inch broad on glandular peduncles; involucres hemispheric, the bracts glandular, pointed and viscid-pubescent.

In dry or sandy soil, southern New York to Pennsylvania, Florida and Louisiana. Flowering in August and September.

THE GOLDENRODS
Solidago

The Goldenrods comprise a large genus of more than one hundred and twenty-five species, all but a few native of North America. In New York there are found about thirty species of this group. They are perennial, erect herbs, often simple or with few branches; alternate leaves which are either toothed or entire, and numerous small heads of both tubular and ray flowers, or rarely whitish flowers, in terminal or axillary panicles, thyrsi, or cymose-corymbose or capitate clusters. The involucre of each head is oblong or narrowly bell-shaped and composed of bracts overlapping each other in several series, the outer ones successively shorter. Disk flowers usually all perfect, that is, with both stamens and pistils, their corollas tubular and five-lobed; ray flowers arranged in one series and pistillate. Achenes in fruit smooth or angled and usually ribbed. Pappus of numerous, hairlike, rough or nearly smooth, white or slightly tawny bristles.

The amateur botanist may experience some difficulty in the use of the following key to the commoner species of Goldenrod, since it is practically impossible to indicate the distinguishing characters without the use of technical terms.

Ray flowers more numerous than the disk flowers; heads corymbose-paniculate (*Flat-topped Goldenrods*)

    Leaves distinctly three-ribbed; heads twenty to thirty-flowered....................
                                  Euthamia graminifolia

    Leaves one-ribbed; involucre campanulate, one-sixth of an inch high or less.........
                                  Euthamia tenuifolia

Ray flowers not more numerous than the disk flowers (*True Goldenrods*)

    Tips of the involucral bracts, or some of them spreading or recurved; leaves smooth..
                                  Solidago squarrosa

    Tips of the involucral bracts all erect and appressed

        Heads in axillary clusters or also in a terminal spikelike sometimes branched thyrsus

            Heads one-sixth to one-fourth of an inch high, chiefly in axillary clusters; achenes pubescent

                Stem and branches terete; leaves lanceolate to oblong................
                                  Solidago caesia

                Stem and branches grooved or angled; leaves broadly oval, contracted into margined petioles...............Solidago flexicaulis

            Heads one-sixth to one-fourth of an inch high, chiefly in a terminal spikelike thyrsus; achenes smooth or nearly so

                Rays white; stem pubescent................Solidago bicolor

                Rays yellow; stem densely pubescent.........Solidago hispida

                Rays yellow; stem smooth or sparingly pubescent; leaves thick, dentate or the upper entire, not acuminate..........Solidago erecta

        Heads about one-half of an inch high; bracts elongated, pointed; leaves ovate..............................Solidago macrophylla

    Heads in a terminal, simple or branched thyrsus, not at all or scarcely secund on its branches; plant glabrous

        Low alpine species, 10 inches high or usually less; heads with thirty flowers or more....................................Solidago cutleri

    Taller species, not arctic-alpine

        Bracts of the involucre linear-subulate, very acute; stem puberulent...
                                  Solidago puberula

Bracts of the involucre blunt or slightly **pointed**; stem glabrous or sparingly pubescent above

Bog species; inflorescence wandlike....Solidago uliginosa

Upland species; inflorescence various

Heads very short-peduncled

Leaves thick, firm in texture, little toothed or entire; very tall with oval or broadly ovate lower leaves which are serrate...................Solidago speciosa

Leaves thin in texture, at least the lower ones serrate; low species......................Solidago randii

Heads distinctly slender peduncled; basal leaves narrowly oblanceolate, one-third of an inch wide or less............

Solidago racemosa

Heads in a terminal, usually large panicle, secund on its spreading or recurved branches

Maritime plants with thick fleshy entire leaves........................

Solidago sempervirens

Not maritime; leaves not fleshy

Leaves all entire, thin and glabrous............Solidago odora

Leaves, at least the lower ones, more or less toothed or serrate

Leaves pinnately-veined, not triple-nerved

Stems densely pubescent; leaves more or less so and rugose-veiny beneath, sharply serrate......Solidago rugosa

Stems glabrous, or merely puberulent above

Leaves very rough on the upper surface, serrulate........

Solidago patula

Leaves smooth, or minutely roughened on the upper surface

Racemes few, widely divergent, very slender, lower leaves oblong, coarsely serrate and thin..........

Solidago ulmifolia

Racemes numerous, spreading, recurved or ascending

Leaves all oblong or oblong-lanceolate and sessile..............Solidago elliotii

Leaves, at least the lower ones petioled, lanceolate or ovate-lanceolate

Leaves firm, ovate-lanceolate or oblong-
lanceolate; heads about one-sixth of an
inch high; racemes short; rays several....
Solidago neglecta

Leaves firm, narrowly lanceolate; heads
about one-sixth of an inch high; racemes
few, short, rays one to five............
Solidago uniligulata

Leaves firm, lanceolate or oval-lanceolate;
heads one-sixth to one-eighth of an inch
high; racemes numerous, slender.........
Solidago juncea

Leaves thin, the lower broadly ovate, short-
acuminate; heads one-sixth to one-fourth
of an inch high; racemes numerous......
Solidago arguta

Leaves triple-nerved, that is, with a pair of lateral veins much
stronger than the others

Heads small, the involucre only $1\frac{1}{4}$ lines high or less; stem
glabrous or pubescent........Solidago canadensis

Heads larger, the involucre one-sixth to one-fourth of an inch
high

Stems glabrous; leaves and involucral bracts thin........
Solidago serotina

Stem pubescent or scabrous

Leaves lanceolate, sharply serrate or entire, rough
above...............Solidago altissima

Leaves oblanceolate, spatulate, oblong or ovate;
minutely rough-pubescent, grayish; lower leaves
oblanceolate; crenate; heads one-sixth to one-
fourth of an inch high
Solidago nemoralis

Heads in a terminal, corymbiform, sometimes thyrsoid cyme, forming a flat-
topped inflorescence.   (genus *Oligoneuron* Small)

Leaves ovate, oblong, or oval, mostly rough on both sides ....
Solidago rigida

Leaves lanceolate, linear, oblong or oblanceolate, glabrous or nearly so
Lower leaves oblong-lanceolate, serrulate; plant 3 to 4 feet tall. . . . .
Solidago ohioensis
Lower and upper leaves all lanceolate or linear, entire, the basal leaves
4 to 5 inches long; plant 5 to 24 inches high. . . . .
Solidago houghtonii

In addition, there has recently been described from Long Island an additional species (Solidago aestivalis Bicknell), said to be like S. arguta Miller, but essentially smooth. The description suggests a form of S. patula Muhlenberg.

Bushy, Fragrant or Flat-topped Goldenrod

Euthamia graminifolia (Linnaeus) Nuttall

Plate 234

Stems erect, paniculately branched above, smooth or nearly so, 2 to 4 feet high, perennial by running rootstocks. Leaves numerous, linear-lanceolate, sessile, 1 to 5 inches long, one-sixth to one-third of an inch wide, three to five-nerved, with rough, hairy edges, and sometimes resinous dotted. Inflorescence a flat-topped compound corymb, the individual golden-yellow heads sessile in capitate clusters. Bracts of the involucre yellowish, oblong or oblong-lanceolate, slightly viscid.

Moist or sandy fields and roadsides, New Brunswick to Saskatchewan, Alberta, south to Florida, Nebraska and Wyoming. Flowering from July to September.

Slender Fragrant Goldenrod; Quobsque Weed

Euthamia tenuifolia (Pursh) Greene

Plate 232b

Stems slender, smooth or usually somewhat resinous, branched above, 8 to 18 inches high. Leaves numerous, narrowly linear, entire, long pointed at the apex, sessile and narrowed at the base, punctate, one-nerved, lateral nerves if present very inconspicuous, 1 to 3 inches long, often with smaller leaves clustered in the axils; heads of flowers about one-eighth of an inch high, very numerous and crowded into a dense, nearly flat corymb; involucre oblong-campanulate, its bracts oblong; ray flowers yellow, six to twelve in number; disk flowers only four to six in number.

In dry, sandy soil, eastern Massachusetts to Florida and Louisiana, and locally inland to Illinois and Wisconsin. Flowering from August to October.

Blue-stemmed or Wreath Goldenrod

Solidago caesia Linnaeus

Plate 235a

A smooth, slender plant, the stem often glaucous and usually bluish or purplish, 1 to 3 feet high from a perennial root, and simple or somewhat branched. Leaves oblong-lanceolate or lanceolate, sessile, long pointed at the apex, smooth, sharply toothed, 2 to 6 inches long, one-fourth to $1\frac{1}{4}$ inches wide. Heads of flowers one-fourth of an inch high or less, in axillary clusters or racemes, sometimes with some or nearly all of them forming a short terminal thyrsus; bracts of the involucre blunt and appressed.

In rich or dry woods and thickets, Nova Scotia to Minnesota, south to Florida and Texas. Flowering from August to October.

Zigzag or Broad-leaved Goldenrod

Solidago flexicaulis Linnaeus

Plate 236

Stems rarely branched, zigzag, 1 to 3 feet high, smooth and angled. Leaves ovate, long pointed at the apex, thin in texture, narrowed and usually abruptly so at the base into margined petioles, smooth or slightly pubescent on the under surface, the margins sharply toothed. Heads of flowers about one-fourth of an inch high in short, axillary, racemose clusters, rarely also in a narrow terminal thyrsus; bracts of the involucre blunt or pointed, appressed.

In rich woods and thickets, Nova Scotia to New Brunswick and Minnesota, south to Georgia, Tennessee and Missouri. Flowering in late summer, usually from July to September.

White or Pale Goldenrod; Silverrod

Solidago bicolor Linnaeus

Plate 237a

Stems stout, hairy or sometimes nearly smooth, 1 to 4 feet high, sometimes branched. Basal and lower leaves obovate or oblong and blunt, narrowed into long, margined petioles, crenulate-toothed, more or less hairy; the upper leaves smaller and narrower, oblong to lanceolate, pointed or blunt, sessile or nearly so and often entire. Heads of flowers one-fourth of an inch high or less, crowded in a terminal thyrsus, 2 to 8 inches long, sometimes also clustered in the upper axils; rays white; bracts of the involucre whitish, the midvein of each bract broadened toward the blunt tip.

In dry or sandy soil, Prince Edward Island west to Ontario and Minnesota, south to Georgia and Tennessee. Flowering from August to October.

Downy Goldenrod

Solidago puberula Nuttall

Plate 237b

Stems rather slender, $1\frac{1}{2}$ to 3 feet high, rarely branched, minutely puberulent or nearly smooth. Basal leaves and often the lowest leaves of the stem spatulate, blunt or pointed, usually sharply toothed, 2 to 4 inches long and 1 inch or less wide, narrowed into margined petioles; stem leaves oblong-lanceolate, pointed, entire or slightly toothed, 1 to 2 inches long, sessile or the lower ones petioled. Heads of flowers numerous, arranged in a terminal, often leafy thyrsus, the branches of which are ascending or spreading; each head of flowers about one-fourth of an inch high with several bright yellow rays. Bracts of the involucre slender and very sharp-pointed.

In sandy or dry soil, Prince Edward Island to Florida and Mississippi, west to Tennessee. In New York most abundant near the coast, but frequent in sandy places as far north as Franklin county.

Seaside Goldenrod

Solidago sempervirens Linnaeus

Plate 235b

Stem stout and leafy, rarely branched, 2 to 8 feet high, smooth or slightly puberulent above. Leaves entire, thick, fleshy with two to five pairs of lateral veins, the lower or basal leaves oblong, spatulate or lanceolate and usually blunt at the apex, often 8 to 12 inches long and narrowed at the base into long petioles; upper leaves smaller, sessile, lanceolate to oblong-lanceolate and pointed. Heads of flowers one-fourth of an inch high or more, in one-sided racemes forming a large terminal, often leafy panicle; rays showy, eight to ten in number in each head; bracts of the involucre lanceolate and pointed.

On salt marshes, sea beaches and along tidal rivers and in sandy soil near the coast, Nova Scotia to Florida and Mexico. Flowering from August to November.

Canada or Rock Goldenrod

Solidago canadensis Linnaeus

Plate 238

Stems slender, smooth or finely hairy above, 1 to 5 feet high, usually several or many plants together and spreading by underground rootstocks. Leaves thin, triple-nerved, linear-lanceolate, 2 to 5 inches long, entire or toothed with somewhat appressed teeth, long pointed at the apex, sessile or the lowest leaves petioled. Heads of flowers very small, about one-eighth of an inch or less high, arranged on one side of spreading branches which form a large, often loose panicle; rays four to six in number, short; bracts of the involucre thin, linear and pointed.

Hillsides and thickets or banks of streams, Newfoundland to Saskatchewan, south to Virginia, Tennessee and South Dakota. Flowering from August to October.

Houghton's Goldenrod

Solidago houghtonii Torrey & Gray

Plate 239a

Stems slender, smooth below, sometimes slightly hairy above, 8 to 24 inches high. Leaves linear, the basal and lower ones petioled, 4 to 5 inches long, one-sixth to one-third of an inch wide, three-nerved and entire, the sessile stem leaves becoming successively smaller upward, the uppermost leaves small and bractlike. Heads of flowers about one-fourth of an inch high, few, forming a small corymbose cyme, each head with twenty to thirty flowers; involucre broadly campanulate, its bracts oblong and blunt.

In swamps and bogs, north shore of Lake Michigan and Lake Huron, and in Bergen swamp, Genesee county, New York. Flowering in August and September.

THE ASTERS

Aster

The Wild Asters comprise a genus of over two hundred and fifty species, of which nearly fifty species occur in New York State. They are mostly perennial, branching herbs with alternate, simple leaves and corymbose or paniculate heads of both tubular and radiate flowers. Involucre varying from hemispheric to campanulate or turbinate, with its bracts overlapping in several series, the outer ones usually shorter and smaller. Ray flowers white, pink, purple, blue or violet, pistillate. Disk flowers perfect, tubular, their corollas five-lobed, usually yellow and changing to red, brown or purple; pappus bristles slender, numerous, rough or minutely toothed, usually in one, sometimes in two series; achenes mostly flattened and nerved.

Key to the Common Species of Aster

A Basal and lower leaves, or some of them, cordate and slender petioled

Stem leaves, or some of them, cordate-clasping; plant rough when dry. . . . .

1 A. undulatus

None of the stem leaves cordate-clasping; rays white, violet or rose

Rays white or rarely rose, usually two-toothed; plants not glandular

Involucre ovoid, campanulate or turbinate: its bracts mostly obtuse
    or rounded; basal leaves few and small, or commonly none
    (except A. g l o m e r a t u s)
    Leaves membranous or thin, smooth or nearly so
        Heads short-peduncled, three-fourths of an inch broad or less,
            the disk turning crimson; leaves acute or short-acuminate
                              2 A. c a r m e s i n u s
        Heads long-peduncled, three-fourths of an inch broad or more,
            the disk turning brown or reddish; leaves long-acuminate
            Heads 1 inch broad or more; leaves of the branches large,
                long, lanceolate, acuminate.......3 A. t e n e b r o s u s
            Heads three-fourths to 1 inch broad; leaves of the branches
                small, obtuse or acute..........4 A. d i v a r i c a t u s
    Leaves thick, firm, rough; heads one-third to one-half of an inch
        high; inflorescence paniculate or glomerate
        Leaves acute or short-acuminate, pilose beneath; inflorescence
            glomerate.........................5 A. g l o m e r a t u s
        Leaves long-acuminate; not pilose beneath; inflorescence open-
            paniculate............................6 A. c l a y t o n i
Involucre cylindric; its bracts tapering to an obtuse apex; basal leaves
    large, tufted
    Bracts of the involucre pale, scarious, usually without herbaceous
        tips.................................7 A. c u r v e s c e n s
    Bracts of the involucre broader, with herbaceous tips...........
                               8 A. s c h r e b e r i
Rays violet, usually three-toothed; plants glandular
    Predominant glands large, capitate; leaves thick, coarse, heavy
        Sinus broad; glands chiefly confined to the inflorescence; plant
            usually harsh.......................9 A. m a c r o p h y l l u s
        Sinus narrow; glands abundant on the leaves and stem; growing
            plant clammy..........................10 A. r o s c i d u s
    Predominant glands minute, scarcely capitate; leaves usually thin
        Inflorescence very irregular, paniculate-corymbose; plants often 4 to
            5 feet high; broader leaves large, cordate, acute..11 A. n o b i l i s
        Inflorescence rather regular, flat, or convex-topped; plants usually
            less than 2½ feet tall

Sinus broad and shallow

Broader leaves orbicular-cordate, their teeth and the inflorescence-leaves inconspicuous..12 A. ianthinus

Broader leaves reniform, sharply incised; some inflorescence-leaves conspicuous................13 A. violaris

Sinus rather deep and narrow; broader leaves ovate-cordate, sharply serrate..................14 A. multiformis

Rays blue or purple; plants not glandular; bracts of the involucre appressed or nearly so; rays eight to twenty

Leaves all entire, or nearly so, thick and firm, rough-puberulent on both sides, the upper bractlike...................15 A. azureus

Leaves nearly all sharply serrate and thin

Heads 2 to 3 lines high, numerous; bracts obtuse or bluntish

Leaves rough; petioles not wing-margined; bracts appressed..
16 A. cordifolius

Leaves smooth, or nearly so; petioles, or some of them wing-margined....................17 A. lowrieanus

Heads 4 to 5 lines high, usually few; bracts acute or acuminate....
18 A. lindleyanus

Heads 3 to 5 lines high, numerous; bracts acute or acuminate; stems glabrous or nearly so; bract-tips spreading..............
19 A. sagittifolius

B   No cordate and petioled leaves; those of the stem, or some of them, with more or less cordate or auricled clasping bases (only slightly auricled in A. tardiflorus and sometimes in A. laevis)

Stem rough, or hirsute-pubescent

Leaves, at least the lower, serrate; stem hispid-pubescent; bracts glabrous or ciliate......................................20 A. puniceus

Leaves entire, oblong, linear or lanceolate

Heads one-half to 1 inch broad, the linear to linear-lanceolate leaves but slightly clasping; bracts hispid or ciliate
21 A. amethystinus

Heads 1 to 2 inches broad; leaves sessile and strongly clasping

Stems hirsute; leaves lanceolate; involucre hemispheric; bracts viscid..........................22 A. novae-angliae

Stems rough; leaves oblong to lanceolate; involucre turbinate

Leaves thick, firm, very rough, oblong to oval. . . . .

23 A. p a t e n s

Leaves thin, roughish, oblong-lanceolate. . . . .

24 A. p h l o g i f o l i u s

Stem glabrous, or only sparingly pubescent above

Leaves sharply serrate

Leaves tapering to the base

Leaves narrowed to the base, the lower into winged petioles. . . . . .

25 A. t a r d i f l o r u s

Leaves scarcely or gradually narrowed at the base. . . . .

20 A. p u n i c e u s

Leaves abruptly contracted into margined petioles, often enlarged near

the base. . . . . .26 A. p r e n a n t h o i d e s

Leaves usually strongly cordate-clasping; bracts green-tipped. . . . .

27 A. l a e v i s

Leaves entire or nearly so

Involucre campanulate, its bracts appressed, green-tipped

Stem leaves oblong, lanceolate or oval-lanceolate. .27 A. l a e v i s

Stem leaves elongated-lanceolate. . . . . .28 A. c o n c i n n u s

Involucre hemispheric

Bracts in one or two series; leaves linear to lanceolate. . . . .

29 A. l o n g i f o l i u s

Bracts in several series, unequal

Bracts linear-subulate; leaves narrowly linear. . . . .

30 A. j u n c e u s

Bracts lanceolate, leaves lanceolate, 2 to 6 inches long. . . . .

31 A. n o v i - b e l g i i

C   Leaves sessile or petioled, scarcely or not at all clasping

Leaves silky or silvery-canescent, entire; heads in a narrow raceme; bracts linear

32 A. c o n c o l o r

Leaves neither silvery, silky nor canescent; leaves entire or toothed

Bracts of the involucre with herbaceous tips

Tips of the involucral bracts spreading (little spreading in A. r a d u l a ,

erect or spreading in A. h e r v e y i); heads large, showy; rays

violet to purple

Leaves oblong-lanceolate, sharply serrate, rugose, the basal leaves
usually wanting..........................33 A. r a d u l a
Leaves lanceolate to oblong, the lower sparingly dentate
　　Basal leaves with unmargined petioles......34 A. h e r v e y i
　　Basal leaves with margined petioles, bracts glandular........
　　　　　　　　　　　　　　　　　35 A. s p e c t a b i l i s
Involucral bracts all appressed (except in A. m u l t i f l o r u s, a
　　small-headed species); rays mostly white, sometimes purple
Heads unilaterally racemose
　　Stem leaves oval, oblong, or lanceolate, serrate, or chiefly so
　　　　Stem pubescent or glabrate......36 A. l a t e r i f l o r u s
　　　　Stem villous; leaves narrowly lanceolate, thin.........
　　　　　　　　　　　　　　　37 A. h i r s u t i c a u l i s
　　Stem leaves linear-lanceolate to linear, nearly entire; stem
　　　　glabrate..........................38 A. v i m i n e u s
Heads not unilaterally racemose, mostly paniculate
　　Involucral bracts spatulate, mostly ciliate, somewhat spreading,
　　　　at least the outer ones obtuse; plants roughish-puberulent
　　　　　　　　　　　　　　　39 A. m u l t i f l o r u s
　　Involucral bracts appressed, acute
　　　　Heads solitary at the ends of very small-leaved branchlets
　　　　　　　　　　　　　　　40 A. d u m o s u s
　　　　Heads paniculate
　　　　　Stem leaves lanceolate, serrate or entire
　　　　　　Heads 8 to 10 lines broad
　　　　　　　Plants glabrous, or sparingly pubescent
　　　　　　　above
　　　　　　　　Leaves firm, roughish or rough; rays
　　　　　　　　often purplish; involucral bracts acute
　　　　　　　　　　　　　41 A. s a l i c i f o l i u s
　　　　　　　　Leaves thin, smoothish; rays chiefly
　　　　　　　　white; involucral bracts acuminate...
　　　　　　　　　　　　　42 A. p a n i c u l a t u s
　　　　　　Plant puberulent all over................
　　　　　　　　　　　　　43 A. t r a d e s c a n t i

Heads 6 to 8 lines broad; stem leaves narrowly
lanceolate...........43 A. t r a d e s c a n t i
Stem leaves linear-lanceolate to subulate, mostly
entire
Heads scattered, 6 to 9 lines broad; upper leaves
linear.....................44 A. f a x o n i
Heads numerous, 4 to 7 lines broad; upper leaves
subulate; involucre subhemispheric, $2\frac{1}{2}$ to
3 lines high; rays usually white
Paniculately branched, bushy.............
45 A. e r i c o i d e s
Simple, or with slender ascending branches
46 A. p r i n g l e i
Bracts of the involucre without herbaceous tips
Bracts linear-subulate, acuminate
Leaves firm, 3 inches long or less, entire or sparingly serrate......
47 A. n e m o r a l i s
Leaves thin, 6 inches long or less, sharply serrate...............
48 A. a c u m i n a t u s
Bracts oblong or oblong-lanceolate, obtuse or acutish; leaves narrow,
entire................................49 A. p t a r m i c o i d e s
D Leaves fleshy, narrow, entire; plants of salt marshes or saline soil
Perennial; heads 6 to 12 lines broad; involucral bracts lanceolate, acuminate.....
50 A. t e n u i f o l i u s
Annual; heads 3 to 5 lines broad; involucral bracts linear-subulate; disk flowers
fewer than the very short rays......................51 A. s u b u l a t u s

Large-leaved Aster

Aster macrophyllus Linnaeus

Plate 240

Stems rather stout, rough, reddish, angled, 1 to 3 feet high from a
thick, long, perennial rootstock. Basal leaves forming large patches, three
to four to each stem, broad, cordate, with a large, irregular sinus at the base,
rough above, harsh, thick, the marginal teeth with curved sides; petioles
long and slender, upper leaves oblong with short, broadly winged petioles,

the uppermost sessile and pointed. Inflorescence hairy and glandular, broadly corymbose and more or less irregular; heads of flowers each about one-half of an inch high; peduncles rigid, thickish; ray flowers about sixteen, each about one-half of an inch long, chiefly lavender colored, sometimes violet or paler blue; bracts conspicuously green-tipped, the lower ones pointed, the inner ones oblong and blunt; disk flowers turning reddish brown with age.

In moist or dry, shaded places, Quebec to Minnesota, south to North Carolina. Flowering in August and September. Consists of numerous races, many of them described as species, differing in leaf character, pubescence, shape of inflorescence and other characteristics.

Red-stalked or Purple-stemmed Aster

Aster puniceus Linnaeus

Plate 241

Stem rather stout, more or less branched above, hispid with stiff hairs or nearly smooth, reddish, 2 to 8 feet high. Leaves lanceolate to oblong-lanceolate, long pointed, sessile and clasping the stem by a broad or narrowed base, sharply toothed or nearly entire, usually rough above and pubescent on the midrib or smooth below, 3 to 6 inches long, one-half to $1\frac{1}{2}$ inches broad; bracts of the hemispheric involucre linear or oblong and long pointed, overlapping in about two series, smooth or ciliate, green, loose and spreading, nearly equal in length; ray flowers twenty to forty in number, violet-purple or sometimes paler, one-half of an inch long or longer, showy; pappus nearly white.

In swamps, marshes and along margins of ponds, Newfoundland to Manitoba, south to Georgia, Tennessee, Ohio and Minnesota. Flowering from July to late fall.

Late Purple Aster

Aster patens Aiton

Plate 242a

Stems rather stiff, slender, somewhat rough, 1 to 3 feet high, with several spreading branches toward the summit. Leaves ovate-oblong to oblong-lanceolate, rough or pubescent, thick and somewhat rigid, clasping the stem by a deeply heart-shaped base, margins rough-ciliate and entire, the apex pointed, or the lower leaves blunt 1 to 3 inches long, those of the branches much reduced in size.   Heads of flowers 1 inch broad or sometimes broader, solitary at the ends of the branches; bracts of the broadly turbinate involucres linear-oblong, finely pubescent or roughish and somewhat glandular, overlapping in several series, their green, pointed tips spreading.   Ray flowers twenty to thirty, purplish blue or deep violet, one-third to one-half of an inch long; pappus tawny.

In dry, open thickets and fields, Maine to Minnesota, south to Florida and Texas.   Flowering from August to October.

Smooth Aster

Aster laevis Linnaeus

Plate 243

Stems rather stout, or slender and stiff, smooth and usually glaucous, branched above or simple, 2 to 4 feet high, from a thick, perennial root. Leaves thick, smooth, slightly rough on the entire or slightly toothed margins, the upper ones sessile and clasping the stem by a heart-shaped base, lanceolate to oblong-lanceolate in shape, 1 to 4 inches long, one-third to 2 inches wide; the lower and basal leaves gradually narrowed into margined petioles; the leaves of the branches usually reduced in size.   Heads of flowers numerous, about 1 inch broad; bracts of the bell-shaped involucres rigid, pointed, green-tipped, appressed and overlapping in several series. Ray flowers fifteen to thirty in number, blue or violet; pappus tawny.

In dry or sandy soil of open fields and thickets, Maine to Ontario and Saskatchewan, south to Alabama, Louisiana, Missouri and Colorado. Flowering from late August to October.

Seaside or Low Showy Aster

Aster spectabilis Aiton

Plate 244

Stems erect or ascending, stiff, simple or branched above, usually several or many from a single mat of stout, perennial roots; stems slightly rough below and more or less glandular above, 1 to 2 feet high. Leaves thickish, firm, the basal and lower ones oval, pointed, 3 to 5 inches long, 1 to 1½ inches wide, sparingly toothed with low teeth, narrowed at the base into slender petioles; upper leaves entire or nearly so, sessile, pointed, linear-oblong; heads several or numerous, about 1½ inches broad, corymbose, very showy; bracts of the hemispheric involucre linear-oblong or slightly spatulate, glandular viscid, overlapping in about five series, their green, bluntish tips spreading. Ray flowers fifteen to thirty in number, bright violet or violet-blue, one-half to seven-eighths of an inch long; pappus whitish.

In dry, sandy soil, chiefly near the coast, Massachusetts to Delaware. Flowering from August to October.

New England Aster

Aster novae-angliae Linnaeus

Plate 245

Stems stout, very leafy and hairy, corymbosely branched above, 2 to 8 feet high, from a stout, perennial root. Leaves lanceolate, entire, rather thin, pointed at the apex, hairy, 2 to 6 inches long, one-half to 1 inch wide, clasping the stem by a broad, heart-shaped base. Heads of flowers numerous, each head 1 to 2 inches broad, clustered at the ends of the branches. Involucres hemispheric, their bracts linear-subulate, somewhat unequal, spreading, green and hairy and usually glandular. Ray flowers numerous, forty to fifty in each head, linear, one-half to two-thirds of an inch long, violet-purple, rarely pink or reddish; achenes pubescent; pappus reddish white.

In moist fields, swamps and wet thickets, often along streams or near water, Quebec to Saskatchewan, south to Alabama, Kansas and Colorado. Usually regarded as the most beautiful of the wild asters. Flowering from August to October.

Starved or Calico Aster

Aster lateriflorus (Linnaeus) Britton

Plate 246b

Stems slender, divergently branched, nearly smooth or puberulent, chiefly erect, 1 to 5 feet high. Basal leaves ovate, slender-petioled; stem leaves broadly lanceolate to oblong-lanceolate, pointed, 2 to 5 inches long, one-half to 1 inch wide, more or less toothed. Leaves of the branches smaller, oblong or linear-oblong. Heads of flowers one-fourth to one-half of an inch broad, in one-sided racemes on the branches, usually numerous and crowded. Bracts of the turbinate involucres linear-oblong, blunt or somewhat pointed, overlapping in about four series, their short, green tips appressed or slightly spreading. Ray flowers numerous, short, white or pale purple; disk flowers purplish; pappus white.

In dry or moist soil, open woods, thickets or fields, Nova Scotia to western Ontario, south to North Carolina, Louisiana and Texas. Variable and consisting of several races or varieties, differing in leaf form, inflorescence and pubescence. Flowering from August to October.

Mountain or Whorled Aster

Aster acuminatus Michaux

Plate 247

Stems zigzag, corymbosely branched above, smooth or minutely pubescent, usually leafless below, 1 to 3 feet high. Leaves thin, broadly oblong, sharp pointed at the apex, narrowed to a somewhat cuneate, sessile base, coarsely and sharply toothed on the margins, smooth or pubescent above and pubescent on the veins beneath, 3 to 6 inches long, one-half to 1½ inches wide, the upper leaves often closer together than the lower ones. Heads of flowers several or numerous, 1 to 1½ inches broad; bracts of the nearly hemispheric involucre very narrow and long pointed, the outer ones much shorter. Ray flowers twelve to eighteen in number, one-half to two-thirds of an inch long, white, sometimes purplish; pappus soft, fine and nearly white.

Moist woods and thickets, Labrador to Ontario and western New York, south to the mountains of Georgia and Tennessee. Flowering from July to October.

Upland White Aster

Aster ptarmicoides (Nees) Torrey & Gray
(Unamia alba (Nuttall) Rydberg)

Plate 246a

Stems slender, stiff, usually rough above, frequently several from a single perennial root, corymbosely branched toward the summit, 1 to 2 feet high. Leaves linear-lanceolate, one to three-nerved, entire or with a few distant teeth on the margins, firm, shiny, rough or ciliate on the margins, sessile or very short petioled, the lower and basal ones 3 to 6 inches long, the upper leaves smaller and those of the branches very much reduced in size. Heads of flowers two-thirds to 1 inch broad. Bracts of the nearly hemispheric involucres linear-oblong, smooth, green, overlapping in about four series. Ray flowers ten to twenty in each head, white, one-fourth to one-third of an inch long; pappus white.

In dry or rocky soil, Massachusetts to Vermont and Saskatchewan, south to Pennsylvania, Illinois and Colorado. Flowering from July to September.

Tall Flat-top White Aster

Doellingeria umbellata (Miller) Nees von Esenbeck

Plate 248

Stems rigid, erect, smooth or somewhat pubescent above, striate, corymbosely branched at the top, 1 to 8 feet high from a perennial root. Leaves lanceolate to oblong-lanceolate, ascending, smooth above, usually slightly pubescent beneath, long pointed at the apex, narrowed into short petioles or the upper leaves sessile, hispid-margined, 5 to 6 inches long and one-half to 1 inch wide, the lower leaves reduced in size; basal leaves none. Heads of flowers numerous, one-half to three-fourths of an inch broad in large terminal compound corymbs. Involucres broadly bell-shaped or hemispheric, about one-sixth of an inch high, their bracts lanceolate, appressed, thin, usually pubescent or ciliate, overlapping in three or four series, the outer ones shortest. Ray flowers ten to fifteen in number, white, pistillate. Disk flowers perfect, the corolla with a slender tube, abruptly expanded into a bell-shaped five-lobed limb; achenes obovoid; pappus double, the outer series of numerous short bristles or scales, the inner series of numerous hairlike bristles, some of which have thickened tips.

In moist soil, open woods, thickets and marshes, Newfoundland to Saskatchewan, south to Georgia, Michigan and Iowa. Flowering from July to October.

Stiff or Savory-leaved Aster

Ionactis linariifolius (Linnaeus) Greene

Plate 242b

Stems very leafy, tufted or often several from a perennial root, puberulent or roughish, 6 to 24 inches high. Leaves linear or spatulate, spreading, one-nerved, stiff, entire, rough and usually ciliolate on the margins, three-fourths to $1\frac{1}{2}$ inches long, sessile, those of the branches much smaller. Heads of flowers several, terminating the branchlets, each about 1 inch broad. Bracts of the turbinate involucres linear-lanceolate, appressed, green and keeled on the back, overlapping in four or five series, the inner ones blunt, the outer ones usually pointed. Ray flowers ten to fifteen in each head, violet or rarely white, one-third to one-half of an inch long; pappus tawny, in two series, the inner with long hairlike bristles, the outer much shorter.

In dry or sandy, sometimes rocky, soil, Maine to Minnesota, south to Florida and Texas. Flowering from July to October.

White-topped Aster

Sericocarpus asteroides (Linnaeus) Britton, Sterns & Poggenberg

Plate 233a

Stems rather stiff, erect or ascending, pubescent or nearly smooth, slightly angled, 1 to 2 feet high, from a perennial root. Leaves alternate, thin, smoothish or somewhat pubescent, ciliate, faintly three-nerved and pinnately veined, the basal and lower leaves obovate or spatulate, toothed or rarely entire, 2 to 4 inches long, 1 to 1½ inches wide, narrowed below into margined petioles; upper leaves smaller, oblong or oblong-lanceolate, toothed or entire. Heads of flowers about one-half of an inch high, densely clustered in a terminal, cymose panicle; involucres bell-shaped, their bracts coriaceous, oblong, ciliate or pubescent, the outer ones shorter and with green reflexed tips. Ray flowers white, conspicuous, four to six in each head. Disk flowers perfect, their corollas tubular, narrow, yellowish and five-lobed; achenes slightly compressed, linear-oblong, one-nerved on each side, pubescent; pappus of numerous hairlike, rough, brownish or whitish bristles.

In dry or sandy woods, Maine to Ohio, south to Florida, Alabama and Kentucky. Flowering from July to September.

Philadelphia Fleabane; Skevish; Daisy Fleabane

Erigeron philadelphicus Linnaeus

Plate 239b

A slender-stemmed herb 1 to 3 feet high, softly pubescent, perennial by stolons and offsets. Stem and midrib on the under surfaces of the leaves densely downy-pubescent. Basal and lower stem leaves spatulate or obovate, dentate, 1 to 3 inches long, blunt at the apex, narrowed at the base into short petioles; upper stem leaves cordate-clasping and smaller. Heads of flowers one-half to 1 inch broad, in a corymbose panicle, borne on slender peduncles thickened at the summit. Each head with one hundred to one hundred and fifty ray flowers, one-sixth to one-third of an inch long, fringelike, light rose-purple to pinkish in color, surrounding a yellow center of disk flowers. Involucres of the heads depressed-hemispheric, composed of narrow, linear bracts, pubescent and with dry, membranaceous margins. Buds drooping, but flowers borne erect.

In fields and woods, Labrador to British Columbia, Florida and California. Flowering from May to August.

The Poor-Robin's-plantain (E r i g e r o n p u l c h e l l u s) resembles this species but is not as tall and has smaller heads with shorter ray flowers.

Spicy or Salt-marsh Fleabane

Pluchea camphorata (Linnaeus) DeCandolle

Plate 249b

An annual, branching herb with nearly smooth, or sometimes puberulent, and somewhat grooved, stout stems, 2 to 3 feet high. Leaves alternate, ovate, serrate or denticulate, 3 to 8 inches long, 1 to 3 inches wide, short petioled, the upper leaves almost or quite sessile. Heads of flowers about one-fourth of an inch high, composed entirely of tubular flowers, purplish or pinkish in color, the heads arranged in terminal corymbose cymes, usually several or many on a plant. Involucres bell-shaped, composed of several series of appressed, ovate-lanceolate pubescent bracts, somewhat purplish in color. Outer flowers of each head with threadlike corollas, three-cleft or toothed at the apex and pistillate; center flowers with five-cleft corollas.

In salt marshes along the coast from Massachusetts to Florida, Texas and Mexico. Flowering from August to October. Flowers with a faint odor of camphor.

Pearly Everlasting; Moonshine

Anaphalis margaritacea (Linnaeus) Bentham & Hooker

Plate 211b

A white-tomentose or woolly perennial herb, the erect leafy stem corymbosely branched at the summit, 1 to 3 feet high. Leaves alternate, entire, linear-lanceolate, sessile, revolute on the margins, green but pubescent above and woolly beneath, 3 to 5 inches long. Heads of flowers numerous in a compound corymb, 2 to 8 inches broad, each head one-fourth to one-third of an inch broad when expanded; involucres campanulate, their bracts ovate-lanceolate, blunt, pearly white; flowers cream-colored becoming yellowish; the staminate flowers with a slender or filiform corolla, an undivided style and pappus bristles not thickened at the summit or scarcely so; pistillate flowers with a tubular five-toothed corolla, two-cleft style and a pappus of distinct capillary bristles which fall away separately.

A common plant, often present as a weed in fields and meadows, throughout nearly the entire United States and Canada, except the extreme north. Flowering in July and August.

The dry, chaffy character of the involucres of the heads suggests the appropriate name of Everlasting. Clusters may be gathered and placed in a vase or other receptacle without water and kept for an indefinite period. They are sometimes subjected to various dyes but it is doubtful if this adds anything to their attractiveness. In florists' shops they are frequently seen dyed a brilliant red or blue.

Elecampane; Horseheal

Inula helenium Linnaeus

Plate 250

A large, woolly, perennial herb, with a stout, thick mucilaginous root. Stems stout, usually unbranched, 2 to 6 feet high and densely woolly-pubescent. Leaves alternate, rough-hairy above, densely woolly on the under surface; basal leaves large, 10 to 20 inches long, 4 to 8 inches wide, narrowed into long petioles; upper leaves sessile or clasping the stem by a heart-shaped base, smaller than the basal leaves. Heads of flowers large and showy, 2 to 4 inches broad, yellow, terminal on stout peduncles, the inflorescence consisting of few or several heads. Involucres hemispheric, nearly an inch high, their outer bracts large and almost leaflike in character. Ray flowers numerous, linear, 1 to 1$\frac{1}{2}$ inches long, yellow; the disk flowers dingy yellow or brownish.

Along roadsides and in fields, Nova Scotia to Ontario and Minnesota, south to North Carolina and Missouri. Flowering from July to September. Native of Europe and naturalized in this country.

Cup Plant; Indian Cup

Silphium perfoliatum Linnaeus

Plate 251

A tall, perennial herb, with resinous juice. Stem usually smooth, square, branched above, 4 to 8 feet high. Leaves opposite, ovate or deltoid-ovate, the upper ones united around the stem, the lower leaves abruptly contracted into margined petioles. Rather thin in texture, usually rough on both surfaces, the margins coarsely angulate-dentate or the upper ones often entire, the larger leaves 6 to 12 inches long and 4 to 8 inches wide. Heads numerous, yellow, nearly flat, 2 to 3 inches broad, composed of yellow ray flowers and disk flowers, the ray flowers twenty to thirty in number, each about 1 inch long and one-sixth of an inch wide, in two or three series. Outer bracts of the involucres broadly ovate, ciliolate, foliaceous and spreading.

Moist soil, chiefly on prairies, southern Ontario to Minnesota and South Dakota, south to New Jersey, Georgia, Louisiana and Nebraska. Naturalized about New York City and in a few other localities in the east. Sometimes as an escape from cultivation.

Oxeye; False Sunflower

Heliopsis helianthoides (Linnaeus) Sweet

Plate 252

Heliopsis, the False Sunflower, differs from the true Sunflowers (Helianthus) chiefly in having both the ray and disk flowers fertile, that is, capable of producing seed. In the true Sunflowers, the ray flowers are neutral. The Oxeye or False Sunflower is 3 to 5 feet high. Leaves opposite, petioled, ovate to lanceolate, thin, rather evenly toothed on the margins, 3 to 6 inches long and 1 to $2\frac{1}{2}$ inches wide. Heads of flowers yellow, borne on long peduncles; bracts of the involucres oblong or linear-oblong, the outer ones usually longer than the inner.

In low or moist soil, usually in open places and along streams, Ontario to New York, west to Illinois and North Dakota, south to Florida and Tennessee. Flowering from July to September. Closely resembling the Pale-leaved Wood Sunflower.

Thin-leaved Coneflower

Rudbeckia triloba Linnaeus

Plate 253

Similar in appearance to the Black-eyed Susan (R u d b e c k i a h i r t a), but more branched and with smaller heads of flowers. It is rather tall, 2 to 5 feet high with rough and pubescent stems but scarcely hairy. Leaves thin, rough on both surfaces, bright green and the lower at least three-lobed, 2 to 4 inches long, one-half to 1 inch wide. Heads about 2 inches broad, numerous, in terminal corymbs. Ray flowers bright yellow, sometimes orange or orange-purple at the base, eight to twelve in number; disk flowers purple, forming an ovoid center to the head, about one-half of an inch broad. Bracts of the involucres linear, pubescent and reflexed.

In moist soil, southern New York to Georgia, west to Michigan, Minnesota, Missouri, Kansas and Louisiana. Flowering from June to October.

Black-eyed Susan; Yellow Daisy

Rudbeckia hirta Linnaeus

Plate 254

A coarse, native biennial, or sometimes annual, with rough, hairy stems and foliage, the stems rather bristly-hairy, 1 to 3 feet high. Leaves thick, sparingly toothed or entire, oblong to lanceolate, the lower ones petioled, 2 to 7 inches long, one-half to 2 inches wide, the upper leaves sessile and narrower than the lower ones. Heads of flowers very showy, usually few or several borne on stout terminal and axillary stalks, each head $1\frac{1}{2}$ to 3 inches broad. Disk flowers purple-brown, forming a cone-shaped center to the head. Ray flowers ten to twenty in number, orange-yellow in color, or sometimes purplish brown or reddish at the base. Bracts of the involucres hairy, spreading or reflexed, much shorter than the ray flowers.

Native of the plains and prairies of the western states, now well established in meadows and fields throughout the east. Flowering from June to August. In meadows and hay fields it is frequently an obnoxious weed.

The Common White Daisy (C h r y s a n t h e m u m   l e u c a n t h e- m u m Linnaeus), perhaps even more abundant in meadows and fields, with its bright yellow center and white ray flowers, needs no description or illustration for its identification. Native of Europe and introduced very early into America and now thoroughly established in the north-eastern states.

Tall or Green-headed Coneflower

Rudbeckia laciniata Linnaeus

Plate 255

Stems tall, leafy and much branched, sometimes 10 or 12 feet tall, from a perennial root. Leaves thin in texture, minutely hairy above and on the margins, both basal and upper leaves pinnately divided and toothed, the lower into three to seven segments and long petioled, the upper leaves into three to five lobes and short petioled or sessile. Heads 3 to 4 inches broad. Ray flowers yellow, six to ten in number, surrounding the columnar, dull greenish-yellow disk which becomes oblong-shaped in fruit and two or more times as long as thick.

Moist thickets and low woods, especially along streams, Quebec to Manitoba and Idaho, south to Florida, Colorado and Arizona. Flowering from July to September.

This plant is the origin of the Golden Glow, a common garden variety in which the disk flowers are all transformed into ray flowers.

Narrow-leaved or Swamp Sunflower

Helianthus angustifolius Linnaeus

Plate 249a

Easily distinguished from the other Sunflowers by its narrow, linear leaves and yellow heads with purplish disks. Perennial by slender root-stocks; stem rough, 2 to 7 feet high; slender and branched above, usually somewhat hairy below. Leaves firm and tough, slightly rough, linear, entire and sessile, 2 to 7 inches long, one-sixth to one-third of an inch wide, the margins becoming revolute with age or in drying. Lower leaves opposite, the upper ones alternate. Heads with twelve to twenty yellow ray flowers and a purplish disk, the entire head 2 to 3 inches broad. Bracts of the involucres linear-lanceolate and pubescent, their tips scarcely spreading. Chaff of the receptacle entire or three-toothed. Pappus usually two short awns.

In swamps mainly near the coast, Long Island to Florida, Kentucky and Texas. Flowering from August to October.

Tall, Giant or Wild Sunflower

Helianthus giganteus Linnaeus

Plate 256

Stems tall and rather stiff, hairy and rough to the touch, 3 to 12 feet high, often purplish, perennial by fleshy roots and creeping rootstocks. Leaves sessile or short petioled, firm, lanceolate, very rough above, margins serrate, long pointed at the apex, narrowed at the base, opposite or alternate, 2 to 6 inches long, one-half to 1 inch wide. Heads of flowers on long peduncles, $1\frac{1}{2}$ to $2\frac{1}{2}$ inches broad. Ray flowers ten to twenty in number, surrounding the yellow or yellowish brown disk. Bracts of the involucres lanceolate, ciliate, with slender, spreading tips. Receptacle chaffy, the chaff oblong-linear and pointed.

In swamps and wet meadows, Maine to Ontario and Saskatchewan, south to Florida, Louisiana and Colorado. Especially abundant in swamps and marshes along the coast. Flowering from August to October.

Rough or Woodland Sunflower

Helianthus divaricatus Linnaeus

Plate 257

A slender perennial with erect stems, 2 to 7 feet high from perennial roots and rootstocks; smooth nearly to the summit. Leaves rough on the upper surface, lanceolate or ovate-lanceolate in shape, tapering at the apex to a long point, 3 to 8 inches long, one-fourth to one-half of an inch wide, toothed, sessile and usually opposite, spreading at right angles from the stem. Heads of flowers yellow, about 2 inches broad; bracts of the involucres ovate-lanceolate or lanceolate, the outer ones spreading.

In dry woodlands, thickets and roadsides, Maine and Ontario to Manitoba, south to Florida, Louisiana and Nebraska. Flowering from July to September.

Hairy Wild Sunflower

Helianthus mollis Lamarck

Plate 258

A tall, perennial plant, with densely soft-hairy stem and downy-pubescent leaves. Stem stout, usually but sparingly branched. Leaves ovate with a heart-shaped base closely clasping the stem, softly pubescent on both surfaces, opposite, 2 to 5 inches long, 1 to 2½ inches wide, with serrulate margins. Heads of flowers yellow, 2 to 3 inches broad, borne solitary on few or several stout peduncles. Disk yellow, about 1 inch broad, surrounded by the numerous bright yellow ray flowers. Bracts of the involucre lanceolate, somewhat spreading and canescent with whitish hairs.

In dry or barren soil, Massachusetts to Iowa, Missouri and Kansas, south to Georgia and Texas. Flowering in August and September.

Pale-leaved Wood Sunflower

Helianthus strumosus Linnaeus

Plate 259

Perennial by branched and sometimes tuberous-thickened rootstock; stems smooth, sometimes glaucous below and branched above, usually somewhat pubescent, 3 to 7 feet high. Leaves short petioled, ovate to ovate-lanceolate, rough above, pale beneath, the margins serrate, 3 to 8 inches long, 1 to 2½ inches wide, mostly opposite, sometimes the upper ones alternate. Heads yellow, 2½ to 4 inches broad, consisting of from five to fifteen neutral ray flowers surrounding the yellow disk flowers. Bracts of the involucres lanceolate and ciliate. Receptacle with pubescent chaff.

In dry woods and on banks, Maine and Ontario to Minnesota, south to Georgia, Tennessee and Arkansas. Flowering from July to September.

Lance-leaved Tickseed

Coreopsis lanceolata Linnaeus

Plate 260a

An erect, perennial herb, 1 to 2 feet high, stems slender, striate, smooth or more or less pubescent, especially below. Leaves smooth or somewhat hairy, opposite; the basal and lower stem leaves spatulate or oblong, entire, sometimes with a pair of lateral lobes, 2 to 6 inches long, on slender petioles; upper stem leaves few, lanceolate to oblong, nearly sessile. Heads of flowers usually few, 1½ to 2½ inches broad, showy, bright yellow, borne on long, slender peduncles often 8 to 12 inches long. Involucres rather flattened, their bracts ovate-lanceolate, in two series, the outer narrower than the inner but nearly as long. Ray flowers six to ten in number, wedge-shaped, three to seven-notched at the apex, forming a single row around the darker yellow disk. Achenes oblong, winged on the edges, with two short teeth projecting from the summit, giving it somewhat the appearance of a bug. It is from this character of the achene that the generic name Coreopsis, meaning " buglike," is derived.

In moist or dry soil, Ontario to Michigan, south to New York, Virginia, Florida, Louisiana and Missouri. Flowering from June to August.

Small Rose or Pink Tickseed

Coreopsis rosea Nuttall

Plate 261b

Stems slender, smooth, wiry, erect or at least the tips ascending, 6 to 24 inches high, perennial by slender, creeping rootstocks, usually much branched and smooth. Leaves opposite, linear, entire, 1 to 2½ inches long, sessile. Heads of flowers small, one-half to 1 inch broad or less, on slender peduncles. Each head consisting of four to eight pink or rose-purple rays, oblong to obovate and slightly three-toothed or sometimes entire, surrounding the yellow disk. Bracts of the involucre in two series, the inner oblong and longer than the outer lanceolate bracts. Achenes (seeds) oblong, not winged, the pappus reduced to a very short truncate crown.

Open swamps near the coast, Massachusetts to Georgia. Flowering in July and August.

Small or Nodding Bur Marigold
Bidens cernua Linnaeus
Plate 262

An annual, with erect or partially prostrate stems, smooth or hispid and usually much branched, from a few inches to 3 feet high. Leaves sessile, opposite, usually somewhat united around the stem. Lanceolate to oblong-lanceolate in shape, coarsely and sharply toothed, smooth, long pointed, 3 to 6 inches long, one-fourth to 1 inch wide. Heads numerous, at least on vigorous plants, globose, short-stalked, one-half to 1 inch broad, nodding after or during flowering, consisting of six to ten short, yellow ray flowers, one-fourth to one-half of an inch long, surrounding the globose, yellow or brownish-yellow disk. Very often the ray flowers are absent. Bracts of the involucre in two series, the outer green and leaflike and much larger than the membranaceous, yellowish-margined inner bracts. Seed a wedge-shaped achene, about one-sixth of an inch long, retrorsely hispid on the margins, and with usually four downwardly barbed awns at the summit.

In wet soil and swamps, Nova Scotia to Hudson bay and British Columbia south to North Carolina, Missouri and California. Also found in Europe. Flowering from July to October. Dwarf forms are frequent.

Sneezeweed; False or Swamp Sunflower
Helenium autumnale Linnaeus
Plate 261a

Stems stout and branching, 2 to 6 feet high, aromatic and resinous, from a perennial root. Leaves firm, oblong-lanceolate, narrowed to a sessile base and pointed at the apex, usually toothed, 2 to 5 inches long, one-fourth to 2 inches wide, the bases of the leaves decurrent on the stems, and making the stem appear wing-angled. Inflorescence composed of yellow heads of flowers on long peduncles; each head with ten to eighteen drooping ray flowers, wedge-shaped and three-notched at the apex, surrounding the globose, darker yellow disk.

In swamps, wet meadows and along streams, Quebec to Manitoba and Oregon, south to Florida and Louisiana. Flowering from August to October. The far western form is sometimes regarded as a distinct species.

Yarrow; Milfoil

Achillea millefolium Linnaeus

Plate 260b

A very common weed, found everywhere; the feathery, finely dissected leaves, when the plant is small and not in flower, often mistaken by those not acquainted with it for fern leaves. It is perennial by means of rootstocks. Leaves lanceolate or oblong in outline, very finely dissected into narrow, pinnatifid segments. Inflorescence consists of dense, flat-topped clusters of numerous, small, white heads (sometimes pink or purplish), one-sixth to one-fourth of an inch broad, borne on erect stems 6 to 18 inches high. Disk flowers yellow, surrounded by four to six gray-white, or sometimes pink or purplish ray flowers; both ray and disk flowers fertile. Entire plant aromatic and pungent, but bitter to the taste.

Waste ground, fields, roadsides and various other situations throughout eastern North America; naturalized from Europe, where it is native. Flowering from June to November.

Golden Ragwort; Swamp Squawweed

Senecio aureus Linnaeus

Plate 263

Stems slender, smooth, erect, 6 to 28 inches high, solitary or tufted from a perennial, strong-scented root. Basal leaves ovate, orbicular or oblong-ovate, heart-shaped at the base and long petioled, usually pointed at the apex, the margins crenately toothed, 1 to 6 inches long; lower stem leaves lanceolate or oblong, usually deeply cut or cleft, the upper leaves small, sessile and clasping the stem. Heads of flowers numerous, on slender peduncles, forming an open corymb, bright golden yellow; each head one-half to three-fourths of an inch broad and one-third to one-half of an inch high. Ray flowers eight to twelve in number, linear-lanceolate; pappus white.

In wet meadows, marshes and swamps, Newfoundland to Ontario and Michigan, south to Florida, Texas and Missouri. Flowering from late in May to July or August.

Swamp Thistle

Cirsium muticum Michaux

Plate 264

An erect, biennial, prickly herb, with spiny leaves and smooth stem, 3 to 8 feet high, slender, leafy, striate and branching above. When young the stem is woolly or hairy, becoming smooth when older. Leaves when young, densely white tomentose on the under surface, becoming glabrous when mature and then green on both sides, or somewhat hairy on the upper surface, deeply pinnatifid into lanceolate or oblong, toothed, spiny segments tipped with slender prickles. Basal leaves petioled, 4 to 8 inches long, upper leaves sessile and smaller. Inflorescence consisting of a solitary or several large terminal heads of flowers, about 1½ inches broad and as high, on naked peduncles or the peduncles with a few small, bractlike leaves. Flowers all tubular, and purple in color. Involucre of the heads glutinous and webby, composed of closely appressed bracts, the outer ones ovate or ovate-lanceolate, the inner linear-lanceolate, pointed and all of them unarmed or without prickles.

Common in swamps and moist soil, Newfoundland to Saskatchewan, south to Florida and Texas. Flowering from July to October.

LIST OF ILLUSTRATIONS OF WILD FLOWERS

ARRANGED ACCORDING TO FAMILIES

Santalaceae
Bastard Toadflax (*Comandra umbellata*).   Plate 28b

Aristolochiaceae
Wild or Indian Ginger (*Asarum canadense*).   Plate 46

Polygonaceae
Swamp Smartweed (*Persicaria muhlenbergii*).   Plate 47a
Lady's-thumb; Heartweed (*Persicaria persicaria*).   Plate 47b
Arrow-leaved Tearthumb (*Tracaulon sagittatum*).   Plate 48a
Halberd-leaved Tearthumb (*Tracaulon arifolium*).   Plate 48b
Climbing False Buckwheat (*Bilderdykia scandens*).   Plate 15b
Coast Jointweed (*Polygonella articulata*).   Plate 49a

Chenopodiaceae
Slender or Jointed Glasswort (*Salicornia europaea*).   Plate 49b

Phytolaccaceae
Poke; Scoke; Pigeon Berry; Garget (*Phytolacca americana*).   Plate 50

Portulacaceae
Narrow-leaved Spring Beauty (*Claytonia virginica*).   Plate 51a
Carolina or Wide-leaved Spring Beauty (*Claytonia caroliniana*).   Plate 69a

Alsinaceae
Field or Meadow Chickweed (*Cerastium arvense*).   Plate 63a

Caryophyllaceae
Bladder Campion; White Ben (*Silene latifolia*).   Plate 52
Wild Pink (*Silene caroliniana*).   Plate 53
Cuckoo-flower; Ragged Robin (*Lychnis flos-cuculi*).   Plate 54a

Nelumbonaceae
American Nelumbo or Lotus (*Nelumbo lutea*).   Plate 55

INDEX